HETEROCYCLIC CHEMISTRY

Heterocyclic Chemistry

AN INTRODUCTION

by

ADRIEN ALBERT

Ph.D., D.Sc., F.R.I.C.

Professor of Medical Chemistry in the
Australian National University, Canberra

UNIVERSITY OF LONDON
THE ATHLONE PRESS
1959

Published by
THE ATHLONE PRESS
UNIVERSITY OF LONDON
at 2 *Gower Street London* WC1
Distributed by Constable & Co. Ltd
12 *Orange Street London* WC2

Canada
University of Toronto Press
Toronto 5

U.S.A.
Essential Books Division
Oxford University Press Inc
New York

Printed in Great Britain by
WESTERN PRINTING SERVICES LTD
BRISTOL

Preface

THE PRESENT WORK is intended to provide an introduction to heterocyclic chemistry along rational lines. It aims to supply a sound framework to which each reader can attach new information as it comes his way. This framework, derived from the most familiar concepts of general organic chemistry, divides the subject into hetero-paraffinic, hetero-ethylenic, and hetero-aromatic substances. Hetero-aromatic substances, which have the greatest individuality, are further subdivided on the basis of the π-electron content of the ring: this achieves a separation of *π-deficient* N-heterocycles (allied to nitrobenzene in their chemical nature) from the *π-excessive* N-heterocycles (allied to aniline). Throughout, emphasis has been placed on principles rather than on isolated facts.

The (at first bewildering) diversity of heterocyclic chemistry should make this comparative method an ideal first approach. It is believed that honours students in chemistry will derive the greatest help from this book by first achieving an understanding of its plan, followed by selected reading in it. However the text is designed to help more advanced readers also, among whom the special needs of research workers in biology and medicine have been kept in mind.

In this book, more emphasis is laid on the connexion between structure and properties than on methods of synthesis, although these are by no means neglected. More prominence has been given to parent substances than to their highly substituted derivatives. It is believed that the principle of simplicity preceding complexity will add to the teaching value of the work. For the same reason much attention has been given to the interpretation of physical properties especially ionization constants, spectra, dipole moments and reduction potentials. Technical applications are mentioned throughout.

In several places, attention is called to gaps in the fundamental knowledge of the subject and it is hoped that this will stimulate further research.

The literature is covered to mid-1958.

The author wishes to thank Professor F. G. Young, F.R.S., for the first opportunity to give a course of lectures along these lines (in the Biochemistry Department, University College, London), Professor W. O. Kermack, F.R.S., for encouragement in the use of the comparative method, Professor D. P. Craig for help in selecting material for Chapter III, Drs. D. J. Brown, S. F. Mason, D. D. Perrin, E. Spinner and F. Reich for helpful discussions, and Miss M. Bell for preparing the manuscript for press. Dr. C. W. Rees gave most valuable help in re-reading the proofs and making a number of suggestions.

A.A.

Contents

ERRATA

p. 25, l. 12. *for* is unknown *read* was discovered in 1949 (Holley and Holley)

p. 122, ll. 4–3 from foot. *for* a stable monohydrate, m.p. 28° *read* a stable monohydrate, m.p. 37°

p. 136, ll. 33–4. *delete* Triazole . . . substitution, and

p. 208, l. 3 from foot. *for* stable to acid *read* stable to aqueous acid

p. 259, l. 5. *for* the simplest known member *read* a simple member

p. 314, Fig. 5. *for* B. Quinoline . . . 1951) *read* B. *Iso*quinoline (in 95% ethanol (Ewing and Steck, 1946)

p. 336

$$\textit{for} \quad K_a = \frac{[HX^+]}{[H^+]\,[X]} \quad \textit{read} \quad K_a = \frac{[H^+]\,[X]}{[HX^+]}$$

p. 345, col. 1, ll. 8–7 from foot.

for 3:4-Benzocinnoline	2·2	*read* 3:4-Benzocinnoline	2·2
2-amino-	6·7	2′-amino-5′:6′-	6·7

p. 346, col. 2, ll. 16–12 from foot.

for	4-Methyl-	*read*	4-Methyl-
	5-Formyl-		5-Formyl-
	5-Acetyl		5-Acetyl-
	5:8-Diacetyl-		5:8-Diacetyl-

p. 376. ALBERT and BARLIN. for *J. Chem Soc.* 1958 read *J. Chem. Soc.* 1959, p. 2384.

p. 385. FELTON, OSDENE and TIMMIS. *for* p. 298 *read* p. 2895.

p. 388. HOLLEY. *add* HOLLEY and HOLLEY (1949). *J. Amer. Chem. Soc.* **71**, 2129.

To the memory of the pioneers of heterocyclic chemistry, on whose secure foundations we build today.

CHAPTER I

General Introduction to Heterocyclic Chemistry

HETEROCYCLIC CHEMISTRY contains much to interest the theoretical organic chemist, but there are also two practical sources of interest in this subject. Firstly there is the steady stream of discovery of new heterocyclic substances playing an important part in the metabolism of all living cells, and secondly the increasing availability of intermediates suitable for the large-scale production of heterocyclic substances, many of which are finding important new uses in industry.

Among the *metabolically important substances*, special mention must be given to such vitamins and coenzyme precursors as thiamine, riboflavine, nicotinic acid, pyridoxine, folic acid, thioctic acid, adenine, biotin, the B_{12} family, the vitamin E family; to the photosynthesizing pigment chlorophyll, the oxygen-transporting pigment haemoglobin (and its breakdown products, the bile-pigments); to the purine and pyrimidine components of nucleic acid and their breakdown products uric acid, allantoin and alloxan; to the amino-acids histidine, tryptophan and proline; and to such other metabolically active substances as heteroauxin, serotonin and histamine.

Drugs, another section of important heterocyclic chemicals, form a bridge between the natural and the purely synthetic divisions of the subject. The natural drugs include the purines (e.g. caffeine, theobromine); the alkaloids (including nicotine); the cardiac glycosides (e.g. those of digitalis); penicillin. Some economically important insecticides such as rotenone must be mentioned here.

Synthetic heterocyclic drugs are used as hypnotics (e.g.

barbiturates), anticonvulsants, analeptics, antihistaminics, anti-thyroid drugs (e.g. thiouracil), antiseptics (e.g. 5-aminoacri-dine), fungicides (e.g. 8-hydroxyquinoline) and vasopressor modifiers. Polyvinylpyrrolidone is used as a replacement for serum lost in haemorrhage and shock. Many of the most promising cancer-arresting substances are heterocyclic.

Dyes. Interest in the non-biological heterocyclic substances was at first largely concentrated upon their use as dyes, parti-cularly such basic dyes as mauveine (the first synthetic dye), rhodamine, methylene blue (still one of the most frequently used microscopical stains), saffranine, nile blue and acridine orange. Today many of the most durable dyes are heterocyclic, par-ticularly the indanthrene and indigoid colours for dyeing cotton by the vat process, melamine-azo colours for the direct dyeing of cotton, the pyrazole-azo yellows for wool, and the phthalo-cyanine series of insoluble blue pigments which are far more durable than their inorganic rivals. All the sensitizers in photo-graphic films and some of the best developers are heterocyclic.

Other Uses. Melamine and coumarone (benzofuran) are poly-merized to yield useful plastics and resins. The rubber industry uses many heterocyclic antioxidants and vulcanization accelera-tors such as 2-mercaptobenzothiazole, and piperidine and its derivatives. Useful heterocyclic analytical reagents include *o*-phenanthroline, dipyridyl, oxine (8-hydroxyquinoline), rho-damine and nitron. The ready availability of furfural from agricultural sources has made the furans valuable industrial sources of the aliphatic chemicals which are formed upon reduc-tion or acid decomposition.

Many molecules not commonly thought of as being hetero-cyclic nevertheless have rings not wholly composed of carbon atoms. Where there is easy ring-chain tautomerism, as with glu-cose and other hydroxyaldehydes, the heterocyclic character may not be of great interest, but this character cannot be over-looked when the rings are fairly stable as in ethylene oxide, succinic anhydride and phthalimide.

Because it is intended only as an introduction to heterocyclic chemistry, this book is concerned mainly with the substances having N, O, or S as the hetero-atom: these constitute the greater bulk of the literature. But other hetero-elements can be involved. Of *The Heterocyclic Derivatives of Phosphorus, Arsenic, Antimony, Bismuth and Silicon*, Mann's works (1950, 1958) give an excellent account. Heterocyclic rings containing B, Al, Se, and Te have also been made. Finally there are the chelates which bi- and poly-dentate organic substances form with the cations of heavy metals (Martell and Calvin, 1952).

The plan on which this book operates has been described in the Preface. The main divisions are into heteroparaffinic, hetero-aromatic and heteroethylenic substances, with the hetero-aromatics further divided into π-deficient and π-excessive families. It is hoped that this classification will not be found too rigid: the copious cross-indexing plus a comprehensive subject index should overcome any such difficulties. Where tautomer-ism makes it uncertain if a substance is aromatic or not, it has been given the benefit of the doubt and classified as (hetero) aromatic.

The last five chapters, none of them lengthy, serve to consoli-date and expand some special themes which run through the main body of the work. References to original literature have been confined to papers published since 1930. Thus the reader is at once put in contact with recent work, from which it is almost always possible to obtain references to what has gone before. Direct access to the older work is easily made from Beil-stein's *Handbuch* and Volume IV of Richter's *Chemistry of the Car-bon Compounds*. Omission of historical material has been made with regret, but existing texts do justice to this subject.

The contents of this book should be supplemented by wider reading. Elderfield's *Heterocyclic Compounds*, of which the first six volumes have appeared, is recommended. In addition, books are available dealing exclusively with one family: e.g. pyridines (Maier-Bode and Altpeter, 1934), pyrroles (Fischer and Orth, 1934–40), acridines (Albert, 1951), thiophens (Hartough, 1952), and phenazines (Swan, 1957). For alkaloids, the five volumes of Manske and Holmes (1952) can be consulted.

B

CHAPTER II

Heteroparaffinics

[i.e. Completely saturated heterocycles]

THE MAJORITY of saturated heterocyclic substances exhibit ordinary aliphatic properties. In fact, as a first approximation, the chemical properties of any completely saturated heterocyclic substance may be taken to be those of the corresponding aliphatic substance obtained by (mentally) splitting the ring at a point remote from the hetero-atom. For example, tetrahydrofuran (I) would be expected to resemble ordinary ether (II), and piperidine (III) should resemble *n*-propylethylamine (IV).

     I   II   III   IV

Thus, tetrahydrofuran (I) smells like ethyl ether and it is cleaved to 1:4-di-iodobutane under the same conditions as ethyl ether is cleaved to two molecules of ethyl iodide. Like ether, it is chemically inert. As we shall see in Chapter VI, the unsaturated analogue, furan (V), is an extraordinarily reactive substance. Tetrahydropyran (VI) resembles tetrahydrofuran, as would be expected of the higher homologue of a saturated ether. Pyran (VII), the corresponding unsaturated substance, remains unknown in spite of many attempts to prepare it, and this failure suggests that it may have a high degree of chemical reactivity.

$$V \qquad VI \qquad VII \qquad VIII$$

Again piperidine (III) and pyrrolidine (VIII) are highly stable substances with the typical smell of an aliphatic secondary amine. They form oily N-nitroso-derivatives and give all the other reactions typical of aliphatic secondary amines. Moreover, these heterocyclic amines give very few reactions not given by aliphatic amines.

On the other hand, pyrrole (IX), the unsaturated analogue of pyrrolidine, is an extraordinarily reactive substance and its reactions are quite individual and in no way resemble those of aliphatic amines (see Chapter V). Likewise pyridine (X), the unsaturated analogue of piperidine, is entirely individual in its properties (see Chapter IV), although it is by no means as reactive as pyrrole. What particularly differentiates the saturated heterocyclic amines from their unsaturated analogues is basic strength. Pyrrolidine and piperidine, as can be seen from Table 1, are bases of the same strength as the aliphatic amines (for the significance of pK_a values, see Chapter IX). On the contrary, pyridine is seen to be about one million times weaker, and pyrrole is almost completely lacking in basic properties. Another property which differentiates saturated from unsaturated heterocyclic substances is the absence of ultraviolet absorption in the former at wavelengths of 200 mμ or greater. This difference is plainly shown in Table 1 and again brings together the saturated heterocyclic and aliphatic substances. Ultraviolet spectra are further discussed in Chapter VIII.

TABLE 1. Completely Saturated Substances

	Base strengths pK_a 20°	u/v absorption spectrum λ max (mμ)	m.p.	b.p.	Refractive index n_D^{20}	Density d_{20}
Oxygen series						
Diethyl ether	a	b	−117°	34°	1·35	0·72
Ethyl propyl ether	a	b		64	1·37	0·74
Di-*n*-propyl ether	a	b		91	1·38	0·74
Tetrahydrofuran	a	b	−65	67	1·41	0·89
(Furan: for						
comparison)	a	205	−86	31	1·42	0·94
Tetrahydropyran	a	b		88	1·42	0·88
Nitrogen series						
Diethylamine	11·1	b	−48	56	1·39	0·71
n-Propyl-						
ethylamine	*ca.* 11	b		80		
Di-*n*-propylamine	11·0	b	−60	110	1·40	0·74
Pyrrolidine	11·3	b		88		0·85
(Pyrrole: for	~0·4	{ 210 +240 (slight)		131	1·51	0·97
comparison)						
Piperidine	11·2	b	−9	106	1·45	0·87
(Pyridine: for						
comparison)	5·2	250	−42	115	1·51	0·98
N:N′-Dimethyl-						
ethylenediamine	10·2	b		119		0·83
Piperazine	9·8	b	104	145		
Pyrazine	0·6	316	55	118	1·50	1·03 (60°)

a. Not appreciably basic (pK_a is below 0).
b. Not absorbing at wavelengths above 200 mμ.

Further reference to Table 1 shows that boiling-points (and melting-points, where known) are not characteristic. The densities of cyclic substances are naturally higher than those of open-chain analogues, and the unsaturated heterocyclic substances containing less hydrogen, and packing better because of their flat structure, have higher densities than their saturated analogues. It would be reasonable to expect the refractive index of unsaturated heterocyclic substances to be about 1·5 because of the presence of conjugated double bonds. However Table 1 shows furan to be 1·4, a figure typical of fully saturated substances. It was pointed out by v. Auwers (1915) that this lack of exaltation by two double-bonds in a five-membered ring is quite common and is also shown by thiophen and *cyclo*pentadiene.

CH——CH
CH CH
N
H
IX

CH
CH   CH
CH   CH
N
X

H
N
CH₂   CH₂
CH₂   CH₂
N
H
XI

H
N
CH₂   CH₃
CH₂   CH₃
N
H
XII

N
N
XIII

Piperazine (XI) is an example of a saturated ring with *two* heterocyclic atoms. As Table 1 shows, its basic and spectroscopic properties are analogous to those of the corresponding aliphatic substance, N:N′-dimethylethylenediamine (XII), and quite distinct from those of the corresponding unsaturated ring, pyrazine (XIII).

The above remarks apply particularly to rings with five or more members. Saturated heterocyclic rings with only four members are more unstable, being under compression strain. Those with three members (e.g. ethylene oxide (XIV)) are under great strain and take part in many reactions with nucleophilic substances. These reactions permit ring-opening and thus the strain is released. For example, in ethylene oxide the C—C—O angle is only 57°, but on polymerization, or reaction with methanol or hydrogen chloride, the normal tetrahedral angle of carbon (109°) is re-formed. Rings with more than six members are often thought of as being under expansion strain, and hence unstable according to Baeyer's strain hypothesis. Experience has shown that these substances are usually as stable as six-membered rings and this stability is attributed to the relief of strain by puckering of the ring. The factors making for stability, and the different meanings that the word 'stability' has to different workers, have been discussed by Wheland

(1949). In general, it is easier to form rings with fifteen to eighteen members than those with nine to thirteen members. No correlation need exist between ease of formation and stability.

It has been pointed out that six-membered rings are more stable than five-membered rings, except where an exocyclic double-bond is present: then the five-membered ring is the less strained and more stable (Brown, Brewster and Schechter, 1954). Thus hydroxyaldehydes (see below) cyclize to five- or six-membered rings, when the position of the hydroxy-group permits: there is no exocyclic double-bond, and the six-ring is more stable than the five-ring (Hurd and Saunders, 1952). But hydroxyacids (see below), which can also form five- or six-membered rings, have an exocyclic $C=O$ bond: here the six-ring is much less stable than the five-ring (rate of hydrolysis by alkali is twenty-two times, and by acid 170 times, faster). Of the two cyclic glycol esters, ethylene carbonate (five-ring) and trimethylene carbonate (six-ring), the former is much the more stable, as would be expected from the presence of an exocyclic double-bond. Thiolactones also follow this generalization, and also the cyclic imides of dicarboxylic acids.

Having established the thesis that saturated heterocyclic substances have, in the main, the properties of their aliphatic analogues, it is interesting to examine the minor features which differentiate these two classes of substances. These differences are mainly of a steric nature, and the freedom of motion of the component atoms of the aliphatic molecules must be contrasted with the comparative restraint of the saturated heterocycles. The latter, for example, are somewhat more soluble in water, the alkyl chains being forcibly held away from the oxygen atom, thus permitting its freer association with water molecules (Ferguson, 1955). Possibly for the same reason, the cyclic analogues are more basic towards boron trifluoride (Brown and Adams, 1942). Piperidine reacts 100 times faster (than aliphatic amines) with active halogens in such substances as 1-chloro-2:4-dinitrobenzene (Brady and Cropper, 1950); this is attributed, similarly, to the larger number of effective collisions possible through the piperidine being in a state of less thermal agitation.

Moreover saturated heterocyclic rings are capable of geometrical isomerism, of the chair and boat type, brought about by ring-folding. As with the carbocyclic analogues, two fused rings are required to stabilize such pairs of isomers, hence an isolated ring merely takes up a preferred arrangement.

The dipole moments of saturated heterocyclic substances are often surprisingly large because of a conformational effect. The low dipole moments of aliphatic esters and anhydrides is due to the flexibility of the open chains which permit the component dipoles to take up such an orientation (by rotation of bonds) that their external fields are partly neutralized by one another. This rotation is limited in small saturated rings, and hence we find many examples with dipole moments considerably higher than their aliphatic counterparts. Thus butyrolactone (4·1 D) is much higher than the open chain esters (1·9 D); ethylene carbonate (4·6 D) is very much higher than open chain carbonates (0·8 D); and succinic anhydride (4·2 D) is higher than acetic anhydride (2·6 D). Such increases in dipole moments bring about an increased adhesive effect towards other polar molecules whether of the same substance (resulting in an increase in boiling-point), or of other substances (resulting in increased solvent action). No noteworthy increases in dipole moment follow the cyclization of ethers, ketones, amides or sulphones (Longster and Walker, 1953).

Finally, the heterocycles, unlike their aliphatic analogues, can be dehydrogenated to heteroaromatic substances. This is not always easy to effect. Refluxing with palladium in an aromatic hydrocarbon is usually most successful, and selenium would be the next choice or, perhaps, chloranil; but sulphur is seldom useful.

1. OXYGEN-CONTAINING SYSTEMS

(a) The cyclic ethers

Ethylene oxide (XIV) (oxiran) was discovered in 1859 by Wurtz when mixing together potassium hydroxide and ethylene chlorhydrin (2-chloroethanol). It is now a chemical of great industrial importance, and is readily available from direct (catalytic) oxidation of ethylene. Its high reactivity makes it a valuable chemical intermediate. It is also used as a toxic agent, e.g. against the flour-moth.

Ethylene oxide is a gas (b.p. 13°). The liquid has a density of 0·89 and is miscible in all proportions with water. When heated to 400° (or at 200° with an alumina catalyst) it isomerizes to acetaldehyde. With cold, dilute hydrochloric acid it quickly and quantitatively forms ethylene chlorhydrin. It reacts vigorously with ammonia to give a mixture of mono-, di- and tri-ethanolamines, separable by fractionation. The polymerization of ethylene oxide to straight-chain polyglycols containing from 2 to 100 molecules can be effected at room temperature by zinc chloride, or by a trace of alkali. The higher polyglycols are wax-like, soluble in water and benzene, but not in light petroleum or ether: they are used as ointment-bases. Glycol is formed from ethylene oxide by heating with water at 100° (under pressure), polyglycols being formed as by-products (the reaction goes only slowly in the cold). Ethylene oxide reacts with ethyl alcohol to give the important solvent 2-ethoxy-ethanol ('cellosolve'), and with phenol to give the phenyl ethers of polyglycols, much used as non-ionic wetting-agents.

XIV   XV   XVI   XVII

For further reading on ethylene oxides see Winstein and Henderson (1950).

Trimethylene oxide (XV) (oxetan) has been prepared (but only in poor yield) from 3-chloropropanol and potassium hydroxide. The rate of this reaction is 10^4 times slower than for the corresponding three-membered ring (Evans, 1891). It is a pleasant-smelling, colourless liquid, b.p. 48°. When heated with hydrobromic acid, it readily gives 1:3-dibromopropane. Beyond this, it has been little investigated. The name 'propylene oxide' refers to the C-methyl-derivative of ethylene oxide.

Tetrahydrofuran (I) (tetramethylene oxide) may be prepared quantitatively by the catalytic hydrogenation of furan over Raney-nickel (at 80° and 50 atmospheres). It is also prepared commercially from acetylene which is condensed with formaldehyde to butyndiol. This is reduced to 1:4-butanediol which is catalytically dehydrated to tetrahydrofuran. Tetrahydrofuran is a colourless liquid with a penetrating smell and a burning, slightly bitter, taste (other physical properties are given in Table 1). It is miscible in water and the majority of organic solvents; it is a good solvent for organic solids. It is unchanged by heating with water to 150°, but heating with fuming hydrobromic acid converts it to 1:4-dibromobutane. 1:4-Dichlorobutane, similarly produced, is a source of adiponitrile, a key intermediate in the production of nylon (Dunlop, 1956). 2-Tetrahydrofurylcarbinol (known as tetrahydrofurfuryl alcohol) is available commercially from the hydrogenation of furfural. This alcohol is readily dehydrated over alumina at 270° to dihydropyran (Chapter VII), a valuable intermediate for the production of 1:5-disubstituted aliphatic substances. Muscarine, the toadstool alkaloid, is 2-methyl-3-hydroxy-5-trimethyl-ammoniomethyl-tetrahydrofuran.

For further reading on tetrahydrofurans see Elderfield and Dodd (1950).

Tetrahydropyran (VI) (pentamethylene oxide) can be made by heating 1:5-dibromopentane with water (plus zinc oxide as a catalyst); alternatively, 1:5-dihydroxypentane is heated with 60% sulphuric acid. The usual preparation is by the quantitative catalytic hydrogenation of dihydropyran (Chapter VIII) over Raney-nickel. It is a colourless liquid with a penetrating smell (see Table 1 for physical properties). It is slightly soluble in cold water, miscible with most organic solvents and a good general solvent for organic solids. It is unchanged by heating with water to 200°, but hot, fuming hydrobromic acid gives 1:5-dibromopentane. Nitric acid (50%) oxidizes it to succinic acid.

For further reading on tetrahydropyrans, see Elderfield and Dodd (1950).

Dioxolan (XVI) (formaldehyde ethylene acetal; glycol methylene ether) is obtained by heating formaldehyde and glycol in the presence of phosphoric acid. It is a pleasant-smelling liquid, b.p. 78°, miscible with water and stable to hot, dilute mineral acids. For a review on dioxolans, see Elderfield and Short (1957).

Dioxan (XVII), i.e. 1:4-dioxan, the cyclic ether of glycol, is obtained by distilling glycol with zinc chloride or concentrated sulphuric acid. It is a colourless liquid (m.p. 11°, b.p. 102°) of density 1·04. The odour is agreeable, not unlike that of acetone, but dioxan is poisonous and has caused several deaths (Browning, 1953). It is miscible with water and the majority of organic solvents. It has a low dielectric constant and is often used to lower that of aqueous solutions for experimental purposes. It is stable towards heating with water, but hydriodic acid at 140° converts it to ethyl iodide. Dioxan is produced commercially in quantity as a solvent, but such material requires careful purification for experimental work if the presence of acids, or of substances absorbing in the ultraviolet, is objectionable. 1:2-Dioxan is also known (Criegee and Müller, 1956).

For further reading on dioxans, see Kremer and Rochen (1957).

XVIII

1:3:5-*Trioxan* (XVIII) (trioxymethylene) is a white solid, m.p. 64°, with a weak chloroform-like odour. It is obtained by polymerizing formaldehyde, e.g. by leading the vapour into ice-water. It is soluble in six parts of water at 20° and very soluble in organic solvents. It is unchanged by boiling with water and gives no reaction for aldehydes. Trioxan is used as a fuel in military field kits.

Paraldehyde (2:4:6-trimethyl-1:3:5-trioxan), a liquid b.p. 124°, is formed by the catalytic polymerization of acetaldehyde (e.g. with sulphur dioxide) and depolymerizes partly on simple distillation, or completely if a little sulphuric acid is added. It has a penetrating apple-like odour and unpleasant burning taste. It is fairly soluble in cold water and the aqueous solution is stable. Paraldehyde is used in medicine as a hypnotic, particularly for children.

(b) **The cyclic semiacetals**

These substances (e.g. XX) are quite distinct from the above cyclic ethers. They are formed when attempts are made to prepare γ- or δ-hydroxy-aldehydes. Thus any attempt to prepare γ-hydroxyvaleraldehyde (XIX) gives only 2-hydroxy-5-methyl-tetrahydrofuran (XX). The latter combines with phenylhydrazine to give the phenylhydrazone of (XIX); and with acetic anhydride, the acetate of (XX). δ-Hydroxycapraldehyde and 2-hydroxy-6-methyltetrahydropyran form a similar pair. The relationship (XIX) ⇌ (XX) is one of the most often quoted examples of ring-chain tautomerism. A study of ratios at equilibrium has shown that γ- and δ-hydroxyaldehydes are predominantly in the cyclic form, e.g. (XX), but that the higher aldehydes and some hydroxy-ketones (in particular (XXI)) are mainly in the chain form (Hurd and Saunders, 1952). Glucose in cold, aqueous solution exists predominantly as a cyclic semiacetal (XXII), and so does fructose although it is a ketone.

$$
\begin{array}{ccc}
& & CH_2\!-\!CH_2 \\
& & | \qquad | \\
CH_2\!-\!-CH_2 & CH_2\!-\!CH_2 & CH_2 \quad COCH_3 \\
| \qquad | & | \qquad | & | \\
H_3C\!-\!CH \quad CHO & H_3C\!-\!CH \qquad CHOH & CH_2 \\
& \diagdown\!O\!\diagup & | \\
| & & CH_2 \\
OH & & | \\
& & OH \\
XIX & XX & XXI
\end{array}
$$

$$
\begin{array}{c}
CHOH \\
CHOH \quad CHOH \\
| \qquad\qquad | \\
OHCH_2CH \qquad CHOH \\
\diagdown\!O\!\diagup \\
XXII
\end{array}
$$

(c) **Lactones** (the cyclic esters)

Traditionally, the terms β-, γ- and δ-lactones have been applied to internal esters consisting of four-, five- and six-membered rings respectively. α-Lactones are unknown.

The β-hydroxycarboxylic acids have no evident tendency

to form even traces of lactones on standing in solution. However, aqueous solutions of γ- and δ-hydroxy-acids always form equilibrium mixtures containing the respective lactones. At $25°$, equilibrium favours the open chain for δ-hydroxy-acids (Hurd and Saunders, 1952), but good yields of lactones can be had by warming the solutions. Thus γ-lactones are more difficult to form and also more difficult to hydrolyse than δ-lactones.

The C_4–C_6 members have abnormally high dipole moments, compared to esters, because ring-strain forces them into a *cis* conformation (see p. 9). These members also hydrolyse with abnormal ease: in warm solution they can be instantly titrated with $0 \cdot 1$ N-sodium hydroxide. The high energy-level of the *cis* members enables the transition state (i.e. addition of a hydroxyl anion to the carbonyl-group) to be reached with little further activation energy. The higher members (C_9 and upwards) have dipole moments and rates of hydrolysis similar to those of ordinary aliphatic esters (see Table 2). The difference in potential energy between the two kinds of lactone is about 4 Kcal per Mole.

TABLE 2. Simple Lactones
(Huisgen, 1957)

Number of atoms in ring	Dipole moment in benzene D	Rate of alkaline hydrolysis in 60% dioxan-water at $0°$, $10^4 k_2$ (sec^{-1} . Mole)
5a	4·09	1,480
6	4·22	55,000
7	4·45	2,550
10	2·01	0·22
11	1·88	—
12	1·86	3·3
13	1·86	6·0
14	1·86	1·8
16	1·79	—

a. butyrolactone

β-*Propiolactone* (XXIII) was obtained for the first time in 1916 when it was prepared (in poor yield) by the action of silver nitrate on sodium β-iodopropionate. It is now more readily available from the reaction of formaldehyde with ketene (Küng, 1941). It is a colourless liquid of sharp, aromatic odour (m.p. $-33°$, b.p.$_{11}$ $51°$; d_{20} $1 \cdot 15$; n_D^{20} $1 \cdot 41$). It is soluble in two parts of cold water and this solution becomes completely hydrolysed (to hydracrylic acid) in five days. It is stable in the anhydrous condition. Propiolactone reacts, even in the presence of water, with amino-, hydroxy- and activated methylene-groups. An example of the latter is its reaction with an aqueous suspension of sodio-acetoacetic ester to give $CH_3COCH(COOC_2H_5)CH_2$ CH_2COOH. For other reactions, see Gresham, Jansen and Shaver (1948).

XXIII   XXIV   XXV   XXVI

Other β-lactones are known (Zaugg, 1954), but have been little studied.

γ-*Butyrolactone* is a colourless liquid (b.p. 204°), miscible with water but salted out by potassium carbonate. It is formed by heating aqueous γ-hydroxybutyric acid (a reaction accelerated by acids). The aqueous solution hydrolyses only slowly to hydroxybutyric acid unless accelerated by sodium hydroxide. γ-Butyrolactone is available commercially in quantity and is used as a solvent (especially for polyacrylonitrile) and intermediate.

δ-*Valerolactone* can be prepared in excellent yield by Reppe's process, heating tetrahydrofuran with carbon monoxide, nickel carbonyl and halogens at 250° and 200 atmospheres. It is a liquid of b.p. 220° and is only sparingly soluble in water. The isomeric γ-*tetrahydropyrone* (XXIV) is obtained by the catalytic hydrogenation of γ-pyrone (Chapter VII). It is a liquid, b.p. 166°, miscible with water. Unlike γ-pyrone, it is a typical aliphatic ketone, readily forming a semicarbazone and oxime.

β-Hydroxy-β-methyl-δ-valerolactone is utilized by the mammalian liver for the biosynthesis of cholesterol, and is believed to be the normal precursor (Tavormina, Gibbs and Huff, 1956).

Lactide (3:6-dimethyl-2:5-dioxodioxan) is a dilactone obtained by heating lactic acid. It is a solid, slightly soluble in cold water which hydrolyses it to lactic acid. It is available commercially in quantity.

The α- and β-tetronic acids are five-membered ring substances, the lactones of α- and β-keto-γ-hydroxybutyric acid respectively. Derivatives of β-tetronic acid are produced by the mould *Penicillium charlesii*.

Lactones with C_{15}–C_{18} are easily made and have a musk-like odour, of interest to the perfumery industry. The C_{15} member, exaltolide by name, is found in angelica root. Lactones with C_7–C_{13} are not easily formed. Unsaturated lactones are dealt with in Chapter VII.

(d) The cyclic acid anhydrides

Those of C_4 and C_5 dibasic acids, e.g. succinic anhydride (XXV) and glutaric anhydride, are derivatives of furan and pyran respectively. Few cyclic anhydrides of C_3 acids are known; those of C_6 and higher acids are usually in the form of polymeric chains. Succinic and glutaric anhydrides are soluble in water and have (unimolecular) velocity constants for hydrolysis at room temperature, of 0·04 and 0·05 respectively (min., $\log_{10}$). Thus they hydrolyse at about the same rate as acetic anhydride. These cyclic anhydrides are usually prepared by heating the acid with phosphorus oxychloride. Acids substituted by one or more methyl-groups tend to form anhydrides much more readily, but such anhydrides are usually more easily hydrolysed. Dimethylmalonic anhydride is an example of the rare four-membered ring anhydrides. It breaks down on heating to dimethylketene: $(CH_3)_2C{:}CO$.

For further comparison between aliphatic and cyclic anhydrides, see the notes on dipole moments (p. 9).

(e) The cyclic carbonates

Ethylene carbonate (XXVI) (glycol carbonate) is representative of these. It is prepared by the action of phosgene on glycol at room-temperature. It is a white solid, m.p. 39°, very soluble in water and the majority of organic solvents, but poorly soluble in dry ether. On boiling with alkalis, glycol is regenerated. Ethylene carbonate has been found a very useful reagent for the introduction of β-hydroxyethyl-groups into alcohols and amines. See also the notes on dipole moments (p. 9).

2. SULPHUR-CONTAINING SYSTEMS

Sulphur analogues are known of many of the oxygen-containing systems which have been discussed. A few examples will now be given. These substances can all be oxidized by potassium permanganate to the corresponding sulphones. They form methylsulphonium iodides with methyl iodide. Neither of these reactions is given by their completely unsaturated analogues (e.g. thiophen).

XXVII   XXVIII   XXIX

Ethylene sulphide (XXVII) is prepared (in 80% yield) by the action of phosgene on 2-mercapto-ethanol (Reynolds, 1957). It is a colourless liquid (b.p. 56°), insoluble in water, and it polymerizes on storage. *Trimethylene sulphide* (b.p. 94°) is formed in 10% yield by the action of sodium sulphide on 1:3-dibromopropane. It has a disagreeable smell and has been little studied.

Tetrahydrothiophen (thiolan), the sulphur analogue of tetrahydrofuran, is similarly prepared from 1:4-dibromobutane. It can be obtained in 71% yield by the hydrogenation of thiophen over palladium (Mozingo *et al.*, 1945). It is a colourless liquid with an unpleasant penetrating odour, insoluble in water, but soluble in organic solvents, b.p. 119°; *d.* 0·98; n_D^{20} 1·49; log ε_{max} 2·9 at 220 mμ. Biotin, an important growth-factor, contains the thiolan ring, not as such but fused to an ethyleneurea ring (XLIX).

Tetrahydrothiapyran (XXVIII) is formed similarly from 1:5-di-iodopentane. It forms crystals, m.p. 13°, b.p. 142°; *d.* 0·99; n_D^{20} 1·50. It has a penetrating smell, is insoluble in water but volatile in steam. It is more stable than its four- and five-membered analogues and is unchanged by long heating with aqueous acids and alkalis. Sulphur has little tendency to form larger rings by the above type of reaction.

Dithiolan (trimethylene disulphide, XXIX, R=H) may be prepared from trimethylene dibromide and sodium disulphide. It is an unpleasant-smelling, yellow oil which polymerizes (by ring-opening) on heating. Unlike aliphatic disulphides, it is stable to aqueous potassium cyanide but is readily reduced to the (ring-opened) dithiol by zinc and hydrochloric acid. The dithiol, in turn, is oxidized to dithiolan by iodine. Thioctic acid (XXIX, R = $(CH_2)_4 \cdot COOH$) is an important coenzyme in the oxidative decarboxylation of pyruvic acid and other α-keto-acids, and it seems to play an important role in linking photo-synthesis in plants with the citric acid cycle. It is prepared in six stages from ethyl δ-chloroformylvalerate (Reed and Niu, 1955).

Dithian and *trithian* the sulphur analogues respectively of dioxan and trioxan are colourless, odourless solids, m.p. 112° and 218° respectively. They are almost insoluble in water.

For further reading, see Elderfield (1957). For thiolactones, see Korte and Löhmer, 1958.

3. NITROGEN-CONTAINING SYSTEMS

(a) **The cyclic amines**

These simple nitrogen-containing rings are usually formed:

(*a*) By heating the salt of an aliphatic α:ω-diamine, with elimination of ammonia;

(*b*) By heating an α-bromo-ω-amine with aqueous alkali (hydrogen bromide is eliminated);

(*c*) By heating an α:ω-dibromo-hydrocarbon with ammonia, or with a primary amine (for an N-alkyl-derivative), or with *p*-toluenesulphonamide followed by saponification or reduction to remove the toluenesulphonyl-group;

(*d*) By hydrogenation of the corresponding unsaturated heterocyclic substances;

(*e*) By reduction of the α-hydroxy-derivatives (e.g. piperidine from 2-ketopiperidine).

They are colourless liquids, having the typical odour of aliphatic secondary amines and forming N-nitroso-compounds with nitrous acid. Methyl iodide gives first the N-methyl-derivatives, and (in excess) the corresponding dimethyl-quaternary salts.

The kinetics for reaction (*b*) have been investigated. As the table below indicates, ring-closure is fastest for the five-membered and slowest for the four-membered rings. Corresponding figures for reactions (*a*) and (*c*) would be of great interest.

First-order Rate Constants for Ring-closure
of Bromoalkylamines $Br(CH_2)_nNH_2$
(Freundlich and Kroepelin, 1926)

n	$k_{25°}$
2	0·036
3	0·0005
4	approx. 30
5	0·50
6	0·001

Ethylenimine (XXX) (aziridine) is best made by heating 2-aminoethanol in turn with sulphuric acid (which forms the O-sulphate) and sodium hydroxide. Unlike the higher homologues, it cannot be prepared by heating the appropriate diamine because ethylenediamine gives piperazine (XI) when treated in this way. It is a colourless, stable liquid, b.p. 56°, *d.* 0·83, completely miscible with water. The aqueous solution is strongly alkaline and hydrolyses even at 20°, to 2-aminoethanol. Solutions in dilute hydrochloric acid change to 2-chloroethylamine (a second-order reaction). It does not react with bromine nor with acidic or alkaline potassium permanganate at room-temperature. The low basic strength ($pK_a = 8·0$), relative to piperidine and pyrrolidine, is attributed to an increase of ring-strain upon quaternization (Brown and Gerstein, 1950; O'Rourke *et al.*, 1956).

XXX   XXXI   XXXII

Ethylenimine is highly toxic. It blisters the skin, apparently because it reacts vigorously with thiols to give the S-aminoethyl-derivatives, even in aqueous solution. Substances of the nitrogen

C

mustard series, such as (XXXI), have been shown to form blistering ethylenimmonium salts (XXXII) as intermediates in their hydrolysis to substituted ethanolamines which are quite bland (Hanby *et al.*, 1947). The details of this reaction, which is reversible, have been fully worked out.

For further reading on ethylenimines, see Fruton (1950).

Trimethylenimine (azetidine) is best prepared by condensing 1:3-dibromopropane with toluenesulphonamide and reducing the resultant sulphonazetidide (XXXIII) with sodium in alcohol (36% yield). It is a colourless, strongly basic liquid, b.p. 63°. It is stable to heating, even at 360°, but is hydrolysed to 3-chloropropylamine by dilute hydrochloric acid. Azetidine-2-carboxylic acid has been found in lily-of-the-valley (Convallaria) leaves (Fowden, 1956), and in other plant material.

$$\begin{array}{c} CH_2 \!-\! N \!-\! SO_2C_6H_4CH_3 \\ | \qquad\quad | \\ CH_2 \!-\! CH_2 \end{array}$$

XXXIII

For further reading on azetidines, see Ballard and Melstrom (1950).

Pyrrolidine (VIII) (tetrahydropyrrole; tetramethylenimine) is conveniently prepared by reaction (*c*) (see above), or by the catalytic hydrogenation of pyrrole (quantitative). Other methods include the electrolytic reduction of succinimide, the reduction of pyrrole with sodium and boiling amyl alcohol, and methods (*a*) and (*b*). Some physical properties are given in Table 1. Pyrrolidine-2-carboxylic acid (proline) is one of the more individual amino-acids present in proteins. Collagen and gelatin are particularly rich in it.

Piperidine (III), commercially the most available of the cyclic amines, is prepared by the catalytic hydrogenation of pyridine, or by the reduction of the latter with (i) zinc and hydrochloric acid, or (ii) sodium and ethyl alcohol. When passed over a nickel catalyst at 250°, it is converted to a mixture of pyridine and hydrogen. It is purified through the N-nitroso-derivative, but commercial material usually contains tetrahydropyridine which can be removed by careful fractionation.

Physical properties are given in Table 1. It is converted to piperidine-N-oxide by aqueous hydrogen peroxide.

The piperidine ring is opened by acting on the N-benzoyl derivative with phosphorus pentachloride, giving ε-benzoyl-aminoamyl chloride. Cyanogen bromide acts on the N-alkyl-piperidines to give ε-alkylaminoamyl bromides, a reaction which has a close parallel in aliphatic chemistry. Piperidine, when exhaustively methylated with methyl iodide, gives 1:3-pentadiene, just as diethylamine gives ethylene, on similar treatment.

Piperidine is used as a catalyst of condensations involving methylene groups. It is also used extensively in the rubber industry as an accelerator of vulcanization, both as such and as the compound which it forms with carbon disulphide (piperidinium pentamethylene dithiocarbamate).

For further reading on piperidines, see Mosher (1950).

Hexamethylenimine, an amine with a seven-membered ring, is conveniently made by reducing caprolactam (see below) with sodium in amyl alcohol or lithium aluminium hydride (Blicke and Doorenbas, 1954). It is a liquid, b.p. 138°. The corresponding eight- and nine-membered rings are made similarly, and are also stable.

All attempts to prepare 2-hydroxypyrrolidine and 2-hydroxy-piperidine, which would be the nitrogen analogues of the *cyclic acetals*, have failed. Thus, the reduction of 2-hydroxypyridine stops at 2-ketopiperidine.

XXXIV   XXXV   XXXVI   XXXVII

Several cyclic amines with more than one nitrogen are known.

Pyrazolidine (XXXIV) is made by the action of hydrazine on 1:3-dibromopropane. It is a stable liquid, b.p. 138°.

Iminazolidine (XXXV) has not yet been prepared but the

N:N'-diethyl derivative is known. The $-NHCH_2NH-$grouping is a point of weakness, in all substances which contain it. This grouping is broken by cold dilute mineral acids with the liberation of formaldehyde. *Bis*diethylaminomethane, for example, is at once converted to diethylamine and formaldehyde by cold, dilute hydrochloric acid. The $-OCH_2O-$grouping is more stable to acids (see dioxolan, above).

The N:N'-dii*so*butyl-derivative, prepared by the action of formaldehyde on 1:2-bis*iso*butylaminoethane, reverts to these intermediates when treated with dilute hydrochloric acid.

Piperazine (XXXVI) is the best known of the six-membered saturated rings containing two nitrogens.[1] It can be made by reducing pyrazine (Chapter IV) with sodium in alcohol; by heating ethylenediamine hydrochloride; by the action of ammonia on 1:2-dichloroethane; and by the action of ethylene bromide on ethylene diamine. The usual method is to heat aniline with ethylene bromide. This gives N:N'-diphenyl-piperazine which is easily converted to piperazine with nitrous acid. It is then purified through the dinitroso-derivative. The physical properties are given in Table 1. It is unchanged by heating with sulphuric acid at 250°. It is used in medicine against roundworms and threadworms in children; the N-methyl-N'-diethylcarbamyl-derivative ('Hetrazan') is the best substance available for treating filariasis, a tropical disease in which mosquito-borne worms invade the blood.

For further reading, see Pratt (1957).

Larger rings containing two nitrogens are readily formed, e.g. the eight-membered *bis*-trimethylenediamine, b.p. 186°.

Hexahydropyrimidine, the 1:3-isomer of piperazine, is made by the action of formaldehyde on trimethylenediamine. It appears to exist only in ring-chain tautomerism with N-methylene-trimethylenediamine (Branch, 1916), but the mixture gives 1:3-dibenzoylhexahydropyrimidine: this, like most cyclic substances containing $N \cdot CH_2 \cdot N$, is ring-opened by acid or alkali. Some other derivatives of hexahydropyrimidine will be found in Chapter VII under 'pyrimidine'.

Trimethylenetriamine (XXXVII) is known as its N:N':N''-trimethyl-derivative, prepared by mixing methylamine and

[1] It is hexahydropyrazine.

aqueous formaldehyde. It is a colourless liquid, b.p. 166°, with a fishy odour. It is soluble in water and organic solvents. Because it contains the $-NHCH_2NH$-grouping (see imidazolidine, above) it is easily split into its components by cold, dilute acids. The 'aldehyde-ammonias', formed by mixing aliphatic aldehydes and ammonia, are 2:4:6-trialkyl-derivatives of (XXXVII).

Hexamethylenetetramine (XXXVIII) (urotropin, hexamine), $(CH_2)_6N_4$ is similarly formed from ammonia and aqueous formaldehyde. It is a colourless solid that sublimes at about 260° without melting. At 12°, 100 g. of water dissolves 81 g. It is less soluble in boiling water, somewhat soluble in chloroform and alcohol but not in ether. It is unchanged by hot aqueous sodium hydroxide, but it is decomposed by cold dilute mineral acids (instantaneously at 100°) into formaldehyde and an ammonium salt. It is sometimes used as a portable fuel for sterilizing surgical instruments. The principal use is as a urinary antiseptic. For this purpose it is given orally and is voided in the urine, the acidity of which decomposes it, liberating formaldehyde which is the true antiseptic.

Hexamine is a cage-shaped molecule, having three-dimensional symmetry. Some simpler cage-molecules will now be described.

XXXVIII   XXXIX   XL

Quinuclidine (XXXIX) (1:4-ethanopiperidine) is made by heating 4-iodoethylpiperidine. It is a colourless solid, m.p. 158°, very soluble in water and organic solvents. The quinine alkaloids all contain a quinuclidine ring, to which they owe their basic properties.

Nortropane (XL) (2:6-ethanopiperidine or 2:5-propanopyrrolidine) is a colourless solid, m.p. 60°, very soluble in water and organic solvents. It is a fairly strong base. Tropane, the

N-methyl-derivative, forms the heterocyclic skeleton of the cocaine and atropine alkaloids. Ecgonine is a hydroxytropane-carboxylicacid.

Cocaine is a di-ester of ecgonine (XLI, a) the acid-group being methylated, and the alcoholic-group benzoylated. A geometric isomer of ecgonine also exists, known as ψ-ecgonine (XLI, b). The stereochemical relationship between ecgonine and ψ-ecgonine has been determined to be as in (XLI, a and b) (Findlay, 1954; Fodor, Kovács and Weisz, 1954).

XLI, a   XLI, b

For further reading on bridged compounds, see Ing in Elderfield (1950).

Pyrrolizidine, b.p. 146°, is a related molecule, but much simpler because only two atoms are shared by the two rings. It consists of two five-membered rings, fused, fully saturated, and sharing a carbon and a nitrogen atom. It forms the skeleton of the Senecio alkaloids, found in *Senecio*, the largest genus of the *Compositae* or daisy family, and in some members of the *Leguminosae* and *Boraginaceae* (e.g. Heliotropum). Cattle eating these plants sustain liver-damage and the blood shows a high content of copper. Pyrrolizidine is prepared by heating 2(γ-aminopropyl)tetrahydrofuran with hydrobromic acid, and cyclizing the resultant 4:7-dibromo-1-aminoheptane with alkali (Sorm and Arnold, 1947).

Norlupinane (octahydropyridocoline; quinolizidine), the parent substance of the lupin alkaloids, found in the *Leguminosae*, is similar to pyrrolizidine, but consists of two fused *hexagons* sharing one nitrogen and one carbon atom. It is obtainable by heating 5-amino-1:9-dibromononane (Prelog and Bozicevic, 1939).

(b) **Lactams** (the cyclic acid amides)

These substances are the nitrogen-analogues of the lactones. They are more difficult to make than the lactones, and harder to hydrolyse. No α-lactams (three-membered rings) have yet been prepared.

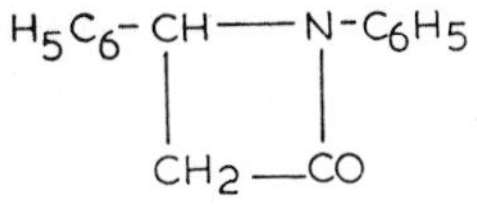

XLII

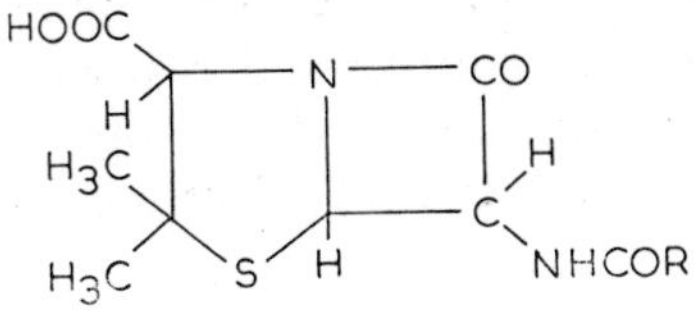

XLIII

R is usually benzyl

Several β-lactams have been prepared. One of the best known is diphenylpropiolactam (XLII), obtained by the action of ketene (or ethyl bromoacetate) on benzylidine-aniline. These diaryl-β-lactams are stable to hydrolysis, whereas the corresponding di-alkyl derivatives (e.g. those made by the action of Grignard reagents on ethyl β-ethylaminobutyrate) are readily hydrolysed by cold dilute mineral acids or alkalis. Propiolactam (unsubstituted lactam of β-alanine) is unknown. β-Lactams are not obtained when β-amino-acids are heated, but β-amino-carboxamides may behave differently because aspartic acid gives propiolactam carboxylic acid (Talley, Fitzpatrick and Porter, 1956). Much of the interest in β-lactams followed the realization that penicillin (XLIII) contained such a ring.

N-Methyl-β-propiolactam (1-methyl-2-azetidinone) hydrolyses with alkali about 10^3 times as fast as an aliphatic amide, but benzylpenicillin (ordinary medicinal penicillin) is hydrolysed 4000 times faster than this lactam. Holley (1953) attributes this heightened instability of penicillin to loss of amide resonance (in the $-\mathrm{CON}\diagdown^{C}_{C}$ group) through steric hindrance, one of the carbons attached to the nitrogen being 55° out of the plane of the amide group.

For further reading on propiolactams, see Ballard and Melstrom (1950); Sheehan and Corey (1957).

2-*Oxopyrrolidine* (XLIV) (2-pyrrolidone; butyrolactam), the next higher homologue, is readily prepared by heating dry γ-aminobutyric acid. It is a colourless solid, m.p. 25°, very soluble in water. The solution is neutral. It requires protracted boiling with aqueous sodium hydroxide or hydrochloric acid to effect hydrolysis. As '2-Ketopyrrolidine' it is available commercially in quantity and is used as a solvent and intermediate. Polymerized N-vinyl-2-ketopyrrolidine (*periston*) is used in transfusions as a partial substitute for blood.

$$CH_2-CH_2$$
$$CH_2 \quad CO$$
$$N$$
$$H$$
XLIV

$$CH_2-CO$$
$$CO-N \cdot C_6H_5$$
XLV

$$CH_2-CH_2$$
$$CO \quad CO$$
$$N$$
$$H$$
XLVI

2-*Oxopiperidine* (α-piperidone; valerolactam) is the corresponding six-membered ring. It can be made by heating δ-aminovaleric acid above its melting-point, by the catalytic hydrogenation of 2-hydroxypyridine, or by the action of concentrated sulphuric acid on *cyclo*pentanone-oxime. It is a colourless solid, m.p. 40°, b.p. 258°, almost odourless and very soluble in water to a neutral solution. For hydrolysis, boiling with strong solutions of acid or alkali is required. It is readily soluble in all solvents. Reduction with sodium in amyl alcohol gives piperidine. The N-acetyl-derivative is formed by acetic anhydride. Unlike δ-aminovaleric acid, 2-oxopiperidine is distinctly poisonous.

The isomeric 4-oxopiperidine (γ-piperidone) is not an acid amide, like the above, but a normal ketone, giving oximes and other ketonic derivatives. Several alkyl-derivatives are well-known substances (e.g. the 2:2:6-trimethyl-derivative, made from acetone and ammonia).

The C_5 to C_9 lactams have dipole moments that *fall* gently with rising concentration: these homologues are believed to have the *cis* conformation (see p. 14) and to be associating in pairs by two hydrogen bonds. The higher homologues (C_{10} and upwards) have moments that *rise* sharply with concentration and hence are believed to have the normal *trans* configuration (Huisgen, 1957). Infrared data support this classification.

2-Oxo-hexa-, hepta- and octa-methylenimines can be prepared in good yield by the action of hydrazoic acid on *cyclo*hexanone and its homologues (Blicke and Doorenbas, 1954). These seven-, eight- and nine-membered rings are quite stable.

ε-Caprolactam is the seven-membered analogue of (XLIV). It is also obtainable by the dry distillation of ε-amino-*n*-caproic acid or by heating *cyclo*hexanoneoxime with sulphuric acid and is commercially available in quantity. It is a colourless solid, m.p. 70°, very soluble in water and organic solvents. When polymerized ε-caprolactam gives Perlon (Nylon 6), a later addition to the nylon family of artificial fibres.

(c) **Cyclic amides of dicarboxylic acids** (cyclic imides)
No three-membered ring of this kind is known. Malonimide, the simplest four-membered ring is unknown, but the N-phenyl-derivative (XLV), (1-phenyl-2:4-diketoazetidine) has been prepared by heating the monoanilide of malonic acid at 200°. It is unaffected by concentrated nitric acid, but sodium hydroxide hydrolyses it to sodium malonate and aniline.

Succinimide (XLVI) (2:5-diketopyrrolidine) is obtained by heating succinic acid in a stream of ammonia at 180°. It is a highly stable, colourless solid, m.p. 127°, b.p. 288°, soluble in about ten parts of cold water. It is an acid of pK_a 9·7, comparable in strength with phenol. Treatment with methyl iodide at 100° gives N-methylsuccinimide exclusively. Hypobromous acid forms N-bromosuccinimide which is widely used as a selective brominating agent. The formula of succinimide can be written tautomerically as 2:5-dihydroxypyrrole, as discussed in Chapter V.

Succinimidine (the di-imine of succinimide) is formed from 1:2-dicyanoethane (succinonitrile) and ammonia at 70° (Elvidge and Linstead, 1954).

Glutarimide (2:6-diketopiperidine) is the corresponding six-membered ring. It is made by heating ammonium glutarate at 175°. It is a colourless solid, m.p. 154°, soluble in water and in boiling benzene but almost insoluble in ether. Glutarimide, pK = 11·4, is a weaker acid than succinimide, and is more readily hydrolysed by alkali.

(d) **Miscellaneous**

2:5-*Dioxopiperazine* (XLVII) (diketopiperazine; glycine anhy-dride) is made by heating glycine (e.g. in glycerol). It is a colourless solid, m.p. 311° (dec.), very difficultly soluble in water and insoluble in most other solvents. It is fairly stable, but can be hydrolysed to glycylglycine with cold 10N-hydrochloric acid or cold N-sodium hydroxide. The carbonyl groups in this substance form part of amide groups, as indicated by electron diffraction measurements (Speakman, 1954), and they yield no ketonic derivatives such as oximes. Evidently the methylene groups are activated because reaction with benzaldehyde and acetic anhydride at 120° gives the 3:6-benzylidine derivative.

XLVII   XLVIII

Pyrazolidone (XLVIII), isomeric with ethylene-urea, is pre-pared from hydrazine and β-chloropropionic acid. Phenidone (N-phenylpyrazolid-3-one) is used to replace metol (elon) as a catalyst for quinol in photographic developers (Kendall, 1951).

XLIX   L   LI   LII   LIII

Ethylene-urea (XLIX) (2-iminazolidone) is made by heating ethylenediamine and diethyl carbonate at 180°. It is a colourless solid (m.p. 131°), very soluble in water, but poorly in ether. The growth factor, biotin, contains the ethylene-urea ring fused to a tetrahydrothiophen ring.

Ethylene-thiourea (2-iminazolidinethione) is the corresponding derivative of thiourea and is prepared quantitatively by mixing ethylenediamine and carbon disulphide (the thiocarbamate: $NH_3^+CH_2CH_2NHCS_2^-$ is an intermediate). It is a colourless solid, m.p. 197°, soluble in alkali, and is oxidized by iodine to a disulphide. It forms complexes with cuprous and silver ions. These reactions suggest that, like thiourea, it exists in equilibrium with a mercapto-tautomer which, in the present case, would be 2-mercapto-Δ^2-iminazoline (L).

4. MIXED SYSTEMS

Several fully-saturated heterocyclic substances are known containing two different hetero-atoms. The following are among the more interesting.

Morpholine (LI) (tetrahydro-1:4-oxazine) is obtainable by heating β:β'-dichloro-diethyl ether (from diethylene glycol) with ammonia. It is commercially available in quantity. It is a hygroscopic liquid with the typical odour of a secondary amine, b.p. 128°; *d.* 1·00; n_D^{20} 1·45. It is a fairly strong base, but weaker than piperidine, and is miscible with water and organic solvents. It is used (*a*) to form wax-emulsions which impart a high gloss to objects without the necessity for polishing, (*b*) as a corrosion inhibitor in boilers, and (*c*) as a raw material for rubber accelerators. N-Ethylmorpholine is a valuable buffer for the pH 7 region when the use of phosphates must be avoided.

Oxazolidine (LII). An aldehyde or ketone, when condensed with a β-aminoalcohol, forms an equilibrium mixture of the azomethine (e.g. $CH_2:NCH_2CH_2OH$) and an oxazolidine. Infrared studies show that the oxazolidine usually preponderates in this mixture (Bergmann, 1953). 2-Oxo-oxazolidine (oxazolid-2-one) is formed by combining phosgene with ethylene oxide to give β-chloroethyl chloroformate which is then cyclized with ammonia. When heated with phosphoric acid, oxazolidone gives phosphorylethanolamine (Jones, 1956). 2:5-Dioxo-oxazolidine, usually referred to as N-carboxyglycine anhydride, will be found in Chapter VI. Troxidone (tridione), a drug used in controlling the *petit mal* type of epilepsy, is 2:4-dioxo-3:5:5-trimethyloxazolidine. The antithyroid (goitrogenic) substance obtained from turnips and cabbage is 5-vinyl-2-thio-oxazolidine (Astwood, Greer and Ettlinger, 1949).

Isoxazolidine, isomeric with oxazolidine, has the $-O-$ and $-NH-$ adjacent. Cycloserine, an antibiotic, is 4-amino-3-oxoisoxazolidine (Hidy *et al.*, 1955).

Thiazolidine (tetrahydrothiazole) and a number of its derivatives have been made, particularly since this nucleus was recognized in penicillin (XLIII). Thiazolidine is prepared by warming β-mercaptoethylamine and formaldehyde (Ratner and Clarke, 1937). The thiazolidines are stronger bases than aniline, but weaker than ammonia. They are not very stable, the aqueous solutions always being in equilibrium with the aldehyde and β-amino-thiol from which they were formed: thus they freely give tests characteristic of these three groups. The $-NH-$ group is easily acylated, and they are then much more stable to hydrolysis. In penicillin, the β-lactam ring hydrolyses much more readily than the thiazolidine ring.

2-*Mercapto*-4-*oxothiazolidine* (LIII) (rhodanine) is an important microanalytical reagent, made from chloroacetic acid and sodium dithiocarbamate. It forms characteristic salts with the ions of heavy metals. The methylene-group is highly reactive and gives azomethine derivatives, of characteristic melting-points, with aliphatic aldehydes. The azomethine formed by *p*-dimethylaminobenzaldehyde is one of the most sensitive reagents known for silver. For a review of thiazolidines, see Cook and Heilbron (1949).

CHAPTER III

A General Discussion on Heteroaromatics

[i.e. Completely unsaturated heterocycles]

MANY OF THE MOST IMPORTANT and chemically interesting families of heterocyclic substances are completely unsaturated, like benzene. These *heteroaromatic substances* are conveniently sub-divided into two classes: ring-systems in which the carbon atoms have a deficiency of π-electrons, and ring-systems with an excess. The nature of this difference will now be explained.

In the second quarter of the present century the results of an investigation into the quantum mechanics of electrons were applied to molecular theory. It became clear that substances whose formulae are commonly written with two or more con-jugated double-bonds actually have a number of electrons which have a much larger mobility than the others. One such electron is derived from each atom contributing to the 'double-bond', and these electrons form a pool which circulates around the molecule in what are termed molecular orbitals. These non-localized electrons are called π-electrons, and their orbitals form layers above and below the molecule and have very little overlap with the orbitals of the other electrons (the σ-electrons). Molecular orbitals are most highly developed in conjugated cyclic structures such as benzene, and are responsible for what is commonly called 'aromatic character'.

The two most important aspects of aromatic character are: (i) a considerable degree of chemical inertness (relative to olefins) especially towards addition-reactions (including hydrogena-tion); and (ii) an ability to concentrate a charge in a distant part of a molecule in response to the insertion of a substituent (or to the approach of a reagent of like charge). The properties of the molecular orbitals which give rise to these aromatic properties are: (i) the delocalization energy (akin to the older concept of resonance energy) arising from the enlarged space in which the electrons move and leading to a lower tendency to chemical reaction; and (ii) the ease with which an electrical influence in one part of the molecule can be instantly carried by the π-electrons to even the remotest part (partial localization). If many powerful electron-attracting substituents are introduced into an aromatic nucleus, localization exceeds delocalization and aromatic character is lost (see pp. 50 and 83).

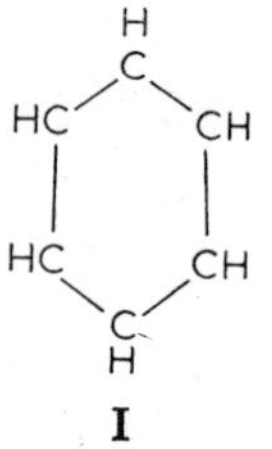

I 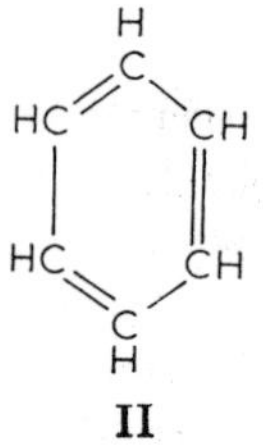   II

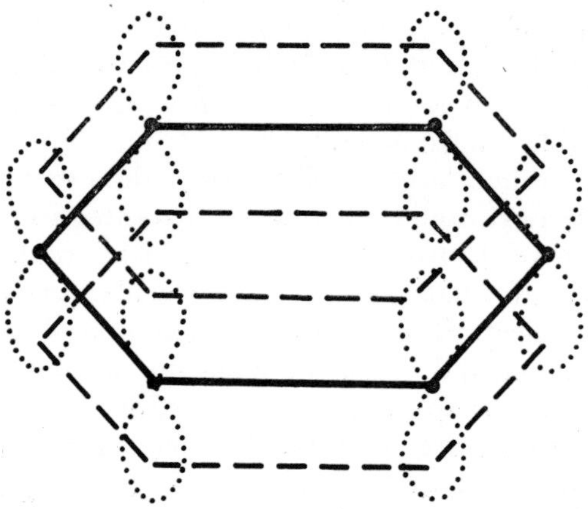

III

As an example of a typical aromatic substance, let us consider benzene whose formula, shorn of its π-electrons, may conveniently be written as (I), only the σ-bonds being shown. (The σ-electrons, which form these σ-bonds, are confined to the two atoms which they connect.) Because no simple convention exists for showing the electron-distribution in benzene, it is

customary still to use the classical formula (II) showing alternat-
ing single and double bonds. The use of this classical formula
entails considerable mental reservations and a much truer picture is given by (III), in which the six large dots represent the
carbon atoms. However this formula (cf. Coulson, 1947) is too
complex for convenient use.

In the last twenty years, the custom has arisen of constructing
'molecular diagrams' to show the distribution of electrons in
aromatic molecules. It is seen from (IV) that benzene has no
charge in excess of the average of one π-electron per carbon
atom. However, when a substituent is introduced into benzene,
a non-uniform distribution of electric charge results from the
partial localization of π-electrons. This effect is most marked in
mesomeric substitution. For example, in aniline the amino-
group shares its lone electrons with the π-electrons of the ring,
resulting in the uneven distribution shown in (V). The amino-
group carries a positive charge as great as the sum of all the
negative charges. In this convention, known as *nett charge*, the
$-NH_2$ is shown with a positive sign because it has a deficit of
electrons. An alternative convention, called *excess charge*, reverses
these signs. Another and more confusing notation is shown in
(VI). The student should practise converting formulae which
use these conventions into those showing nett charge, as used
throughout the present book.

The flow of electrons is not always in the direction shown in
(V). In nitrobenzene, the nitro-group attracts π-electrons with
the result shown in (VII).

These charges can be determined experimentally from
measurements of dipole moments, but the order of accuracy is

insufficient for the purpose. The figures usually quoted are found by rather complex calculations of another kind. Three systems of calculation are in use, (*a*) the method of molecular orbitals (Coulson, 1947; Lennard-Jones and Coulson, 1939); (*b*) the valence bond method (Daudel and Pullman, 1946; Pullman, 1947); and (*c*) Wheland's approximate method of resonance structures. Both methods (*a*) and (*b*) have led to similar conclusions. All examples of nett charge depicted in this book were obtained by the molecular orbital method.[1] Yet even this method, in its present form, gives figures of relative, rather than of absolute, accuracy. Small as the figures in (V) may seem, it is evident from dipole measurements that they are too great and that the true values should lie much nearer to o (it is not yet known by what common factor they should all be divided). Hence we must accustom our minds to the fact that very big differences in chemical reactivity are caused by minute accumulations of excess charge.

The special problems encountered in calculating excess charges in *heterocyclic* molecules have been discussed by Longuet-Higgins and Coulson (1947, 1949).[2] When the heterocyclic ring is derived by replacing =C– by =N– the hetero-atom has an
$$\text{H}$$
overall electron-attracting effect and is able to attract π-electrons, thus conferring positive charges upon the other ring-atoms. Thus pyridine has the distribution of charge shown in (VIII), the most electron-rich atom being the nitrogen (to be compared to the nitro-group of nitrobenzene) whereas all the carbon atoms have a deficiency of π-electrons, the 4-position being the most deficient (the distribution of charge is to be taken as symmetrical in this and other molecules where certain positions are left unlabelled).

Ring-systems whose carbon atoms are deficient in π-electrons will be dealt with at length in Chapter IV. Other heterocyclic rings have carbon atoms with an excess of π-electrons (Chapter V). Such substances are usually those derived from

[1] All the nett charge diagrams in this chapter were constructed by Prof. C. A. Coulson with the same parameters, and hence are comparable with one another.

[2] The numerical values of the heteroaromatic parameters h and k are known only approximately, the best values being for nitrogen (R. D. Brown, 1956).

an unsaturated cyclic hydrocarbon by replacing $-CH_2-$ by $-NH-$, or by $-O-$. In such cases, a lone pair of electrons is contributed by nitrogen, or oxygen, to the ring, giving 'an aromatic sextet of electrons', i.e. a double π-layer as in benzene, and hence increasing the stability of the molecule. Pyrrole (IX) is a typical example. Here the nitrogen contributes to the π-electrons as in aniline, and the nett charge is calculated to be as in (X). It should be noted that *cyclo*pentadiene, the hydrocarbon corresponding to pyrrole, is not aromatic because $-CH_2-$, unlike $-NH-$, has not a lone pair of electrons to make up the aromatic sextet. However, the anion of *cyclo*pentadiene (formed by loss of a proton) has an aromatic nature.

+O·18 +O·O5 +O·15 N -O·58   VIII

4 3 5 2 N H   IX

-O·O6 -O·IO +O·32 N H   X

In a study of aromatic hydrocarbons, the nett charges are small (or absent) and do not govern chemical reactivity to any extent. However, in substituted hydrocarbons (such as aniline) and in heteroaromatic substances, nett charge should have a large influence on substitution reactions (Wheland and Pauling, 1935). Such a correlation has been only imperfectly realized, but it is possible that further experience will enable the ease and orientation of substitution to be predicted, even in hitherto unexplored nuclei. Some semi-quantitative correlations will be pointed out in the following chapters. In general, positions in the molecule with excess charge can easily be substituted by electrophilic reagents (e.g. cold bromine), and those with a deficiency of charge usually react readily with nucleophilic reagents (e.g. sodamide). Reaction with free radicals is believed to depend upon another property (see below under Free Valence).

Present methods of calculating nett charge are at a disadvantage in polycyclic systems (e.g. quinoline), as they do not scale down an inductive effect (by the factor of two or more which laboratory experience indicates) when transferring it to an adjacent ring.

D

Some other aspects of electron-distribution will now be referred to.

Self-polarizability. The approach of a charged reagent to a polar molecule induces a redistribution of charge (Coulson and Longuet-Higgins, 1947). It is believed that this effect sometimes alters the distribution in such a way that an atom with less charge could be augmented to a value exceeding that of one normally more highly charged. Both π and σ bonds contribute to the polarizability of aromatic molecules (Bolton, 1954).

The magnitudes of this effect in N-heterocycles were studied by calculations based on molecular orbital theory (e.g. Sandorfy, Vroelant, Yvan, Chalvet and Daudel, 1950). A more recent reassessment indicates that, to a first order of approximation, the self-polarizabilities for quinoline and naphthalene are the same (Jaffé, 1955). The figures for naphthalene are given by Coulson and Longuet-Higgins, 1947.

Bond-orders. The delocalization of π-electrons causes the distances between atoms in aromatic rings to be less than those of single bonds and greater than those of isolated double bonds. The concept of *percentage double-bond character* was originated by Pauling in 1935 to express the degree to which a given bond approaches the properties of an isolated double-bond (as in ethylene). This property has been empirically related to the bond-length, and Pauling showed how it could be calculated also from resonance considerations. The tendency of aromatic bonds to undergo ethylene-like addition reactions increases progressively with their percentage double-bond character. Coulson showed in 1939 how to calculate percentage double-bond character also from molecular orbital theory and he expressed the result as *fractional bond-orders.* These are numerically one-hundredth of the percentage double-bond character.

The lengths of many bonds have been determined experimentally with great accuracy by electron diffraction and by X-ray diffraction. When plotted against bond-orders obtained by either the valence-bond or the M.O. methods of calculation, these lengths fit on a smooth curve. Hence this curve may be used to predict the bond-lengths for which experimental measurements have not been made.

There is an excellent agreement between all these methods.

Thus bond-orders, together with resonance energies, are those properties of π-electrons which we know with greatest precision. The M.O. bond-orders of benzene (XI), naphthalene (XII) and anthracene (XIII) are shown as examples. (Another notation is sometimes used in which $1 \cdot 0$ has been added to all the figures, in order to include the σ-electrons.)

XI   XII   XIII

XIV   XV   XVI

It is evident that the bonds in benzene are all of the same length and have $66 \cdot 7\%$ double-bond character. In naphthalene the bonds are of unequal length, the most ethylenic bond being that which connects the 1- and 2-positions (the four $\alpha:\beta$-bonds). The correspondingly placed bonds in anthracene (XIII) are also the most ethylenic.

In the light of claims that the magnitude of the bond-order can be used to predict the site where an *addition reaction* occurs, it should be noted that naphthalene adds ozone, osmium tetroxide and ethyl diazoacetate across the 1:2-bond. But hydrogenation with sodium gives 1:4-dihydronaphthalene. Anthracene adds osmium tetroxide and ethyl diazoacetate across the 1:2-bond, but maleic anhydride, hydrogen, halogens, nitric acid and benzoquinone are added across the 9:10-positions (XIV). Thus it seems that the magnitude of the bond-order is not the only factor determining addition reactions. Bond-orders are known for a number of heterocyclic substances, e.g. pyridine (XV) and pyrrole (XVI) (Longuet-Higgins and Coulson, 1947). It will be noted that pyrrole has two bonds which exceed those of benzene in double-bond character. It is well known that pyrrole undergoes addition in the 2:3-position (with 77% double-bond character) and enters into such reactions far more readily than benzene or pyridine. Thus a numerically small difference in bond-order makes for a large difference in reactivity. In such comparisons the mechanism of the reaction is assumed to be the same. This may not always be true.

In general, ring-systems deficient in π-electrons have little tendency towards bonds of an order higher than in benzene, whereas ring-systems rich in π-electrons tend to have some bond-orders of high value. This can be shown to be a consequence of the definition of bond-order.

Index of Free Valence. In an aromatic molecule, such as benzene, the bond-forming power of a carbon atom is not entirely used up in forming bonds to its neighbours. The residual bond-forming power, which is entirely a property of π-electrons, is called the Free Valence. This has nothing to do with excess charge and can sometimes have a large value when there is no excess charge at all, as in certain free radicals. However, the free valence of an atom is related to the bond-orders of the bonds radiating from the atom. High values for these bond-orders make for small values of free valence, and vice versa.

Where excess charge exists, as in aniline, pyridine or pyrrole, the concept of free valence has not been clearly defined. Hence the theoretical treatment of the attack of aromatic substances by free radicals was long delayed because no theoretical justification in terms of approximate activation energies could be made. Good progress in understanding this type of reaction has come more recently from the development of localization theory, which interprets the reactivities in terms of the appropriate atom localization energies, A_r (Wheland, 1942; R. D. Brown, 1952) calculated from molecular orbitals. These localization energies represent that part of the activation energy which arises from the redistribution of π-electrons.

The free phenyl radical, derived from various sources, attacks all positions in pyridine, but particularly the 2-position (see Chapter IV (2j)). The results agree reasonably well with calculations of localization energy, but agreement is not so good as that obtained with purely aromatic substances.

π-Deficient N-Heteroaromatics

[i.e. Completely unsaturated heterocycles, having nitrogen as the sole hetero-element, and a deficit of π-electrons elsewhere]

THIS IS THE FIRST of three detailed chapters dealing with heteroaromatic substances. Those containing nitrogen as the sole hetero-element will be dealt with in the first two of these chapters, for they have the larger literature and the rules relating structure to properties are better understood. These nitrogenous heteroaromatics are further subdivided into systems deficient in π-electrons (this chapter), and systems with an excess of π-electrons (Chapter V).

All π-deficient heterocycles contain nitrogen,[1] and almost all are six-membered rings:[2] pyridine (I) is a typical example. As was explained in Chapter III, the nitrogen atom in a six-membered heteroaromatic ring attracts electrons from the π-double layer. Because the stability of aromatic-type substances is due to the π-electrons, the parent-substances dealt with in this chapter are less stable than benzene. This loss of stability is reflected in the following list of resonance energies obtained from quantum mechanical calculations[3] (Dewar, 1949):

Benzene	36 Kcal/Mole	Pyrimidine	26 Kcal/Mole
Pyridine	31	1:3:5-Triazine	20

When more than one ring-nitrogen is present, this loss of stability is seen in the greater tendency to hydrolytic degradation (see p. 49, below).

The attraction of the ring-nitrogen atom for the π-electrons causes a considerable polarization of the molecule (pyridine has a dipole moment of 2·3 D). This polarization causes the ring-carbon atoms to have low electron densities. As a consequence, the substances dealt with in this chapter should be less readily substituted by electrophilic reagents (e.g. cold bromine), and more readily by nucleophilic reagents (e.g. sodamide), than is benzene. That this is so will be shown (see pp. 62, 69).

1. THE PARENT SUBSTANCES

Apart from pyridine (I) and quinoline (which are commercially available in quantity) and acridine and *iso*quinoline, the parent substances dealt with in this chapter are somewhat rare

[1] Pyrylium salts (Chapter VII), which are oxygen-heterocycles, may be π-deficient, but the evidence is not clear.

[2] The indolenines (Chapter V) and the little-known aza-azulenes are possible exceptions. Also note, in Chapters V and VI, some five-membered rings, π-excessive by nature, but neutralized or even made π-deficient by inserting electron-attracting substituents. The aza*cyclo*heptatriene cation, so far unknown, is likely to be π-deficient.

[3] Resonance energies based on heats of combustion tend to be low for N-heterocycles, because incomplete oxidation of the nitrogen has not always been allowed for; heats of hydrogenation have seldom been attempted for heterocycles.

materials, even though some of their amino-, or hydroxy-derivatives are easily accessible. This rarity arises from difficulties in synthesis, most of the parent-substances being obtained by the removal of substituents from chloro-, mercapto- or carboxy-derivatives that are not commercially available.

Pyridine   Quinoline   Acridine[1]   *Iso*quinoline
I   II   III   IV

Phenanthridine[1]
V

Pyridine (I) may be regarded as the (theoretical) progenitor of this series. The addition of one and two benzene rings gives quinoline (II) and acridine (III) respectively. *Iso*quinoline (IV) is an isomer of quinoline obtained by adding the benzene ring to another position in pyridine (no other isomer is possible). A benzene ring could be added to quinoline to give five different isomers, viz.: in the 2:3-position to give acridine, in the 3:4-position to give phenanthridine (V), and on the three facets of the benzene rings to give the three benzquinolines. This process of adding rings is known as *annelation* (in the laboratory it is usually simpler to form the nitrogen-containing ring last). Quinoline, acridine and their isomers are known as *benzologues* of pyridine.

[1] Other methods of numbering these rings are also in use, but those given here are preferable and will be used throughout this book.

The introduction of further ring-nitrogen atoms into pyridine leads to *azalogues* of pyridine. A nitrogen atom can be introduced in three different positions, giving respectively pyridazine (VI), pyrimidine (VII) and pyrazine (VIII). Of these, pyrimidine is the parent-substance of many biologically important derivatives which have been extensively investigated. To speak in this way of introducing a further ring-nitrogen atom into pyridine is only a theoretical approach to the structures: in practice each must be independently synthesized.

Introduction of one more ring-nitrogen could give three different triazines, of which symmetrical triazine (IX) has been most studied. Of the higher azalogues of pyridine, only 1:2:4:5-tetrazine (X) is known and, as might be expected, it is explosive.

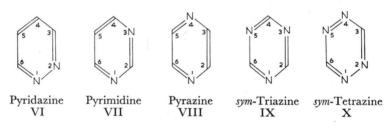

| Pyridazine | Pyrimidine | Pyrazine | *sym*-Triazine | *sym*-Tetrazine |
| VI | VII | VIII | IX | X |

The joining of a benzene ring to these diaza-benzenes leads to diazanaphthalenes such as quinazoline (XI). Other diaza-naphthalenes arise from the fusion of two pyridine rings, e.g. 1:5-naphthyridine (XII).[1]

The triazanaphthalenes have been little explored, but one of the tetra-azanaphthalenes, pteridine (XIII), has attracted considerable attention. Apart from their biological importance, the pteridines are of special chemical interest because the high N:C-ratio of the nucleus allows the characteristic properties of π-deficient systems to appear in a higher degree than in the lower azalogues.

Of the polyaza-anthracenes, phenazine (XIV) is the best known. Several of its derivatives occur in nature, and others are used as dyes. Polyazaphenanthrenes are also known, e.g. the phenanthrolines.

---

[1] The remaining diazanaphthalenes are cinnoline (1:2-), phthalazine (2:3-), quinoxaline (1:4) and the three naphthyridines. They are all numbered as in quinazoline.

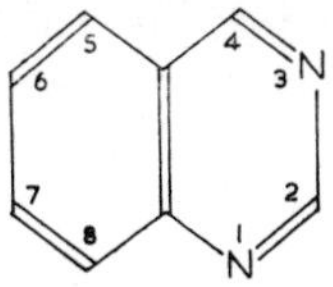

Quinazoline
XI

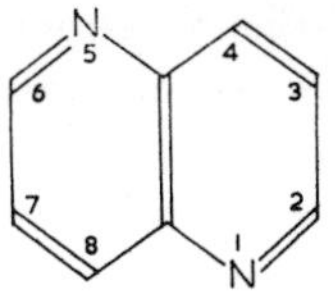

1:5-Naphthyridine
XII

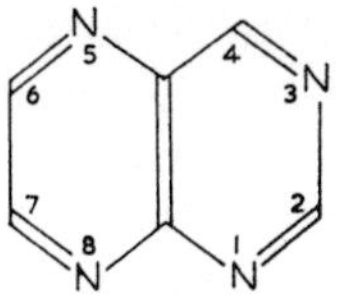

Pteridine
XIII

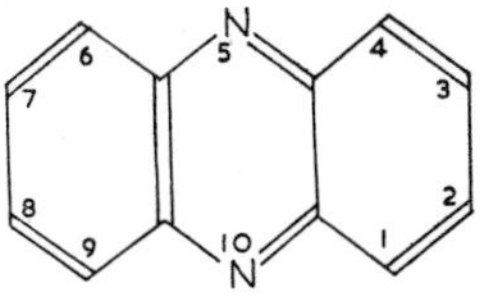

Phenazine
XIV

2. CORRELATION OF STRUCTURE AND PROPERTIES

At first sight, these heteroaromatic substances may seem to have properties at variance with their structural formulae: for example, the insolubilizing effect of hydroxy-substituents[1] seemed unreasonable to earlier workers. Nevertheless, when due attention is given to physico-chemical properties, a close connexion between structure and properties can be seen.

(a) Solubility

The lone pair of electrons on the nitrogen atoms are hydrogen-bonding and make π-deficient N-heterocycles (i.e. the parent-substances) more soluble in water than the corresponding hydrocarbons. For example, pyridine, unlike benzene, is completely miscible with water. The addition of benzene rings to pyridine naturally decreases the aqueous solubility (quinoline is soluble 1 in 150 at 20°),[2] but the insertion of further ring-nitrogen atoms restores high solubility, e.g. pteridine (XIII) is soluble 1 in 7.

On the other hand, substituents having a bondable hydrogen atom decrease the solubility very much, quite contrary to their

---

[1] This effect was first noticed in the purine series (see Chapter V).
[2] (Albert, 1955, c.) The figure, 1–15, found in some handbooks is incorrect.

effect in organic chemistry generally where, for example, hydroxy- and amino-groups increase the solubility in water of aliphatic and aromatic substances. Typical examples of this effect, which arises from the substituent groups forming hydrogen-bonds with water molecules, are given in Table 3.

TABLE 3. Solubility in Water at 20°

Substance	State	1 part in:
Hexane	liquid	7,500
1-Hexanol	liquid	160
2:3-Hexanediol	liquid	(completely miscible)
Benzene	liquid	660
Phenol	solid	14
Resorcinol (1:3-dihydroxybenzene)	solid	3
Aniline	liquid	37
m-Phenylenediamine (1:3-diamizobenzene)	solid	1

However, hydroxy- and amino-groups diminish the aqueous solubility of heteroaromatic substances. This insolubilizing effect is due to hydrogen-bonding, for it is brought about by the amino-, but not by the dimethylamino-, group (also by the hydroxy, but not by the methoxy-, group) (Albert, 1955, a; Albert, Brown and Cheeseman, 1952).

In Table 4, the insolubilizing effect of the hydroxy-group is exemplified in 2:4-dihydroxypyridine which is 160 times less soluble than 2- or 4-hydroxypyridine. It would not be fair (although it would seem to support the argument) to compare these hydroxypyridines with pyridine itself, because pyridine is a liquid and must of necessity be more soluble because there is no crystal-lattice to break. This difficulty does not arise in the pyrimidine and pteridine series, because the parent-substances are solids: Table 4 provides examples of the large insolubilizing effect of the first hydroxy-group, most clearly demonstrated in the pteridine series. Each additional hydroxy-group seems (on the average) to have less effect than the previous one. In the pyrimidine series the third hydroxy-group has even caused a small increase in solubility, but such reversals of the trend are unusual and trihydroxy-*sym*-triazine (cyanuric acid) is much less soluble (1 in 400) than dihydroxy-*sym*-triazine (1 in 7).

TABLE 4. Solubility in Water at 20°
(all solids)

Substance	20° 1 part in:	100° 1 part in:
Pyridine	(see text)	—
2-Hydroxy-	1	—
3-Hydroxy-	30	—
4-Hydroxy-	1	—
2:4-Dihydroxy-	160	—
Pyrimidine	<1	—
2-Hydroxy-	2	—
4-Hydroxy-	3	—
2:4-Dihydroxy-	300	—
4:6-Dihydroxy-	400	—
2:4:6-Trihydroxy-	150	—
Pteridine[a]	7	1
2-Hydroxy-	600	50
4-Hydroxy-	200	29
7-Hydroxy-	900	76
2:4-Dihydroxy-	800	120
4:6-Dihydroxy-	5,000	300
6:7-Dihydroxy-	3,000	290
2:4:7-Trihydroxy-	12,000	1,400
4:6:7-Trihydroxy-	27,000	7,000
2:4:6:7-Tetrahydroxy-	58,000	—

a. For a more complete discussion of the solubilities of hydroxy- and amino-pteridines see Albert, Lister and Pedersen (1957).

The most likely explanation of the insolubilizing effect is that intermolecular hydrogen-bonding, from oxygen atoms to the negatively-charged ring-nitrogen atoms, is preferred to hydrogen-bonding to water. The crystal-lattices formed in this way must be very strong to be so favoured at the expense of hydration. The reason for the unusually high strength of these crystal-lattices is unknown, but may lie in the reinforcement of the hydrogen-bond by a large dipole.

This insolubilizing effect is not connected with the ability of α- and γ-hydroxy-derivatives to tautomerize.[1] In fact the

[1] See formula (XVII) for exposition of α- and γ-orientations.

hydroxypyridine least subject to tautomerism (i.e. 3-hydroxy-pyridine) is the least soluble. Again, 2:4-dihydroxypyridine (Table 4) can have only one tautomeric hydroxy-group, and yet it is much less soluble than either 2- or 4-hydroxypyridine (see p. 57 below for the tautomerism of these hydroxy-derivatives). Curiously enough, only one hydroxy-group in 4:6-dihydroxy-pyrimidine can tautomerize[1] (recourse to pencil and paper will quickly reveal the limitations, imposed by valency, which make this so). Yet this dihydroxypyrimidine is more than 100 times less soluble than the corresponding mono-hydroxypyrimidine.

4-Hydroxypteridine (1 in 200) is less soluble than its O- and $N_{(1)}$-methyl-derivatives (1 in 80 and 1 in 2, respectively), in spite of the well-known water-repelling properties of hydro-carbon-groups. This is because the oxygen- and nitrogen-atoms in these methyl-derivatives are free to form hydrogen-bonds with water; but in 4-hydroxypteridine the presence of the bondable hydrogen favours association between similar mole-cules. (This example was taken from the *pteridine* series to avoid liquid derivatives, such as methoxy-pyrimidines.) There are indications, too, that aliphatic hydroxy-groups (especially the hydroxymethyl-group) are insolubilizing (Albert, 1955, c).

The less soluble these hydroxy-derivatives, the higher their melting-points. Often decomposition occurs before any melting-point is reached. Paper chromatography is used instead as a criterion of purity and identity for these substances (Albert, 1952).

An amino-group has approximately the same insolubilizing effect as a hydroxy-group (but additional amino-groups often exert less effect than is found in the correspondingly poly-hydroxy-derivatives). Examples are the 2- and 3-amino- and 2:6- and 2:3-diamino-pyridines, whose solubilities in water at 20° are 1 in 1, < 1, 10, and 515 respectively (Albert, Lister and Pedersen, 1957, where data on polyaminopteridines can also be found).

The insolubilizing effect of the mercapto-group has also been demonstrated (Albert, Brown and Wood, 1954), but is less sur-prising because sulphur is far less hydrophilic than oxygen and nitrogen.

---

[1] i.e. On to nitrogen.

In lipoid solvents, the hydrogen-bonding heteroaromatic substances are less soluble than their non-bonding methyl-derivatives. But this is a normal trend that needs no further comment.

Closer inspection of Table 4 will reveal differences in solubility between isomers. Steric factors, which play a large part in crystal-lattice formation, may well be responsible for these secondary effects which do not obscure the remarkably large measure of regularity found, remarkable because the physical chemistry of the solid state is still not well understood.

(b) Basic Strength

Pyridine is a far weaker base ($pK_a = 5·2$) than the aliphatic amines (these have pK's around 10, i.e. the K's are 100,000 times greater). This difference is thought to be due to the un-shared electrons of the ring-nitrogen atom being in a plane-trigonal orbital, whereas those of the aliphatic-nitrogen atom are in a tetrahedral orbital, and hence have less s component (Ingold, 1953). Annelation (i.e. to quinoline, acridine, etc.) changes the base-strength only slightly and not in any uniform direction. However, the insertion of an extra ring-nitrogen atom (as in pyrimidine (VII), 1:5-naphthyridine (XII), etc.) produces much weaker bases: this is what would be expected because a ring-nitrogen atom has a similar inductive effect (i.e. electron-attracting) to that of a nitro-group in aromatic and aliphatic chemistry. This is dealt with at greater length in Chapter IX. No simple relationship between the basic strength and the magnitude of the charge on the nitrogen atom has been found.

The insertion of an *amino-group* usually increases or decreases the basic strength by not more than 1 unit of pK, and the ring-nitrogen remains the principal basic centre. However, when the insertion of an amino-group permits more resonance in the cation than in the neutral molecule, a remarkable increase in basic strength results (Albert, Goldacre and Phillips, 1948). For example 4-aminopyridine is four units of pK stronger than pyridine (a figure 10,000 times greater), and other γ-amino-derivatives[1] such as 4-aminoquinoline and 5-aminoacridine show the same effect. The canonical forms of this resonance

---

[1] See (XVII) for exposition of α-, β- and γ-orientations.

hybrid are (XV) and (XVI), i.e. for the cation of 4-amino-pyridine.

Considerations of valency would make us expect the β-amines (such as 3-aminopyridine) to be normal, whereas the α-amines (such as 2-aminopyridine) should show the base-strengthening effect. These expectations are realized (see Chapter IX). The base-strengthening effect is relayed by conjugation to annelated benzene rings, but is simultaneously attenuated.

XV   XVI   XVII

The insertion of a *hydroxy-group* has, in general, little effect on the basic strength, but creates a new (acidic) pK, similar in strength to the nitrophenols (Albert and Phillips, 1956). How-ever, α- and γ-hydroxy-derivatives are exceptionally weak both as acids and bases, an effect which is not relayed by conjugation to alternant positions in an annelated benzene ring. These α- and γ-hydroxy-derivatives (e.g. 4-hydroxypyridine) have essen-tially the structure of acid amides (see pp. 55–62), which ex-plains their feeble basic and acidic properties. The insertion of a second nitrogen atom into α- or γ-hydroxy-derivatives is base-strengthening (contrast the case of pyrimidine above), because this second nitrogen carries no positive charge, and hence does not repel protons (this will become clearer after a study of (*e*), p. 52).

(c) Ultraviolet Spectra

The spectra of π-deficient nitrogenous heterocycles are con-spicuous and easily understood. They will be dealt with more fully in Chapter VIII, the following being by way of introduction.

As a first approximation, it may be said that the spectra of these substances are similar to those of the corresponding nitrogen-free substances, but somewhat less detailed and with the leading edge (the portion of longest wave-length) shifted to slightly longer wave-lengths. Thus the spectrum of acridine (III) is very similar to that of anthracene, but some of the fine structure has been lost; phenazine (XIV), which has one more ring-nitrogen atom than acridine, has still less fine structure (Radulescu and Ostrogovitch, 1931) (see Figure 3, Chapter VIII).

Similarly the spectrum of naphthalene ($\lambda_{max} = 310$ mμ) reappears in quinoline (313 mμ) and the azalogues of quinoline, such as (XI), (XII) and (XIII) but simplified (in different ways for each azalogue), and with the leading edge moved to slightly longer wave-lengths (Albert, Brown and Cheeseman, 1951) (see Figures 5 and 7 in Chapter VIII). The comparison between benzene and pyridine does not follow quite so smoothly. The electronic transition-moments in benzene largely cancel, because they are vector quantities, and the molecule of benzene is completely symmetrical. But pyridine is asymmetrical, so that higher extinction coefficients are found (see Figure 9, Chapter VIII). The rule, that insertion of nitrogen atoms moves the leading edge to longer wave-lengths, holds as before. In all diazabenzenes, a new peak of longer wave-length may be seen in non-polar solvents.

The conversion of π-deficient N-heterocycles to cations usually leaves λ_{max} unchanged or moves it to slightly longer wave-lengths. The aromatic amines, such as aniline, behave quite differently, for λ_{max} moves to much shorter wave-lengths upon salt formation. This clear-cut difference has helped to establish the rule that amino-derivatives of π-deficient N-heterocycles add the first proton to the *ring*-nitrogen atom (Craig and Short, 1945; Hearn, Morton and Simpson, 1951, a).

The addition of various substituents to π-deficient N-heterocycles usually has much the same effect on the spectra as when the same substituents are inserted into the benzene ring.

(d) Action of Acid and Alkali

As was mentioned at the beginning of this chapter, the π-deficient N-heterocycles have a tendency to hydrolytic decomposition, arising from the flight of π-electrons to the nitrogen atom(s). This tendency increases as the N:C-ratio of the ring-atoms increases (Albert, Brown and Cheeseman, 1952). For example, pyridine (N:C = 0·2:1) is stable to hot acid (even at 300°) and alkali; pyrimidine (VII) with the higher N:C-ratio of 0·5:1 is unstable to strong alkali (Lythgoe and Rayner, 1951), and *sym*-triazine (IX) with the high N:C-ratio of 1:1 is completely decomposed by cold water in 10 minutes (Grundmann and Kreutzberger, 1954). It should be pointed out that although the N:C-ratio is the dominant consideration, the orientation of the nitrogen atoms modifies this slightly: for example, *sym*-tetrazine (X) is fairly stable in cold water for an hour.

The same effect operates in substances with two rings. Quinoline (N:C = 0·1:1) can be distilled over calcium oxide and resists hot concentrated sulphuric acid. Similarly, *iso*-quinoline can be taken down to dryness with 50% hydrobromic acid without decomposition. However, quinazoline (XI) (N:C = 0·25:1) is slightly decomposed by hydrobromic acid under these circumstances, and so is 2-methylquinoxaline (no data are available for quinoxaline (LIII)). Finally pteridine (XIII) (N:C = 0·7:1) is unstable to cold N-acid or N-alkali, which convert it to 2-aminopyrazine-3-aldehyde (Albert, Brown and Wood, 1956).

These N:C-ratios are only a rough guide to instability. If it is accepted that the most polar ring will be the most vulnerable to fission, the electronic distribution *in this ring* must be the ruling factor. The presence of nitrogen atoms in a neighbouring ring has significance only in so far as they must strongly influence this distribution. Hence annelation of an unstable system by addition of benzene rings should not greatly improve stability, e.g. 6:7-naphtha-4-hydroxypteridine is not appreciably less stable to acid than 4-hydroxypteridine (Felton, Osdene and Timmis, 1954).

The instability can be counteracted by the insertion of electron-releasing groups such as hydroxy- or amino-groups. It is important to note that hydroxy-groups in α- or γ-positions are quite suitable for this purpose, although they enter into the tautomerism discussed in (*e*) below. Thus, although *sym*-triazine (IX) is instantly decomposed by cold water, its 2:4:6-trihydroxy-derivative (cyanuric acid) resists N-potassium hydroxide at

100°, and also boiling concentrated sulphuric acid. Similarly, the instability of pteridine (XIII) to acid and alkali is largely overcome by the insertion of two or more hydroxy-groups (see Table 5).

TABLE 5. Electron-releasing Groups overcome
the tendency of Pteridine to Hydrolytic Decomposition
(Albert, Brown and Cheeseman, 1952)

	Decomposition in 1 hr. at 110°	
	$N-H_2SO_4$	10N–NaOH
Pteridine:		
(Unsubstituted)	74%	Almost complete
2-Hydroxy-	55	89
4-Hydroxy-	60	94
7-Hydroxy-	52	76
2:4-Dihydroxy-	6	4
6:7-Dihydroxy-	7	12
4:6:7-Trihydroxy-	0	4
2:4:6:7-Tetrahydroxy-	0	(6[a])

a. This decomposition is almost entirely oxidation, typical of polyhydroxy-heterocycles in alkali.

Amino-groups contribute to the stabilization of the pteridine nucleus to about the same extent as do hydroxy-groups, whereas methyl-groups have a much smaller, but similar effect. Again, methyl-groups exert a small stabilizing effect upon *sym*-triazine (Grundmann and Weisse, 1951).

It is evident that pyridine and other π-deficient heterocycles could be made unstable to hydrolysis in another way than by inserting ring-nitrogen atoms, namely by attaching strong electron-attracting groups to the ring-atoms. Nitro- and cyano-groups should be suitable for this purpose. Unluckily, no dinitro- or dicyano-pyridine, and no nitro- or cyano-pyridazine, pyrimidine or pyrazine are yet known. Hence this subject lies wide open for exploration. A few indicative facts are available. Firstly, 6-(and 8-)nitro-4-hydroxyquinazolines are readily hydrolysed to 3-(and 5-)nitroanthranilic acid amides, but 4-hydroxyquinazoline is stable (Taylor, 1954). Again, the quaternary salt of pyridine with 1-chloro-2:4-dinitrobenzene readily undergoes ring-fission in alkali, giving the 2:4-dinitroanil

E

of glutaconic aldehyde (XVIII). Pyridine also gives a quaternary salt (XIX) with cyanogen bromide, and this behaves similarly. For a review of these reactions of pyridine see Mosher (1950).

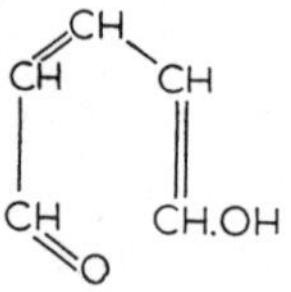

XVIII 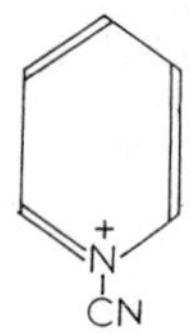   XIX 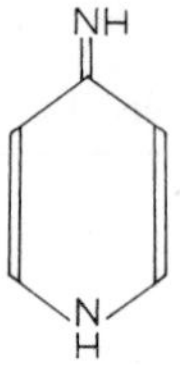   XX 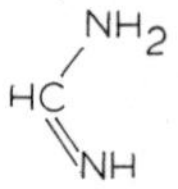   XXI

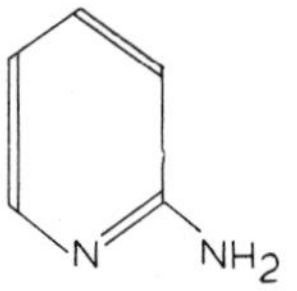

XXII 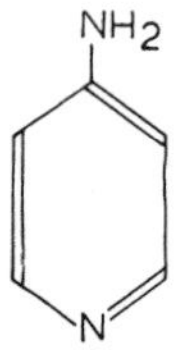   XXIII 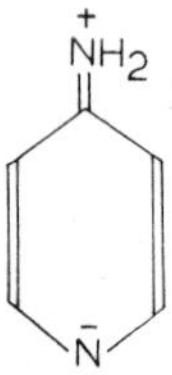   XXIV

(e) The Nature of Amino- and Hydroxy-derivatives

An *amino-group* in π-deficient N-heterocycles usually resembles that in aniline, in that it contributes electrons to the π-layer, and can be diazotized and coupled (e.g. to β-naphthol). In π-deficient N-heterocycles, such an amino-group is almost invariably a weaker base than the ring-nitrogen atom, and hence diazotizes only at a low pH. An amino-group that is α- or γ- to a ring-nitrogen is notoriously difficult to diazotize. Nevertheless, diazotization can be effected in an almost anhydrous medium: 4-aminopyridine has been diazotized thus and then coupled with dimethylaniline and resorcinol (Königs and Greiner, 1931). If water is present, nitrous acid usually converts α- and γ-amines into the corresponding hydroxy-compounds, a reaction which does not necessarily pass through a diazonium stage.

Because of the reluctance to diazotize, it has been argued that α- and γ-amino-derivatives are atypical, and even that they are the isomeric imines, of the type (XX). All the evidence is against such an assumption, and in favour of their being amidines, or vinylogous amidines. The word *vinylogous* refers to the separation of the component parts of a substituent group by one or more ethylene units (Fuson, 1935); thus (XXI) is an aliphatic amidine, viz. formamidine; (XXII) is a cyclic amidine, viz. 2-aminopyridine; and (XXIII) is a vinylogous cyclic amidine, viz. 4-aminopyridine. The difficulty in producing diazonium compounds from α- and γ-amines is in keeping with this amidine character (e.g. nitrous acid converts the amino-groups in guanidine to hydroxy-groups (Hale and Vibrans, 1918).

However, in problems of tautomerism, weight must be given mainly to *physical* properties. The reason for preferring these to evidence from chemical reactivity is that a tautomer present at equilibrium in only minute amount is frequently much more chemically reactive than the tautomer present in major amount; but examination of physical properties leaves the equilibrium undisturbed.

X-ray crystallography can reveal which tautomer is pre-dominant in the solid state, provided that resolution of the hydrogen atoms is achieved (this is a lengthy process). This technique, applied to melamine (2:4:6-triamino-*sym*-triazine), has shown the three α-amino-groups to be primary amines (Knaggs and Lonsdale, 1940). Various aminopyrimidines were examined in this way, and also found to have only primary amino-groups, which formed hydrogen-bonds with the ring-nitrogens of neighbouring molecules (White and Clews, 1956). Infrared spectrometry of the solid state is technically less diffi-cult and often permits a decision as to which tautomer pre-dominates. If the substance dissolves in carbon tetrachloride or disulphide (unfortunately not good solvents for these amines, nor for the corresponding hydroxy-compounds), the infrared spectrum can be measured in solution. Infrared measurements of 2- and 4-amino-pyridines and -quinolines (Goulden, 1952; Angyal and Werner, 1952), of 5-aminoacridine (Short, 1952), and of 2- and 4-aminopyrimidines (Brown, Hoerger and Mason, 1955, b), reveal that the forms with primary amino-groups are those chiefly present in these substances, under the experimental conditions.

From the biological standpoint, the state of tautomerism in aqueous solution is the most important: here ultraviolet spectrometry is most useful. However, it is of value only when two standards for comparison are at hand: (i) the amine methylated on the ring-nitrogen; and (ii) the same amine doubly methylated on the exocyclic amino-group. The spectrum of the amine in question is then compared with that of (i) and (ii), and it is concluded that the predominant tautomer has the structure resembling (i) or (ii), depending on the spectrum obtained. Some necessary precautions are to make sure that (i) and (ii) have very different spectra, and that the methylations do not introduce steric hindrance (a difficulty with 5-dimethyl-aminoacridine). This method, which depends on the virtual transparency of a methyl-group has been applied to 2- and 4-aminopyridine (Anderson and Seegar, 1949), and 2- and 4-aminopyrimidine (Brown, Hoerger and Mason, 1955, b): in each case the primary amines have been found to be the principal species present (see Figure 17 in Chapter VIII).

Dipole moments, which cannot of themselves distinguish between amino- and imino-tautomers, i.e. between (XXIII) and (XX), became of use as soon as the primary amino nature of these α- and γ-amines had been established. The dipole moments show that the primary amines are resonance hybrids of e.g. (XXIII) and (XXIV) (Angyal and Angyal, 1952). This statement refers to the neutral molecules, for the cations have been shown to be resonance hybrids of (XV) and (XVI) (see (b) above).

Finally, studies of ionization constants enable the ratio of amino- to imino-tautomers to be calculated (Angyal and Angyal, 1952). When held in the imino-form, e.g. (XX), by methylation on the ring-nitrogen, stronger bases are obtained than when held in the amino-form, e.g. (XXIII), by double methylation on the exocyclic amino-group. Although substances like 4-aminopyridine are strong bases, they are far from being as strong as these methylated imines. A simplified calculation from the various pK's gives tautomeric ratios (amine:imine) of 2000:1 for 4-aminopyridine and 4-aminoquinoline, and 200,000:1 for 2-aminopyridine.

Vicinal amino-groups, as in 8-aminoquinoline, are internally hydrogen-bonded (Short, 1952).

When a *hydroxy-group* is inserted into a π-deficient N-hetero-cycle, the resultant substance can have properties which fall somewhere on a continuously variable line which begins with the pure phenols, passes through the isomeric zwitterions, and ends with analogues of the acid amides (Albert and Phillips, 1956; Mason, 1957). This state of affairs is more complex than is conveyed by earlier literature, which states that α- and γ-hydroxy-derivatives are abnormal, but that their isomers are normal phenols.

In support of the old simplified subdivision, it has often been written that α- and γ-hydroxy-derivatives give no colours with ferric chloride, whereas the isomers do so. This is demonstrably untrue: 2- and 3-hydroxy-pyridine give identical red colours, and 4-hydroxypyridine a yellow colour, with ferric chloride. A negative result would not exclude their all being phenolic, because the ferric derivatives of phenols that have electron-attracting substituents absorb at lower wave-lengths (but more intensely) than phenol itself, and in fact many give no *visible* colour at all. 2-, 3-, and 4-Hydroxypyridine are all less π-deficient than pyridine: they all readily undergo electrophilic substitution and nitrate, brominate, and couple with diazotized aniline just as phenol does. Thus they are not quinonoid, because quinones react by addition. They give one reaction which is not at all phenol-like: methylation usually favours N-methyl-, at the expense of O-methyl-, derivatives (this is just as true for 3- as for 2-hydroxypyridine (Albert and Phillips, 1956)). The important differences in chemical reactivity are that only the α- and γ-derivatives are converted to α- and γ-chloro-derivatives by phosphoryl chloride (POCl$_3$), and to α- and γ-mercapto-derivatives by phosphorus pentasulphide.

Such evidence, derived as it is from chemical reactivity, is not acceptable for distinguishing between tautomers, and (unlike the corresponding amino-derivatives) *every* hydroxy-derivative in this series can tautomerize. Any chemical reaction that favours the minor tautomer will remove it from the equilibrium mixture, and hence more will continuously be formed so that it may appear to be the major tautomer. Only physical properties can give the true picture of what exists at equilibrium.

It was explained, under (*b*) above, that α- and γ-hydroxy-derivatives are weaker acids and weaker bases than their isomers, and that they owe this property to their amide-like configuration. Before developing this topic, we should give attention to 3-hydroxypyridine (XXV), which, from considerations of valency, cannot assume an amide form such as (XXXI): yet it is subject to tautomerism, and in fact a neutral aqueous solution is a mixture of the normal phenol (XXV) and the corresponding zwitterion (XXVI) in almost equal amounts. The ultraviolet spectrum, in fact, shows two peaks above 250 mμ; that at 313 mμ agrees with the sole peak of quaternized 3-hydroxypyridine[1] (XXVII), the other (at 277 mμ) agrees with that of 3-methoxypyridine (XXVIII) [both (XXVII) and (XXVIII) have only one peak in this region, but it is of double the intensity]. When the dielectric constant of the neutral aqueous solution of 3-hydroxypyridine is lowered, e.g. by adding alcohol, the peak corresponding to that of (XXVII) disappears, and that corresponding to (XXVIII) rises to double the previous intensity (this process can be reversed by adding water) (Metzler and Snell, 1955).

XXV   XXVI   XXVII   XXVIII

The high proportion of dipolar ion in aqueous solutions of 3-hydroxypyridine is due to the mutual inductive effect of the two groups: the cation strengthens the acid group, and the anion strengthens the basic group. This effect should therefore fall off with distance, and in fact it is barely detectable in 6-hydroxyquinoline which may be classed as a normal phenol. Thus 3-hydroxypyridine is intermediate between pyridine-3-carboxylic acid (which is about 95% zwitterionic in neutral solution) and p-aminobenzoic acid (where the two groups hardly interact). Some of the relevant data for 3-hydroxypyridine will be found

[1] This is 3-hydroxypyridine methochloride examined at pH7, its sole pK_a being 4·96 (Albert and Phillips, 1956).

TABLE 6. Ionization Constants and Tautomeric Ratios
of Hydroxy-derivatives
(Albert and Phillips, 1956; see also Mason, 1958)

Substance	Ionization Constants (reported as pK_a values, determined in water at 20°)	Tautomeric Ratios (molecules of zwitterion (or amide) per molecule of enol)
Pyridine	5·23	—
3-hydroxy-	4·86; 8·72	1
O-methyl-	4·88	—
N-methyl-	4·96	—
2-hydroxy-	0·75; 11·62	340
O-methyl-	3·28	—
N-methyl-	0·32	—
4-hydroxy-	3·27; 11·09	2,200
O-methyl-	6·62	—
N-methyl-	3·33	—
Quinoline	4·93	—
2-hydroxy-	−0·31; 11·74	3,000
O-methyl-	3·17	—
N-methyl-	−0·71	—
3-hydroxy-	4·30; 8·06	0·1
4-hydroxy-	2·27; 11·25	24,000
O-methyl-	6·65	—
N-methyl-	2·46	—
5-hydroxy-	5·20; 8·54	0·1
N-methyl-	6·12	—
6-hydroxy-	5·17; 8·88	0·01
7-hydroxy-	5·48; 8·85	3
N-methyl-	5·56	—
8-hydroxy-	5·13; 9·89	0·05
Acridine	5·62	—
5-hydroxy-	−0·32; > 12	10,000,000
O-methyl-	7	—
isoQuinoline	5·46	—
1-hydroxy-	−1·2; > 12	18,000
O-methyl-	3·05	—
N-methyl-	−1·8	—

in Table 6: for a fuller discussion of this isomer, which is the
key to the whole series, see Albert and Phillips (1956).

The α- and γ-hydroxy-isomers differ from those previously
discussed in that the zwitterion tautomer, e.g. (XXIX) for 2-
hydroxypyridine, is stabilized with respect to the enol tautomer

(XXX) by being one of the canonical forms of a resonance hybrid, which includes the amide tautomer (XXXI). Before discussing the evidence, it is necessary to be clear that (XXIX) and (XXXI) cannot exist independently of their resonance hybrid, which for the sake of brevity will be called the 'amide' form of 2-hydroxypyridine. This hybrid could equally be called the 'zwitterion' form, but the name 'amide' is preferred because it draws attention to the source of stability, and provides a clue to chemical properties (e.g. the ready transformation to 2-chloropyridine). 4-Hydroxypyridine is thus a vinylogous amide (see p. 53 for definition of vinylogous). An older nomenclature: '4-pyridone', or the 'keto-form of 4-hydroxypyridine', is objectionable because these substances lack ketonic properties.

XXIX   XXX   XXXI   XXXII   XXXIII

Knowledge of the nature of the α- and γ-hydroxy-derivatives has come from five sources: ionization constants, ultraviolet and infrared spectra, measurements of X-ray diffraction, and dipole moments. Of these, ionization constants have provided most quantitative data of the amide:enol ratio, and hence will be dealt with first.

Table 6 shows that 2- and 4-hydroxypyridine are much weaker acids and bases than 3-hydroxypyridine.[1] The basic strength is, in each case, very much nearer to the N-methyl-derivatives, e.g. (XXXII), than to the O-methyl-derivatives, e.g. (XXXIII). The reasons underlying these big differences in basic strength between N- and O-methyl-derivatives is discussed elsewhere (Albert and Phillips, 1956). Thus equilibrium in these α- and γ-hydroxy-derivatives must favour the amide form

---

[1] Another approach is possible: by concentrating on the zwitterionic contribution, it could be said that 2-hydroxypyridine is an acid of pK_a 0·75 comparable with the mineral acids, and a base of pK_a 11·62 comparable with the aliphatic amines. This is more tortuous reasoning although not incorrect, and leads to the same conclusions.

at the expense of the enol form. It will be recalled that amides owe their feeble acidic and basic properties (cf. acetamide: pK's −0·5; 15·1) to a similar resonance effect, viz. between (XXXIV) and (XXXV). This represents as much as 25 Kcal./mole (Pauling, 1940) and corresponds to an amide:enol ratio of about 10^{11}, the enol in question being (XXXVI).

XXXIV   XXXV   XXXVI   XXXVII   XXXVIII

Table 6 shows that 2- and 4-hydroxyquinoline, 5-hydroxy-acridine and 1-hydroxy-*iso*quinoline (all α- or γ-hydroxy-derivatives) are overwhelmingly in the amide form. An approximate, but serviceable, equation permits calculation of the tautomeric ratio (Ebert, 1926; Edsall and Blanchard, 1933; Tucker and Irvin, 1951):

$$R = \text{antilog } (pK_{\text{OMe}} - pK_{\text{OH}}) - 1$$

where R is the ratio of amide to enol, and pK_{OMe} and pK_{OH} are the observed values for the addition of a proton to corresponding methoxy- and 'hydroxy-' compounds. This method assumes that e.g. the intrinsic basic constant for (XXX) would differ little from that for (XXXIII). That this is a reasonable assumption may be gauged by reference to the pK_a values for *m*-methoxyaniline (4·20) and *m*-hydroxyaniline (4·17). The results, given in the last column of Table 6, show a wide span of values. It is interesting that the vanishingly small proportion of enol in 5-hydroxyacridine is not too small to permit rapid chlorination (to 5-chloroacridine) by phosphoryl chloride, doubtless because more of the enolic form can be regenerated as fast as it is consumed (also the low dielectic constant should increase the proportion of enol). The *methylation* of hydroxy-derivatives is dealt with in section (*h*) below, and the complex pathway of the replacement of −OH by −Cl is discussed on p. 80.

The hydroxyquinolines, other than the 2- and 4-derivatives, are bases of about the same strength as quinoline (Table 6), so that they cannot have high tautomeric ratios. Thus, 5- and 7-hydroxyquinoline have no strong tendency to become stabilized in the amide form through resonance involving tautomers such as (XXXVII). It may well be that, in general, a tendency to form transannular amides is not strong. 8-Hydroxyquinoline is a slightly weaker acid than the 5-, 6- or 7-isomers, apparently because the proton is hydrogen-bonded as in (XXXVIII), which makes it less mobile. The high volatility and liposolubility of this isomer support this concept of hydrogen-bonding. It is the only isomer which forms chelates with metals, for which it has a very high avidity (Albert, 1953).

Similar evidence from ionization constants has shown that there is also a high amide:enol ratio in the α- and γ-hydroxy-derivatives of pyridazine, pyrimidine, pyrazine, phenanthridine, cinnoline, phthalazine, quinoxaline, naphthyridine and pteridine (Albert and Phillips, 1956). When two ring-nitrogens are present, the one bearing the hydrogen can be located from spectra (Chapter VIII), but it is not often possible to extend to systems containing two nitrogen atoms the calculations used for the one-nitrogen systems, for it is not easy to be sure that the *same* nitrogen is protonated in the pair of substances being compared (Mason, 1958).

That α- and γ-hydroxy-derivatives exist mainly in the amide form *in aqueous solution* is supported by ultraviolet spectrometric[1] comparison with the O- and N-derivatives. This has been done for 2- and 4-hydroxypyridine[2] (Specker and Gawrosch, 1942), 2-hydroxyquinoline (Ley and Specker, 1949), 5-hydroxyacridine (Acheson *et al.*, 1954), 2- and 4-hydroxypyrimidine (Brown, Hoerger and Mason, 1955, a) and their C-alkyl derivatives (Marshall and Walker, 1951), 2:4-dihydroxypyrimidine (Marshall and Walker, 1951), 4-hydroxyquinazoline and 4-

---

[1] *Aqueous* ultraviolet spectra are most useful. The pH must be adjusted, from knowledge of the exact ionization constants, so that only a single ionic species is present.

[2] See Figure 15 in Chapter VIII.

hydroxycinnoline (Hearn, Morton and Simpson, 1951, b). This method is inapplicable when both the O- and the N-methyl-derivatives have almost the same spectra, as sometimes happens, e.g. with 4-hydroxypteridine (Albert, Brown and Cheeseman, 1952), and isatin (Morton and Rogers, 1925). Such instances underline the necessity of using *both* O- and N-derivatives for comparison. That α- and γ-hydroxy-derivatives exist mainly as the amide form *in the solid state* has been established by X-ray crystallography for 2-hydroxypyridine (Penfold, 1953), 2:4-di-hydroxypyrimidine (Parry, 1954) and 2:4:6-trihydroxy-*sym*-triazine (Newman and Badger, 1952), and by infrared spectrometry for 2- and 4-hydroxypyrimidine (Brown, Hoerger and Mason, 1955, a), and the hydroxypteridines (Mason, 1957). Infrared studies have shown that 4:5- and 4:6-dihydroxy-pyrimidine have one enolic and one amide group (Tanner, 1956). Dipole moments provide evidence for the essentially amide character of 2- and 4-hydroxy-pyridines in *non-aqueous* solution (Albert and Phillips, 1956).

In conclusion, it may be asked: what is the best nomenclature for α- and γ-hydroxy-derivatives? In discussing this question, it is important to bear in mind the essentially aromatic nature of these α- and γ-hydroxy-compounds. The spectrum of 2-hydroxy-quinoline, although complex, is clearly very similar to that of β-naphthol, and 3-, 6-, and 7-hydroxyquinolines (see Chapter VIII, particularly Figure 14), and this suggests that kekulé forms predominate throughout. In so far as zwitterionic structures, such as (XXIX), can play an important part in the structure of a β-hydroxy-derivative (as was shown on p. 56), there is every reason to believe that they are present in what we have termed the 'amide' form of the α- and γ-hydroxy-isomers, where they are stabilized by resonance with the oxo-structures, such as (XXXI), but not in any overriding proportion. Thus any differences between the α- and γ-hydroxy-compounds on the one hand, and their isomers on the other is only a matter of degree, and it seems best to use the prefix 'hydroxy-' in describing them all.

Both the amide and the enol structures should give the same anion, e.g. perhaps (XXXIX). The hydroxy-nomenclature also serves as a valuable reminder that even in the α- and γ-

XXXIX

positions, these substituents are electron-releasing, and give rise to *ortho*- and *para*-substitution with electrophilic reagents (see (*f*) below). Compared to the simplicity of the 'hydroxy' nomenclature, the amide nomenclature is clumsy, e.g. the tautomer of a 4-hydroxyquinoline is called 1:4-dihydro-4-oxoquinoline.

The nature of hydroxy- and amino-groups in the substituted N-oxides is discussed on p. 89.

Examination of *mercapto*-derivatives is revealing that these favour the thioamide-forms in aqueous solution even more than the corresponding hydroxy-derivatives favour the amide forms (Albert and Barlin, 1958).

(*f*) *Substitution by Electrophilic Reagents*

The substitution of π-deficient N-heterocycles by electrophilic reagents would be expected to be difficult because of the lack of available electrons on the carbon atoms, cf. (XL). Those electrophilic reagents (such as ethyl nitrate) which can be used in neutral solution do not react with the parent substances in this series.

However, the majority of powerful electrophilic reagents, such as nitric acid and bromine, act in an acidic environment, and these obviously are further handicapped by the quaternization of the ring-nitrogen atom, because such a positive charge must repel the attacking cations (NO_2^+; Br^+). Hence it is not surprising that the temperature of 300° is required to nitrate pyridine (den Hertog and Overhoff, 1930) and the yield is only 5%. This leads to 3-nitropyridine, and the nett charge diagram for the cation of pyridine (XLI) is in harmony with this fact. Pyridine also sulphonates reluctantly: it requires fuming sulphuric acid for 24 hours at 220° and a mercury catalyst (McElvain and Goese, 1943). Bromination by heating bromine and pyridine hydrochloride at 160° gives 3-bromopyridine in 40% and 3:5-dibromopyridine in 27% yields (McElvain and Goese, 1943). When pyridine and bromine are heated at 500°, a free-radical attack by bromine atoms gives 2-bromo- and 2:6-dibromo-pyridine. Chlorine cations have little effect on pyridine, but free-radical attack occurs at 270°, giving 2-chloropyridine in 46% yield (Wibaut and Nicolai, 1939). Co-ordination of the lone electrons on the nitrogen can be prevented sterically. Thus, 2:6-di-t-butylpyridine, unlike 2:6-dimethyl-pyridine, hinders the approach of sulphur trioxide to nitrogen, so that nuclear sulphonation occurs even at −10° (Brown and Kanner, 1957).

Formula (XL) gives the charge distribution in pyridine and (XLI) in the pyridinium cation using the parameters employed in the diagrams of Chapter III. It is believed that charges calculated from these parameters are *relatively* correct, although too large in absolute terms. Formula (XLII) has smaller absolute values from more recent calculations and is comparable with formulae (XLIII) to (XLVI) for the polyazabenzenes (Davies, 1955); similar figures for these compounds were calculated by Chalvet and Sandorfy (1949), and Brown and Heffernan (1956). It is unfortunate that a complete set of formulae using the same parameters is not available and until it is, we must have at least two standards of comparison, (XL) and (XLII).

When more than one ring-nitrogen is present, it has been found that reactions with electrophilic reagents are extremely difficult. For example all attempts at nitration have failed with pyridazine (XLIII), pyrimidine (XLIV), pyrazine (XLV) and *sym*-triazine (XLVI) (e.g. Dixon and Wiggins, 1950; Lythgoe and Rayner, 1951). Pyrazine has been chlorinated at 400° (American Cyanamid Co., 1950), but this is probably a free-radical reaction. In comparing pyridine (XLII) with its azalogues, it is evident that increasing the number of ring-nitrogen atoms slightly lowers the charge on each nitrogen (particularly if they are α- or γ- to one another), but the *total* accumulation of π-electrons by the nitrogen atoms is greatly increased (cf. (XLIV) and (XLII)).

Not even pyridine undergoes Friedel-Crafts reactions using aluminium chloride catalyst. However, pyridine condenses with benzyl chloride, using a copper catalyst, to give 2- and 4-benzylpyridines (Crook, 1948).

XL: +0·18, +0·05, +0·15, N −0·58

XLI[1]: +0·29, +0·08, +0·24, N+H −0·93

XLII: +0·06, +0·01, +0·06, N −0·20

Pyridazine XLIII: +0·06, +0·07, N −0·13, −0·13

Pyrimidine XLIV: +0·12, +0·03, N −0·19, +0·12, N −0·19

Pyrazine XLV: N, +0·075, N −0·15

sym-Triazine XLVI: N, N, +0·18, N −0·18

Although electrophilic reagents combine so reluctantly with these parent substances, the reactions go in good yields at room-temperature when electron-releasing substituents are present. The most effective electron-releasing groups are methoxy-, amino-, mercapto- and hydroxy- (even when the latter has the amide configuration). A useful rule is that it usually requires one such electron-releasing group for every ring-nitrogen. This rule applies specially to nitration and diazo-coupling, whereas halogenation is rather easier and nitrosation somewhat more difficult. In pyridine, an electron-releasing group in the 3-position sends the entering substituent to the 2- or 6-position, whereas an electron-releasing group in the 2- or 4-position sends the entering substituent to the 3- or 5-position. Thus *ortho-* or *para-*direction is effected, as in the benzene series, but the 4-position is avoided (see Schofield (1950) for a discussion of this

---

[1] Kindly calculated by Professor C. A. Coulson to match (XL).

avoidance). One methyl group is not enough to activate pyridine for nitration, but 2:4:6-trimethylpyridine nitrates easily at 100° (Plazek, 1939).

As will have been gathered from the above, one alkoxy-, amino-, or hydroxy-group suffices for easy nitration in the pyridine series. Thus 3-ethoxypyridine nitrates in the 2-position (Bernstein *et al*., 1947), as does 3-hydroxypyridine (Plazek and Rodewald, 1936), 2- and 4-hydroxy-pyridine both nitrate in the 3-position (Binz and Maier-Bode, 1936; Bremer, 1937). 2-Hydroxypyridine chlorinates in the 5-position and, when heated with carbon dioxide at 200°, gives the 5-carboxylic acid. 2-Aminopyridine chlorinates, iodinates and nitrates principally in the 5-position (a little 3-nitro-2-aminopyridine can be removed by steam distillation (Caldwell and Kornfeld, 1942)). 2-Dimethylamino-pyridine gives the 5-nitro-derivative in 90 % yield, which suggests that nitration of 2-aminopyridines does not need to go through the well-known nitramines ($-NH \cdot NO_2$). 4-Aminopyridine gives the 3-nitro-derivative (Königs, Bueren and Jung, 1936). 3-Aminopyridine sulphonates readily in the 2-position. Amino- and hydroxy-pyridines with free 3- or 5-positions rapidly couple with diazotized aniline. In the absence of electron-releasing groups, diazonium salts act on pyridine more slowly, and by a free-radical mechanism giving phenyl- (instead of phenyl-azo) pyridines (see (*j*) below).

Formula (XLVII) shows what may be one of the most significant activated states of the 2-hydroxypyridine molecule, in facilitating electrophilic substitutions.

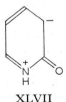

XLVII

The electrophilic substitution of pyrimidine (XLIV), which has two ring-nitrogens, has been well summarized by D. J. Brown (1953) as follows. Electrophilic reagents attack the ring only at the 5-position, and only when there are powerful electron-releasing groups ($-NH_2$, $-OH$, $-SH$) in other positions. Nitration goes readily, but requires two electron-releasing groups. The following have been thus prepared in good yield by nitration in sulphuric acid at 50°: 2-amino-4-hydroxy-5-nitro-, 4-amino-2-hydroxy-5-nitro-, 4-amino-6-hydroxy-5-nitro-, and 4:6-diamino-5-nitro-pyrimidine, and reaction conditions can be made a little milder for 2:4-, and 4:6-dihydroxypyrimidine. Only one powerful electron-releasing group is required for halogenation. Thus, 2-aminopyrimidine and 4-amino-6-methyl-pyrimidine have been chlorinated and brominated, and 4-aminopyrimidine has been iodinated (with ICl), all in the 5-position. It is noteworthy that the mercapto-group in 4-amino-2-mercaptopyrimidine survives halogenation.

Pyrimidines having at least two electron-releasing groups couple well with diazotized aromatic amines (Polonovski and Pesson, 1948; Lythgoe, Todd and Topham, 1944), e.g. 2-methyl-4:6-dihydroxy-5-phenylazopyrimidine is formed in 87% yield, in alkaline solution. Also two electron-releasing groups are the least that suffice for the nitrosation of a pyrimidine with nitrous acid.

For examples of electrophilic substitution in pyridazine, see Dixon and Wiggins (1950), and in pyrazine, see Spring (1945) and Krems and Spoerri (1947). Bromination of 2-bromopyrazine at 95° gives 2:3-dibromopyrazine (Karmas and Spoerri, 1957).

Systems with two or more fused rings will now be discussed.[1] Quinoline (XLVIII) chlorinates and brominates in the 3-position (but 5- and 8- in sulphuric acid, de la Mare, Kiamuddin and Ridd, 1958). It nitrates with great readiness in the benzene ring (the 5- and 8-isomers are formed in almost equal amounts). It also sulphonates exclusively in the benzene ring, the 8-sulphonic acid predominating. These results would hardly be predicted by the nett charge diagram (XLVIII) alone, and together form one of the most often quoted cases of the limitations of such diagrams, even when (admittedly rough) corrections are made for the possibility that the cation of quinoline is the reacting species in one or all cases. The results can be partly explained (but not

---

[1] Although the benzene-rings of quinoline, acridine and their isomers have, in certain positions, a slight electron excess, they are essentially π-deficient substances, and belong here rather than in Chapter V.

predicted) by invoking polarization (which favours the 1-, 4-, 5- and 8-positions), frontier electrons, etc. But assessing the relative importance of these factors has so far proved unrewarding territory in heterocyclic chemistry (cf. Davies, 1955). Progress should be faster when allowance is made for the fact, so well known from practical experience, that a powerful inductive effect in one ring is not transmitted to another ring without attenuation to, at least, half.

By nitrating in acetic anhydride, using a lithium nitrate catalyst, a 2% yield of a nitroquinoline (once thought to be 7-nitroquinoline but now known to be the 3-isomer) can be isolated (Dewar and Maitlis, 1957).

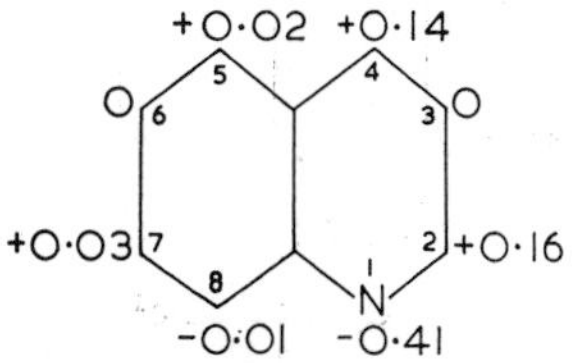

Quinoline
XLVIII[1]

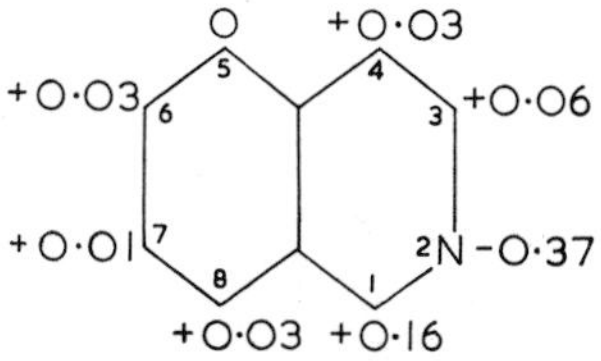

Isoquinoline
XLIX[1]

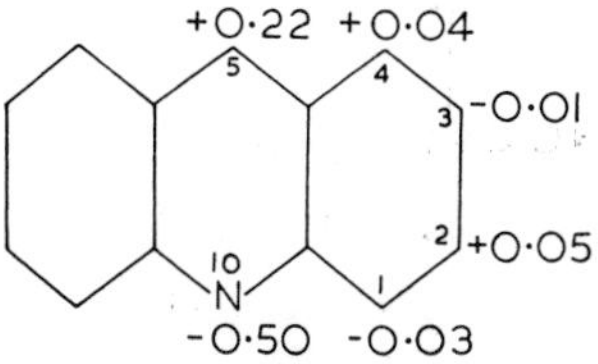

Acridine
L[1]

Isoquinoline (XLIX) gives 5- and 8-nitroisoquinoline in the ratio of 9:1 (Dewar and Maitlis, 1957), and acridine (L) gives mainly 3-nitro- and 3-bromo-acridine: here the nett charge diagrams run parallel to practical accomplishments much better than for quinoline. Phenanthridine (see p. 41) nitrates in the 4-, 5- and 7-positions (Caldwell and Walls, 1952).

Quinolines carrying hydroxy-groups in the 2- or 4-position

[1] These figures (Longuet-Higgins and Coulson, 1949) are comparable with those for pyridine in (XL), but not in (XLII).

F

nitrate in the 6- or 8- position in sulphuric acid, and in the 3-position in the absence of sulphuric acid (Halcrow and Kermack, 1945; see Schofield and Swain, 1949 for a discussion of this phenomenon). Both 2- and 4-aminoquinoline nitrate in the 6-position (Simpson and Wright, 1948). Quinolines with electron-releasing substituents in the benzene ring are sub-stituted, by all kinds of electrophilic reagents, in positions *para* or *ortho* to the electron-releasing group. 5-Hydroxyacridine directs electrophilic reagents to the 3-position (Lehmstedt, 1931; Acheson and Robinson, 1953).

$$
\begin{array}{cc}
\text{Cinnoline[1]} & \text{Quinazoline[1]} \\
\text{LI} & \text{LII}
\end{array}
$$

Cinnoline[1] (LI): +0.02 (5), +0.16 (4), +0.04 (6), +0.06 (3), +0.04 (7), 2 N −0.20, +0.02 (8), −0.25 (N1)

Quinazoline[1] (LII): +0.05 (5), +0.29 (4), +0.01 (6), 3 N −0.36, +0.07 (7), 2 +0.22, −0.01 (8), −0.38 (N1)

Quinoxaline[1] (LIII): +0.04 (7), 2 +0.16, +0.01 (8), −0.38 (N1)

Of the diazanaphthalenes, quinazoline (LII) nitrates in the 6-position (Schofield and Swain, 1949), although the diagram indicates the 8-position, which would also be favoured by polarization. Cinnoline (LI) nitrates in the 5- and 8-positions (Morley, 1951) and quinoxaline (LIII) in the 5-position (it dinitrates 5:6-) (Dewar and Maitlis, 1957). 4-Methylcinnoline gives the 8-nitro-derivative (Schofield and Swain, 1949), and 4-hydroxycinnoline mainly the 6-derivative (Schofield and

[1] These figures (Longuet-Higgins and Coulson, 1949) are compatible with those for quinoline in (XLVIII).

Simpson, 1945), as does 4-hydroxyquinazoline (Morley and Simpson, 1948).

For the ready electrophilic substitution of N-oxides, see p. 88.

(g) Substitution by Nucleophilic Reagents

The substitution of π-deficient N-heterocycles by nucleophilic reagents is easy, whereas that by electrophilic reagents is difficult; in both cases the lack of available electrons on the carbon atoms is responsible. Thus, when pyridine (XL) is treated with sodamide, it would be expected to aminate in the 2- and 4- (but on no account in the 3-) positions.

Amination. Actually pyridine aminates exclusively in the 2-position and, on pushing the reaction further, 2:6-diamino-pyridine is formed. Thus, as in (*f*) above, electron-density diagrams prove a good, but not sufficient, guide to the positions occupied.

Nitrobenzene, which has an electron distribution comparable to that of pyridine, see Chapter III, also reacts with nucleophilic reagents in a similar position, giving e.g. *o*-nitrophenol (45% yield) when heated at 70° with sodium hydroxide (Wohl, 1901). Sodamide reduces nitrobenzene and hence no comparison can be made. The postulated course of the Tschichibabin reaction between sodamide and pyridine is as follows (Ingold, 1953):

(i)

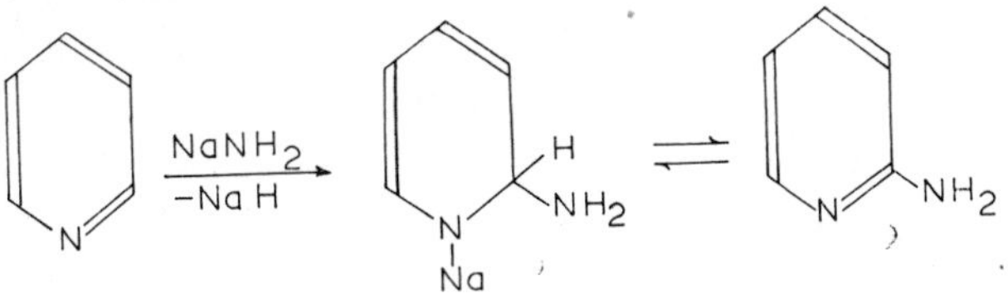

then

(ii)

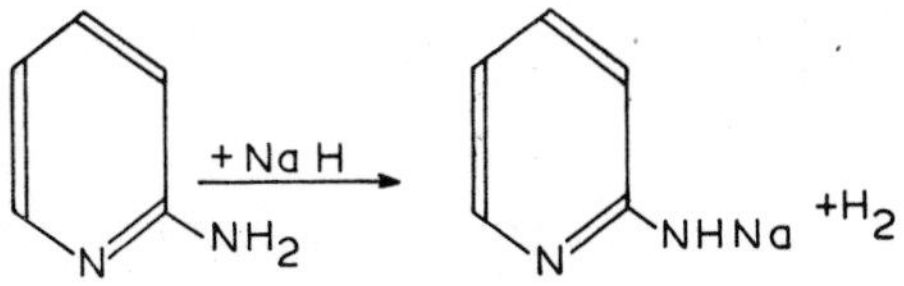

Thus, the attack by the amide-anion produces 2-amino-pyridine and sodium hydride. But the sodium at once exchanges anions, so that hydrogen is liberated and it is as the sodioderivative that 2-aminopyridine is isolated: this must be decomposed by water to get 2-aminopyridine. The reaction with sodamide goes best in cold liquid ammonia. An oxidizing agent such as a ferric salt, or potassium nitrate (Bergstrom, 1937) helps in cases where the reaction is tardy. Quinoline (XLVIII) gives a mixture of 2- and 4-aminoquinoline; *iso*quinoline aminates in the 1-, acridine in the 5-, and phenanthridine in the 9-positions, as would be expected from the diagrams. Phenanthridine can be directly aminated by ammonia. For a review on amination, see Leffler (1942).

Hydroxylation. The action of dry potassium hydroxide at 250–300° appears to be similar, and produces 2-hydroxy-pyridine and -quinoline in approximately 50% yields (Tschichi-babin and Kursanova, 1930; Tschichibabin, 1932).

All nucleophilic reactions go more readily when the ring-nitrogen is quaternized, because the drain on π-electrons is intensified by quaternization. Thus, when a cold aqueous solution of N-methylquinolinium chloride (LIV) is basified, the initially high alkalinity slowly decreases, and there is a parallel drop in conductance. The product, 2-hydroxy-N-methyl-1:2-dihydroquinoline (LV), is the result of an attack by a hydroxyl anion under very mild conditions. The reaction is rapidly reversible on acidification. This phenomenon was investigated by Hantzsch in 1899, who termed (LV) the 'pseudo-base' of (LIV). *Iso*quinoline reacts similarly but in the 1-position, and acridine in the 5-position.

LIV   LV   LVI

The secondary alcohol (LV) is easily oxidized by potassium ferricyanide to (LVI), the N-methyl-derivative of 2-hydroxy-quinoline (encountered previously, in (*e*) above). Another property of (LV) is that it easily forms ethers with alcohols; also two molecules of (LV) readily unite to form a self-ether.

If ammonia is used instead of sodium hydroxide, the primary amine corresponding to (LV) is formed.

The point of equilibrium for alkylpyridinium salts is such that they do not give appreciable amounts of the secondary alcohol ('pseudo-base'). However in the presence of alkaline potassium ferricyanide, good yields of the N-methyl-derivative of 2-hydroxypyridine are produced.

Ingold (1953) has suggested that the favouring of the 2-, rather than the 4-, position in quinoline is due to the longer conjugated pathway in the final product. A 4-substituted product (LVII) is formed if sodium cyanide is used instead of sodium hydroxide.

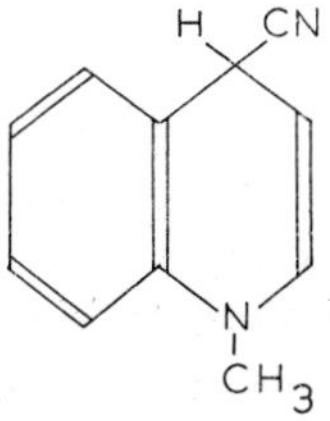

LVII

Hydroxylamine is a nucleophilic reagent that inserts a primary amino group (it is used at 50°, as the neutral molecule). 3-Nitroquinoline gives 2-amino-3-nitroquinoline, and 5-, 7-, and 8-nitroquinoline are similarly substituted in the 8-, 8- and 5- positions respectively, all in good yield (Colonna and Montanari, 1951).

Carbanions. Several nucleophilic reactions are known in which carbanions appear to be the active agent. For example, pyridazine (VI) and lithium butyl give 3-butylpyridazine in 50% yield (Letsinger and Lasco, 1956). The following scheme for lithium alkyls has something in common with that outlined above for sodamide (cf. Ziegler and Zeiser, 1930):

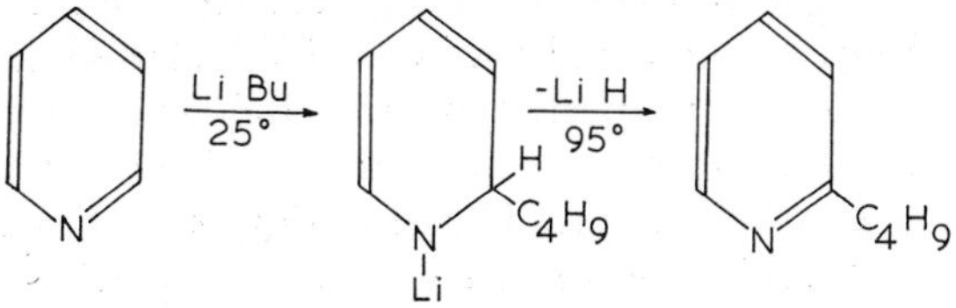

Similarly, Grignard reagents add quantitatively to pyridine: when the adduct is heated to 150° under pressure 2-alkyl- (or 2-aryl-) pyridines are formed (Bergstrom and McAllister, 1930). Less readily classified is the formation of 2- and 4- methylpyridine upon heating methylpyridinium chloride:

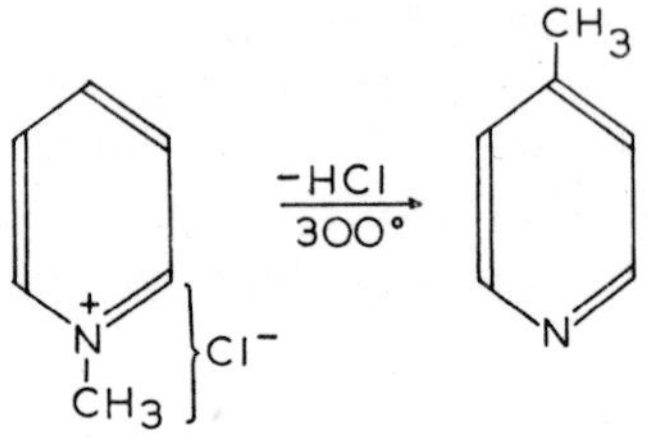

The formation of 2-benzoylpyridine (50% yield) from pyridine, magnesium and dimethylbenzamide may be similar (Bachman and Schisla, 1957).

The 3-position of iso*quinoline.* It is noteworthy that in all the nucleophilic reactions listed, *iso*quinoline reacts exclusively in the 1- (and never in the 3-) position, although both 1- and 3-positions are α- to a ring-nitrogen atom. Inspection of the electron-density diagram (XLIX) throws some light on this difference. The positive charge needed for nucleophilic attack is present to a much greater degree in the 1- than in the 3-position. Longuet-Higgins and Coulson (1949) consider that +0·15 is needed for nucleophilic attack (in diagrams constructed from their parameters, such as this). The case of 3-chloro*iso*quinoline, discussed below, is also relevant.

Replacement of halogen. The above nucleophilic substitutions, where hydrogen is replaced, are less frequently used than those where halogen is replaced. The greater stability of the halide anion than that of the hydride anion facilitates this type of replacement. The replacing reagents make a nucleophilic attack on the carbon atom to which the halogen is attached. Halogens in the α- and γ-positions are the most easily detached, because the electron-attracting properties of the halogen and the ring-nitrogen combine to produce a higher positive nett charge on the α- and γ-carbon atoms. This situation is well known in the *o*- and *p*-chloronitrobenzenes. Activation by a ring-nitrogen atom is not relayed to annelated rings. Halogen may be replaced nucleophilically in the following ways.

(i) By *methoxyl*, e.g. 4-methoxyquinazoline by mixing 4-chloroquinazoline with sodium methoxide in methanol without any heating (Keneford *et al.*, 1950); 2:4:6-trimethoxypyridine similarly from the trichloropyridine, but at 135° in a sealed tube (den Hertog *et al.*, 1950).

(ii) By *phenoxyl*, e.g. 6-nitro-4-phenoxyquinoline from 6-nitro-4-chloroquinoline with phenol and potassium hydroxide at 130° (Simpson and Wright, 1948).

(iii) By *hydroxyl*: this is effected with alkali, acid, or acetate buffer (see below).

(iv) By *amino*, e.g. by passing ammonia through a solution of a 4-chloroquinoline in phenol (Backeberg and Marais, 1942); by heating a 5-chloroacridine with ammonium carbonate in phenol at 120° (Albert and Gledhill, 1945); by passing ammonia through 6-chloropteridine in benzene at 20°, a method suitable for a highly activated chlorine (Albert, Brown and Cheeseman, 1952); by heating a 2-chloroquinoline with zinc chloride diamine at 240° in a sealed tube, a method often suitable for chlorine which is not activated enough to yield to ammonia under pressure even when catalysed by a trace of copper acetate (Backeberg and Marais, 1942; Albert, Brown and Duewell, 1948). Finally, 4-phenoxy-quinoline, -cinnoline and -quinazoline have been converted to amines by heating with ammonium acetate in an open vessel at 185–195° (Keneford *et al.*, 1950).

(v) By *substituted amino*. The reaction with weak bases, e.g. aniline, is acid catalysed (Banks, 1944; Keneford *et al.*, 1950), but basic conditions are preferable for strong bases such as piperidine, morpholine and the aliphatic amines (Maggiolo and Phillips). The reaction may be carried out in phenol (Albert, Goldacre and Heymann, 1943), alcohol (under pressure), or water.

(vi) By *mercapto*, e.g. the action of potassium hydrogen sulphide on 2-chloropyridine (Thirtle, 1946), or of thiourea on various 2- and 4- chloropyrimidines (Polonovski and Schmitt, 1950; Boarland and McOmie, 1951).

(vii) By *cyano*, e.g. the action of cuprous cyanide on 2-bromopyridine (Craig, 1934).

(viii) By *sulphonic acid*, e.g. the reaction of 4-chloroquinolines with aqueous sodium sulphite (Walker, 1947; Rubtsov and Arendaruk, 1946). This reaction permits an easy conversion of chloro- to cyano-derivatives via the sulphonic acid (Ochiai and Yamanaka, 1955).

Bunnett and Zahler (1951) have found the following order of reactivities for the replacement of chlorine in dinitrochlorobenzene, an order which may be relevant to the present series:

$$\text{-OEt} > \text{-OPh} \sim \text{piperidine} > \text{aniline} > \text{-I} > \text{-Br}$$

These replacements are all bimolecular reactions, and are S_N2 in Ingold's classification.

All who have prepared a number of α- and γ-chloro-compounds will know that the lability of the chlorine varies over a wide range. For example 2-chloro- and 2-bromo-pyridine are not appreciably hydrolysed by heating with 6N-hydrochloric acid for 24 hours, whereas 2-chloroquinoline is totally hydrolysed (Bradlow and Vanderwerf, 1949). Moreover, 5-chloroacridine, which is far more sensitive, is completely hydrolysed in an hour by cold 0·1N-hydrochloric acid. Again, 2:4-6-trichlorotriazine (cyanuric chloride) gives monosubstituted derivatives, esters or amines, at 0°, disubstituted derivatives at 20–30°, and trisubstituted derivatives at 90°.

When the more reactive of these chloro-compounds are exposed to moist air, they hydrolyse (to hydroxy-compounds) at an ever-increasing rate because of autocatalysis by the hydrochloric acid formed. This acceleration of hydrolysis by acid is due to the stronger electron-withdrawing effect of the ring-nitrogen atom when quaternized. Thus the carbon atom to which the chlorine is attached acquires a stronger positive charge, and more strongly attracts a polarized water molecule. Alkali-catalysed hydrolyses, where the hydroxyl-anion attacks the neutral molecule, are also known, but are not so rapid. Acetate-catalysed hydrolyses are valuable for substances sensitive to acid (Boon, Jones and Ramage, 1951).

In view of the quite small amount of kinetic work available in the heterocyclic field, it is gratifying that some of these nucleophilic replacements have been investigated. Excellent work has been done by Chapman and his school (Chapman and

Russell-Hill, 1956; Chapman and Rees, 1954). Reactions with sodium ethoxide, morpholine and piperidine gave consistent results at various dilutions and temperatures. From these results there were calculated rate coefficients and Arrhenius parameters (measures of the energy and entropy of activation).

The aromatic amines were unsatisfactory, because the replacement of $-Cl$ by $-NR_2$ is catalysed by cation-formation in the chlorine-containing species (Banks, 1944), and aromatic bases are too weak to prevent this. Pyridine was also unsatisfactory, apparently because the required reaction to give, say, (LVIII) from 2-chloropyrimidine, was not sufficiently faster than self-quaternization to give (LIX). It may be appropriate to mention here that 4-chloropyridine has a great tendency to self-quaternization, and can be kept unchanged for only a few days; 4-chloropyrimidine is still more troublesome in this respect and has to be used as soon as it is made. For steric reasons, self-quaternization gives little trouble in 4-chloroquinoline.

Fractional double-bond
character of *iso*quinoline
(Longuet-Higgins and Coulson,
1947)

| LVIII | LIX | LX |

The data in Table 7 may be compared with (i) the hydrolysis of 2-chloronaphthalene by sodium ethoxide under the same conditions, which has a log rate coefficient of only $\overline{7}\cdot96$, and (ii) that of 1-chloronaphthalene which is almost inappreciable.

Table 7 shows the effect of annelating (i.e. adding $-CH:CH\cdot CH:CH-$ to) a pyridine or pyrimidine ring. It can be seen that this annelation has been done in the 5:6-, 3:4- and 4:5-positions of 2-chloropyridine and in the first two cases this has increased the activation of the halogen, possibly because

TABLE 7. Comparison of Reactivities of Chloro-derivatives
(From Chapman and Russell-Hill, 1956)

Rates of reaction (log rate coefficients) at 20°	2-Chloropyridine	2-Chloroquinoline
Ethoxide ion 10 + log k	1·34	3·80
Piperidine 10 + log k	0·28	3·18

	1-Chloro*iso*quinoline	3-Chloro*iso*quinoline
Ethoxide ion 10 + log k	3·84	1̄·07
Piperidine 10 + log k	3·40	—

	2-Chloropyrimidine	2-Chloroquinazoline
Ethoxide ion 10 + log k	7·23	7·47
Piperidine 10 + log k	6·47	6·63

TABLE 7, *continued*

Rates of reaction (log rate coefficients) at 20°	2-Chloroquinoxaline	1-Chlorophthalazine
Ethoxide ion 10 + log k	7·92	7·27
Piperidine 10 + log k	5·79	5·31
	4-Chloropyridine	4-Chloroquinoline
Ethoxide ion 10 + log k	2·94	3·81
	5-Chloroacridine	4-Chlorocinnoline
Ethoxide ion 10 + log k	5·79	7·68
	4-Chloropyrimidine	4-Chloroquinazoline
Piperidine 10 + log k	7·2	10·49

of a wider delocalization of the charge imposed on the transition state. However the third example (annelation to 3-chloro*iso*quinoline) results in a considerable decrease in activity. Chapman and Russell-Hill believe that this is due to the feeble double-bonded character of the 2:3 bond in *iso*quinoline (LX) just as in naphthalene (see Chapter III). The result of this bond-fixation is that the activating influence of the hetero-atom is poorly transmitted to the 3-position (for another example, see (*k*) below). On the other hand the 1:2-bond has a high double-bond character, and this helps the activation in 1-chloro*iso*quinoline and 2-chloroquinoline. It is likely that the low reactivity of 2-chloroquinazoline compared to 2-chloropyrimidine is to be explained similarly, the increase of reactivity due to annelation being offset by bond-fixation. 4-Chloroquinazoline, where such an effect could not operate, is notably more reactive than 4-chloropyrimidine. An alternative theoretical treatment is to compare the nett charges of the 1- and 3-positions on the electron-density diagram (XLIX). 5-Chloroacridine shows the powerful effect of annelating first one, and then two, benzene rings to 4-chloropyridine.

Amstutz and his school have carried out similar kinetic studies using piperidine and, amongst other halo-compounds, 2-chloropyrazine (Brower, Way, Samuels and Amstutz, 1954), and the seven mono-halogenoquinolines (*idem*, 1953).

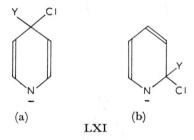

(a)   (b)
LXI

It has been shown by kinetics that a γ-nitrogen atom and a *para* nitro-group are roughly equal in the activation of a halogen, but that an α-nitrogen atom is not so effective as is an *ortho* nitro-group (Chapman and Russell-Hill, 1956). From this work it would appear that a transition state (or intermediate) with a predominating *para*-resonance structure is more likely to form than one with a predominating *ortho*-resonance structure; i.e. that (LXI, a) is more stable than (LXI, b). However, the similar reactivities of 2- and 4-chloroquinoline show that some unknown factor is also involved.

Nuclear methyl-groups, if substituted *meta*- to the chlorine atom, reduce the reaction-rate by a factor of about 2·5 per methyl-group. This (slight) deactivation is due to the inductive effect of the methyl-group, i.e. electron release (Chapman and Rees, 1954).

Other labile groups compared with chlorine. Because of resemblances between the nitrochlorobenzene series and the chloro-derivatives of π-deficient N-heterocycles, *iodine* would be expected to be less activated than chlorine in the latter series, as is the case in the former (Briner *et al.*, 1954). What little evidence is available seems to confirm this. On the other hand, if it is desired to exchange a halogen that has no α- or γ-activation, it has been found that iodine and bromine are more labile than chlorine. Thus 3-bromopyridine and cuprous cyanide give a 55% yield of 3-cyanoquinoline at 170° (3-iodopyridine gives 85%, Caldwell, Tyson and Lauer, 1944). Also 3-methoxy- and 3-amino-pyridine can be prepared in good yield from 3-bromopyridine, but 24 hours at 150° are required. In all these reactions, 3-chloropyridine is unreactive.

When an active halogenated substance is not easily prepared, the analogue with a *methylsulphonyl*-group ($-SO_2CH_3$), obtained by oxidizing a methylmercapto-group ($-SCH_3$), has been found equally reactive (Andrews, Anand, Todd and Topham, 1949). Also α- and γ-*nitro*-groups are very labile. For example 2-nitro-5-ethoxypyridine is easily converted to 2-bromo-5-ethoxypyridine by hydrobromic acid (Königs, Gerdes and Sirot, 1928; cf. Ochiai, 1953).

As with aromatic hydrocarbons, a sulphonic acid group in the benzene-ring of quinoline can be replaced by a hydroxyl-group through alkaline fusion. *Methylmercapto*- (e.g. Albert, Brown and Wood, 1954), *methoxy*-, and *phenoxy*- (e.g. Keneford, Schofield and Simpson, 1948) groups (when α- or γ-) have all been replaced by the amino-group. The mercapto-group is not so labile as the methylmercapto-group. It often permits differential replacement: for example 2:4-dimercaptopyrimidine is easily converted to 2-mercapto-4-methylaminopyrimidine (Russell, Elion, Falco and Hitchings, 1949).

Replacement of hydroxyl by halogens. Only α- and γ-hydroxyl-groups can be replaced by halogens. For replacement by chlorine, refluxing with phosphorus oxychloride is usually the best method. In difficult cases, it is advantageous to add phosphorus pentachloride, but this is not so often necessary as the older literature implies, and it complicates the working up. N:N-Dialkylanilines are useful accelerators of chlorination (Baddiley and Topham, 1944), and diethyl- is superior to dimethyl-aniline for this purpose.

As far as can be deduced from aliphatic analogues (Gerrard, Green and Nutkins, 1952), the first reaction is esterification of the hydroxy-derivative, followed by reaction with the liberated hydrogen chloride. As is well known, phenols can be converted to chlorobenzenes provided electron-attracting groups are present (Sané and Joski, 1924), and it would appear that a stage in the reaction is favoured by a low electron density on the carbon-atom to which the hydroxy-group is attached. This stage is probably the last one, which is a nucleophilic substitution.

The methochlorides of α-hydroxy-compounds lose methyl chloride when heated with phosphorus pentachloride at 170°, giving α-chloro-compounds, e.g. 2-chloroquinoline from 2-oxo-N-methylquinoline (cf. Deinet and Lutz, 1946).

The replacement of *hydroxy-groups* by the amino-group has not often been successful, and is usually mediated through the -chloro or -mercapto compounds. However, 2:4:6-trihydroxy-triazine (cyanuric acid), heated with ammonia gas to 350° is said to give a 70% yield of the triamine (melamine) (American Cyanamid Co., 1948). Moreover 5-, 6- and 8-hydroxyquinoline give the corresponding amines when heated with the zinc-chloride ammonia complex, temperatures from 180° to 300° being required for the various isomers. Similarly 2-, 3-, 7-, and 8-hydroxyquinolines exchange the hydroxyl-group with primary amines when heated with sulphurous acid (catalyst) under slight pressure (Hartshorn and Baird, 1946).

The replacement of the hydroxy- by the anilino-group is much more common (e.g. Albert and Ritchie, 1943). The methylation of hydroxy-groups usually leads to a mixture of O- and N-methyl-derivatives, even when the hydroxy-group is neither α- nor γ-. Diazomethane is the reagent likely to produce the highest possible yield of O-methyl-derivative.

Interconversion of hydroxyl- and mercapto-groups. Mercapto-groups are successfully hydrolysed in the pyrimidine series by refluxing with dilute chloroacetic acid (e.g. Brown, 1952). The reaction appears to go through a carboxymethyl stage ($-SCH_2COOH$), and may prove applicable outside the pyrimidine series.

Hydroxyl-groups (if α- or γ-) can be converted to mercapto-groups by phosphorus pentasulphide, in pyridine (Klingsberg and Papa, 1951) or tetrahydronaphthalene (Elion and Hitchings, 1947). This reaction is based on the usual way of forming thioamides from amides.

Replacement of diazo- and amino-groups. Except when in α- or γ-positions, amino-N-heterocycles diazotize normally and the diazo-group undergoes the usual Sandmeyer replacement by chlorine and all the other nucleophilic replacements. A little more care must be taken with *peri*-amino-derivatives, such as 8-aminoquinoline, which form triazinum compounds unless strong acid is present.

When the amino-groups are α- or γ-, the chloro-compound is obtainable from a solution in concentrated hydrochloric acid on adding sodium nitrite (e.g. Parker and Shive, 1947). Similarly a solution in concentrated hydrobromic acid gives excellent yields of the bromo-compound if free bromine is present (Craig, 1934; Allen and Thirtle, 1946).

All amino-pyridines and -quinolines can be converted to the corresponding hydroxy-compounds by treatment with nitrous acid (e.g. Tschichibabin and Rjazancev, 1915; Adams and Schrecker, 1949; Albert and Phillips, 1956 (3-hydroxyquinoline); Erickson and Spoerri, 1946 (2-hydroxypyrazine)).

Even α- and γ-amino-pyridines and -quinolines are not hydrolysed by acid or alkali at 100° unless a strong electron-attracting group is present ($-NO_2$ or a further ring-nitrogen atom). However, at 180–200°, even 5- and 7-aminoquinolines, and 2-, 3- and 4-aminoacridines, are smoothly hydrolysed by 10N-hydrochloric acid to the corresponding hydroxy-compounds. In the pteridine series, where all amino-groups are α-, both acid and alkaline hydrolyses (at atmospheric pressure), and also nitrous acid treatment, have all been applied successfully (Albert, 1952).

Replacement of a pyridinium group. 4-Pyridyl pyridinium chloride, a quaternary salt analogous to (LVIII), is easily prepared by the action of thionyl chloride on pyridine (Bowden and Green, 1954). The pyridinium ring in this substance is easily displaced by hydrogen sulphide, phosphorus pentachloride, amines, phenols, and hydroxyl ions to give respectively 4-mercapto-, 4-chloro-, 4-amino- (dimethylamino-, etc.), 4-phenoxy-, and 4-hydroxy-pyridine (Jerchel, Fischer and Thomas, 1956).

(h) Addition Reactions

Addition across a double-bond. In some aromatic molecules, delocalization of π-electrons creates a bond (between two neighbouring ring-atoms) that has a considerably higher fractional double-bond character than the standard aromatic bond of benzene. This bond should more readily take part in addition reactions. Thus, comparison of the bond-orders of benzene and naphthalene (see Chapter III, p. 37) shows that the $\alpha:\beta$-bond of naphthalene has the bond-order 0·73 (cf. 0·67 for benzene). Similarly, delocalization of electrons in π-deficient N-heterocycles is often associated with a double-bond of even higher bond-order. However, the substances added across double-bonds by these π-deficient substances are not those added by ethylene, viz. bromine or strong acids (e.g. HCl). Rather they are those added by ethylenic bonds conjugated to an electron-attracting group (an $\alpha:\beta$-unsaturated ketone has such a bond). It is characteristic of these bonds to add the anions of weak acids, such as HCN, $NaHSO_3$, NH_3, H_2O, the hydride anion, and the anions of pseudo acids such as acetone and ethyl malonate. An example is:

$$(CH_3)_2C = CH \cdot COCH_3 + HCN \rightarrow (CH_3)_2C(CN) \cdot CH_2COCH_3$$

It is a special difficulty in classification to say which is an addition reaction of this kind, and which is a nucleophilic reaction, as in (g) above, because the addition begins with a nucleophilic attack (the amination and carbanion sections of (g) should be re-read in this connexion). Because the double-bond of highest order often springs from the carbon atom of most positive charge, the causes are difficult to disentangle. However common usage is to speak of nucleophilic *substitution* only when the act of addition is followed by elimination and the double-bond is restored.

Addition reactions in π-deficient heterocycles seem to occur more easily the greater the π-deficiency. Perhaps the best model in the benzene series is the addition of sodium ethoxide to trini-trobenzene (Caldin and Long, 1955). Pyridine does not readily add reagents across its double-bonds, although quinoline and acridine readily dissolve in sodium hydrogen sulphite solution. Quinoxaline (LIII) easily adds two equivalents of hydrogen cyanide, or sodium hydrogen sulphite to give (LXII), where —R is —CN or —SO₃Na (Bergstrom and Ogg, 1931). These substances are re-converted to quinoxaline by alkali, or on heating. Acridine similarly reacts with these two reagents, but vinylogously, viz. across the 5:10-positions to give (LXIII) (Lehmstedt and Wirth, 1928). After quaternization, many pyri-dines add hydrogen cyanide.

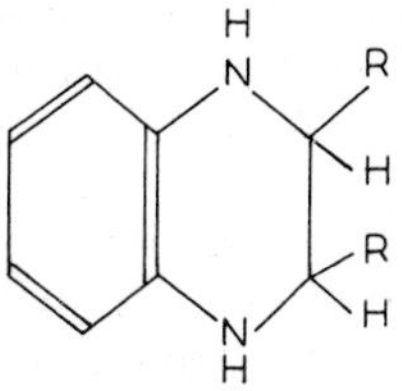

LXII 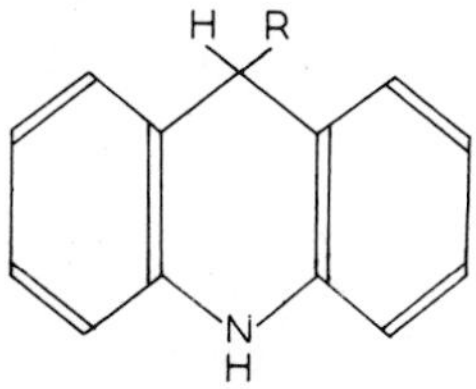   LXIII 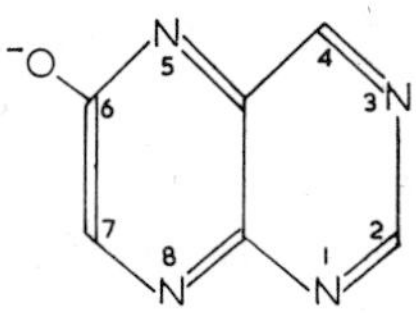   LXIV

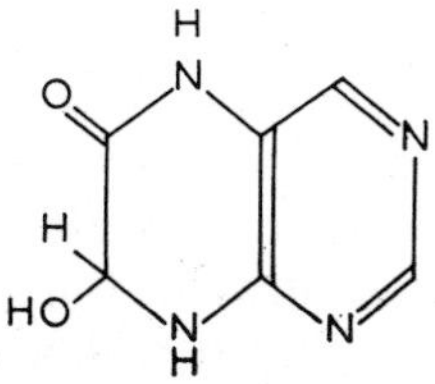

LXV

In the pyrimidine and pteridine series, it is a common experience to find, at the end of a reaction in which sodium bisulphite was present (or was generated), that the elements of

G

H_2SO_3 remain in the product, not as a salt, but in a form only expelled by boiling with mineral acid for several minutes.[1] The sulphur-containing products, although not characterized, resemble those already discussed.

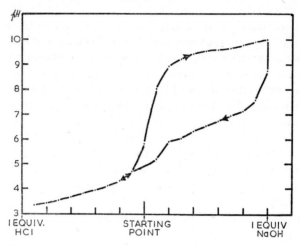

Fig. 1. Hysteresis loop produced on titration of 6-hydroxypteridine (250 ml. of 0·002 M, aqueous) with 1 equiv. (5 ml.) of 0·1 N-acid and -alkali at 20°.

The addition of water across a double-bond, in the more highly π-deficient-N-heterocycles, may be commoner than has been realized. The most studied example is the anion of 6-hydroxypteridine (LXIV), which changes rapidly, but at a measurable rate, to the substance (LXV) upon acidification. This substance, 6:7-dihydroxy-7:8-dihydropteridine, is 6-hydroxypteridine plus the elements of water covalently bound across the 7:8-double-bond. When titrated with alkali, (LXV) slowly gives the anion of 6-hydroxypteridine (LXIV) again. If promptly titrated, and back-titrated, 6-hydroxypteridine gives a hysteresis loop (Figure 1), from which two ionization constants can be calculated. The upper curve, that of a weak acid ($pK = 9·7$), belongs to the hydrated substance (LXV), and the ower curve, that of a stronger acid ($pK = 6·7$), is that of 6-hydroxypteridine itself (LXIV, and the relevant neutral

[1] Alternatively, cold strong alkaline treatment is often effective.

molecule) (Albert, Brown and Cheeseman, 1952). When the titrations are repeated, the loop is retraced. The possibility that this reaction is ring-opening and -closing was investigated, and disproved. Its true nature was revealed by properties of the $N_{(5)}$-methyl-derivative, viz. the ultraviolet spectra, the pK, and lack of hysteresis on titration, and by agreement between ionization constants and spectra of all species of 7:8-dihydro-6-hydroxypteridine (Brown and Mason, 1956).

It is also fairly certain that the anion of 2-hydroxypteridine adds water across the 3:4-double-bond when acidified. If this is so, this reaction must be fast, for it does not show hysteresis in titration. The hydrated product (unlike that from 6-hydroxypteridine) can be dehydrated on heating to 200°. Spectrometric evidence from the $N_{(1)}$- and $N_{(3)}$-methyl-derivatives supports the hypothesis of hydration. It should be added that the abnormally large shifts to shorter wave-lengths occurring on acidifying alkaline solutions of 2- and 6-hydroxypteridines strongly support this conception of a chemical change more complex than simple de-ionization. The remaining isomers, 4- and 7-hydroxypteridine, seem to be normal, spectrometrically and in all other ways. Finally, the ability of pteridine to give an anion, although lacking an ionizable hydrogen, can be explained by hydration in the 3:4-position (Albert, Brown and Wood, 1956).

A possibly similar phenomenon is encountered when ethyl 2:4-dichloropyridine-5-carboxylate is refluxed with dilute sodium hydroxide, and gives a 'hydrate' (m.p. 198°) of the corresponding carboxylic acid, unchanged by recrystallization from petroleum, or sublimation. When heated with phosphorus halides, it gave anhydrous 2:4-dichloropyridine-5-carboxylic acid, m.p. 152° (from water) (den Hertog et al., 1950).

2:4-Dihydroxypyrimidine (uracil), irradiated with ultraviolet light of 254 mμ, adds water across the 5:6-double-bond to give 2:4:6-trihydroxy-5:6-dihydropyrimidine (Moore and Thomson, 1955; Wang, Apicella and Stone, 1956). This is reminiscent of the addition of hypobromous acid across the same double-bond in 5-nitrouracil (Behrend, 1887), and of nitric acid in 5-bromouracil (Johnson, 1908) (irradiation was not used in these additions).

Addition to the ring-nitrogen. These additions result in an increase in valency of the nitrogen atom. The simplest example is quaternization, undergone with great vigour, and without prior warming, by pyridine and quinoline on simple admixture with a methyl, allyl or benzyl iodide, and more reluctantly with ethyl iodide (and its higher homologues), and phenyl iodide. The reaction can be abated by solvents of low dielectric constant, such as ether. Conversely the more difficult quaternizations go better in nitrobenzene. Acridine, because of steric hindrance, is slow to quaternize at 20°, but methyl sulphate or methyl *p*-toluenesulphonate in nitrobenzene at about 120° is effective. Methyl 2:4-dinitrobenzenesulphonate is excellent for quaternizing unstable bases (at 20°) and resistant bases (140°) (Kipriyanov and Tolmatschev, 1957).

When quaternizing primary amino-derivatives, it is usual to protect the exocyclic nitrogen by acetylation. This is unnecessary for α- and γ-amino-derivatives which alkylate only on the ring-nitrogen. Also α- and γ-hydroxy-derivatives usually methylate exclusively on the nitrogen atom if alkyl halides or sulphates are used: but diazomethane either effects methylation exclusively on oxygen (cf. v. Pechmann, 1895; Brown, Hoerger and Mason, 1955, a), or a mixture of both O- and N-methyl-derivatives is obtained (Albert, Brown and Wood, 1956).[1] Mercapto-derivatives, even if α- or γ-, methylate on the sulphur atom.

π-Deficient N-heterocycles also readily form quaternary compounds with acyl halides. These are readily hydrolysed by cold water. Reissert found that the combined action of benzoyl chloride and aqueous potassium cyanide on quinoline gave N-benzoyl-2-cyano-1:2-dihydroquinoline (LXVI), which can be rearranged to benzaldehyde and 2-cyanoquinoline. This reaction has been adapted to the production of aldehydes from aroyl halides.

The self-quaternization of 4-chloropyridine was mentioned in (*g*) above (p. 75). 4-Pyridylpyridinium chloride (LXVII) is

---

[1] By adding diazomethane *slowly* to a hydroxy-derivative, the proportion of O- to N-methyl-derivatives can sometimes be increased, because the enol has time to regenerate (Arndt, 1953). This fact disposes of the principal assumption of the 'mesohydry' hypothesis (Hunter, 1945) that the two tautomers cannot exist independently.

usually made by the action of thionyl chloride on pyridine (Königs and Greiner, 1931; Bowden and Green, 1954; Bak and Christensen, 1954).

Bromine (e.g. in carbon tetrachloride) adds to π-deficient N-heterocycles to give such substances as N-bromoacridinium bromide (LXVIII) (Acheson, Hoult and Barnard, 1954).

The migration of methyl from a methoxy-group to a ring-nitrogen upon heating can be catalysed by acids (Eichenberger, Staehlin and Druey, 1954). Conversely, methyl-groups 'wander' from a ring-nitrogen to an α- (but not to a γ-) amino-group upon gentle treatment (e.g. Brown, Hoerger and Mason, 1955, b; Carrington, Curd and Richardson, 1955), an effect caused by ring-opening.

LXVI	LXVII	LXVIII

LXIX	LXX	LXXI	LXXII

During the last two decades, investigations of the *N-oxides* of π-deficient N-heterocycles have opened up new territory in pyridine chemistry and made available many heterocyclic substances previously difficult of access (Katritzky, 1956). In 1926, Meisenheimer made N-oxides from pyridine, quinoline and *iso*quinoline by the action of perbenzoic acid. This reaction remained neglected until it was shown that sulphuryl chloride converted pyridine N-oxide into a mixture of 2- and 4-chloropyridine, and quinoline-N-oxide behaved similarly (Bobranski, Kochanska and Kowalewska, 1938; Bachman and Cooper, 1944). This initiated a stream of excellent and original papers from Japan, beginning in 1943 (summarized by Ochiai, 1953). Similar studies were independently conducted in Holland (den Hertog *et al.*, 1950, 1951). The discovery that heterocyclic N-oxides are obtainable in good yield by heating the parent-substance with acetic acid and hydrogen peroxide (den Hertog and Combe, 1951; Ochiai, 1953) avoided the troublesome preparation and standardization of per-acids.

Pyridine N-oxide is much more reactive to electrophilic reagents than pyridine, e.g. potassium nitrate in fuming sulphuric acid at 100° gives 4-nitropyridine-N-oxide in 90% yield (den Hertog and Overhoff, 1950; Ochiai, 1953). Quinoline-N-oxide similarly gives 4-nitroquinoline-N-oxide, but below 0°, 5- and 8-nitroquinoline-N-oxide are slowly produced.

This comparatively high reactivity of pyridine-N-oxide has been attributed to the high proportion of (LXX) in the resonance hybrid, cf. the nett charge diagram (LXXI) (Jaffé, 1954). The small dipole moment reveals that the moment of pyridine is opposed by that of the N-oxide group (Linton, 1940). The result is that a small negative charge accumulates in the 4-position. This diagram falls short of what is required, because the oxygen atom is basic ($pK_a = 0.8$) and will carry a proton during nitration. However, this salt formation protects the ring-nitrogen from protonation (coulombic effect) and thus keeps the cation more reactive than the pyridinium cation.

The N-oxide function is resistant to many common reducing agents such as sulphurous acid, but the parent-substances can be regenerated by iron and acetic acid, catalytic reduction, or by the action of phosphorus trichloride. Thus 4-nitropyridine-N-oxide can be converted at will to 4-nitropyridine, 4-aminopyridine, or 4-aminopyridine-N-oxide.

When refluxed with acetic anhydride, the N-oxides isomerize to α-hydroxy-derivatives. This reaction is believed to proceed through 1:2-diacetoxy-1:2-dihydropyridine, apparently a nucleophilic substitution. The ability of heterocyclic N-oxides to give both electrophilic and nucleophilic substitution in conjugated positions is attributed to the nitrosobenzene-like property of being polarizable in opposite directions depending on the charge of the reagent, and (LXXII) is put forward as the resonance contribution that is specially favoured in the hydroxylation reaction (Ochiai, 1953). The alternative polarizabilities have been confirmed by dipole moment measurements of a series of derivatives (Katritzky, Randall and Sutton, 1957).

At equilibrium in water, 2- and 4-aminopyridine-N-oxide have been shown to have the true primary amine structure, whereas 2- and 4-hydroxypyridine-N-oxide contain both enol and amide forms in comparable amounts (Gardner and Katritzky, 1957). The methods used were potentiometry and ultraviolet spectrophotometry of the substances and their various methyl-derivatives.

Diels-Alder reagents. These reagents have not much affinity for π-deficient-N-heterocycles. The action of maleic anhydride on 2:3-dimethylquinoxaline is attributed to the methylene ($CH_2=$) nature of the methyl-groups (Schönberg and Mostafa, 1943). Methyl acetylenedicarboxylate reacts with π-deficient-heterocycles more readily than maleic anhydride, but usually only achieves quaternization of the nitrogen atom (Holmes, 1948).

(i) Oxidations and Reductions

Oxidations. The formation of N-oxides has been discussed under (*h*) above, as well as the formation of C-hydroxy-compounds from these by rearrangement. This seems to be the mechanism by which hydrogen peroxide converts pteridine to 4-hydroxy-pteridine. However, the formation of 6:7-dihydroxy- from 7-hydroxy-pteridine with nitric acid appears to be an electrophilic substitution (Albert, Brown and Cheeseman, 1952). Chromic acid oxidations are apparently nucleophilic: a few examples are known, notably 3-nitro- to 5-hydroxy-3-nitro-acridine, and 2-methyl- to 4-hydroxy-2-methyl-quinazoline. Ammonium persulphate can introduce a hydroxy-group into either electron-rich or electron-deficient positions, e.g. 2:4-diaminopyrimidine is converted to the 5-hydroxy-derivative (Hull, 1956), but quinoxaline to 2:3-dihydroxyquinoxaline.

In most cases, the oxidation of π-deficient heterocycles causes ring-opening. That there is little difference in the stability to oxidation of the benzene and pyridine rings is shown by the oxidation of 2-phenylpyridine with potassium permanganate: in hot alkaline solution 63% of benzoic acid, and in hot acid solution 99% of pyridine-2-carboxylic acid, are formed. When not heated, pyridine is very stable to potassium permanganate for which it forms a useful solvent in oxidation reactions.

A cold solution of chromium trioxide in sulphuric acid hardly affects quinoline, but alkaline potassium permanganate gives a good yield of pyridine-2:3-dicarboxylic acid, a reaction that helped to establish the constitution of quinoline. *Iso*quinoline similarly gives pyridine-3:4-dicarboxylic acid plus a little phthalic acid; when an electron-attracting group is present in the 5-position, only phthalic acids (substituted in the 3-position) are formed. Polyhydroxy-pyridines and quinolines are easily oxidized by air, but the products have not been characterized. Both the 2- and 4-hydroxyquinolines, also the N-alkylquinolinium salts, are stable in air, but give substituted anthranilic acids with alkaline permanganate solutions. Solutions of permanganates in N-acid destroy both quinoline and *iso*quinoline, even at 20°.

Occasionally, mercapto-groups can be removed by oxidation (with hydrogen peroxide or nitric acid) to the corresponding sulphinic acids, which hydrolyse readily:

$$R \cdot SH \rightarrow R\text{-}SO_2H \rightarrow RH + SO_2$$

For example 2-mercapto-4-hydroxy-6-methylpyrimidine gives 4-hydroxy-6-methylpyrimidine (Williams, Ruehle and Finkelstein, 1937).

Hydrogenations (catalytic and otherwise). The hydrogenation of double-bonds can occur by three different mechanisms. The reaction can be *homolytic*, i.e. the hydrogen is transferred as atoms. This apparently happens in metal-catalysed hydrogenation, in electrolytic reduction, and in reduction during radiation. Or the reaction can be *heterolytic* and involve hydrogen cations, or even hydride anions. Hydrogen cations are believed to be the active agent in sodium hydrosulphite (dithionite) reductions, and in some enzymic reductions (Burton and Kaplan, 1954), whereas hydrogen anions are involved in sodium borohydride and lithium aluminium hydride reductions, and apparently in reductions with dissolving metals (Na, Zn and Sn for example).

Pyridine is reduced to piperidine (i.e. the three double-bonds are hydrogenated) by hydrogen gas over Adams' platinum catalyst (or Raney-nickel above 100°), by tin and hydrochloric acid, or by sodium in absolute alcohol. Tetrahydropyridine is a contaminant of commercial piperidine, but can be removed by adding bromine and fractionating.

Dihydropyridines can be prepared by gentler reduction. They tend to dimerize and the most stable seem to be those with electron-attracting substituents. One of the most important coenzymes in cellular metabolism is a dihydropyridine, viz. DPN or diphosphopyridine nucleotide. In its reduced form (LXXIV) (where R is a ribose residue connected to pyrophosphoric acid which is, in turn, linked to adenosine), this coenzyme functions by handing hydrogen to an acceptor of higher E_0, usually a similarly constituted riboflavine nucleotide, and this in turn passes it to more highly poised oxidizing systems (see Figure 2).

Meanwhile the dehydrogenated DPN is reduced apparently as follows (Burton and Kaplan, 1954), the hydrogen coming from the substrate (e.g. lactic acid), with the aid of a specific enzyme (in this case lactate dehydrogenase):

LXXIII $+2H^+ + 2\underline{e}$ LXXIV

[Where A^- is a phosphoric group on R.]

That the hydrogen is added (both enzymically and in hydrosulphite reductions) to the 4-, and not to the 2- or 6-positions as had been thought, followed from deuteration experiments

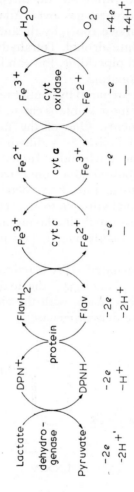

FIG. 2. Chain of heterocyclic coenzymes metabolizing a typical substrate (lactate) by transferring hydrogen ions and electrons stepwise to the oxygen of air.

DPN = defined above
Flav = riboflavine nucleotide
Cyt = cytochrome (see Chapter V)

(Pullman, San Pietro and Colowick, 1954). Reduction of (LXXIII) with sodium borohydride gives other isomers (Stein and Stiasny, 1955). Oxidation of (LXXIII) with potassium ferricyanide, a general reaction described above, on p. 71, gives both the 2- and 6-oxo-derivatives.

Quinoline hydrogenates in the presence of platinum, to the 1:2:3:4-tetrahydro-derivative in neutral solution, and to decahydroquinoline (80% *trans* and 20% *cis*) in glacial acetic acid. Raney-nickel at room-temperature also catalyses formation of 1:2:3:4-tetrahydroquinoline. Hydrogen iodide and phosphorus at 200° converts quinoline to a mixture of 1:2:3:4- and 5:6:7:8-tetrahydroquinoline and decahydroquinoline.

Gentle acid (or alkaline) reduction gives dimers of dihydroquinolines, but monomers have been obtained by other methods. For example 3:4-dihydro-2-hydroxyquinoline is obtained by catalytic hydrogenation (Späth and Galinowski, 1936) of 2-hydroxyquinoline under conditions which would produce 1:2:3:4-tetrahydroquinoline from quinoline. This failure of a −CO·NH − group to hydrogenate readily is usual in the π-deficient heterocycles (cf. Albert, Brown and Cheeseman, 1952). Lithium aluminium hydride was used to make certain 1:2-dihydroquinolines (Schmid and Karrer, 1949).

*Iso*quinoline gives 1:2:3:4-tetrahydro*iso*quinoline with tin and hydrochloric acid, with sodium in alcohol or with hydrogen (platinum catalysed) in glacial acetic (and further catalytic hydrogenation gives *cis*-decahydro*iso*quinoline, which can be dehydrogenated to 5:6:7:8-tetrahydro*iso*quinoline). Lithium aluminium hydride reduces *iso*quinoline to 1:2-dihydro*iso*quinoline in good yield (Jackman and Packham, 1955). Acridine is readily reduced to acridan (5:10-dihydroacridine) by catalytic hydrogenation at atmospheric temperature and pressure, by sodium hydrosulphite, and by dissolving metals, but 1:2:3:4-tetrahydroacridine is not obtainable by hydrogenating acridine. The catalytic hydrogenation of acridan or acridine at 100° gives a mixture of *sym*- and *as*-octahydroacridines and dodecahydroacridine; at 240°, tetradecahydroacridine results, no double-bonds remaining (Albert, 1951). Using copper chromite catalyst at 190°, only *as*-octahydroacridine is produced, because this catalyst hydrogenates pyridine-, rather than benzene-, rings (the same isomer is obtained with hydriodic acid and phosphorus at 225°).

Very little information is available about reduction of diazanaphthalenes. Quinoxalines are reduced to 1:2:3:4-tetrahydro-derivatives by catalytic hydrogenation, or by dissolving sodium. 4-Phenylcinnoline gives the 1:2-dihydro-derivative with zinc and ammonia. Phthalazine gives 1:2:3:4-tetrahydrophthalazine with dissolving sodium.

Pyrazines are easy to hydrogenate catalytically under alkaline conditions (Krems and Spoerri, 1947), whereas pyrimidines are almost unaffected (Lythgoe and Rayner, 1951). Hence it is not surprising that pteridines hydrogenate exclusively in the pyrazine ring, taking up four hydrogen atoms (minus two for each $-CO\cdot NR-$ group present, e.g. 7-hydroxypteridine hydrogenates in the 5:6-position, and 6-hydroxypteridine in the 7:8-position). Suitable reagents are sodium amalgam, sodium hydrosulphite (Albert, Brown and Cheeseman, 1952), and lithium aluminium hydride (Taylor, 1954). The reduction of 7-hydroxypteridine to the 5:6-dihydro-derivative by light (Albert, 1956) is typical of pteridines and phenazines.

Reductive removal of oxygen, sulphur or chlorine. The circumstances under which a *hydroxy-group* can be replaced by hydrogen are not well understood. So far, the reaction is confined to the 5-position in a 5-hydroxyacridine, the 7-position in a 6:7-dihydroxypteridine, and the 2-position in a 2:3-dihydroxyquinoxaline. In all cases dissolving sodium or zinc is used, and $-CO\cdot NR-$ is replaced by $-CH_2-NR-$, where R is H or alkyl (Albert, 1951; Albert, Brown and Cheeseman, 1952; Elion, 1954). Pyridine 2- and 4-carboxylic acids give methylpyridines with zinc (Sorm, 1948).

In 1945, Roblin and his colleagues demonstrated that a *mercapto-group* can be replaced by hydrogen, merely by refluxing with Raney-nickel, and many other examples, principally in the pyrimidine series, have since been provided (Brown, 1950, 1952). Only mercapto-groups that are α- to a ring-nitrogen atom have so far been removed in this way.

The replacement of *chlorine* by hydrogen can often be carried out by heating with hydriodic acid and phosphorus, or boiling with zinc and dilute ammonia. Both methods are unsuitable for readily hydrolysed chlorine atoms. For these, catalytic hydrogenation is to be preferred, or gentle warming with *p*-tosylhydrazide to give e.g. (LXXV), followed by a mild alkaline treatment (Albert and Royer, 1949). Another method is to warm with hydrazine, then oxidize the resulting hydrazide with a cupric salt (Baumgarten and Su, 1952).

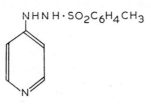

LXXV

Catalytic hydrogenation is suitable for the replacement of chlorine provided that an acid-binding agent is present. Thus 5-chloroacridine is dehalogenated in cold alcoholic potassium hydroxide over Raney-nickel (Albert and Willis, 1946). For the more difficult dehalogenation of chloropyrimidines, palladium has given better results, particularly that prepared by the method of Rampino and Nord (1941). In this way, pyrimidine has been obtained in good yields from 2-chloro-, 2:4-dichloro-, 2:4:6-trichloro- and even 2:5-dichloropyrimidine (Boarland, McOmie and Timms (1952), Whittaker (1951; 1953), and Lythgoe and Rayner (1951) respectively). By far the best acid-binder for this catalyst is magnesium oxide. Many dehalogenations of pyridines and quinolines in the older literature would probably be improved by the use of palladium in this way.

In some cases, catalytic dehalogenation is accompanied by hydrogenation, e.g. 4-chlorocinnoline gives 1:2-dihydrocinnoline, which is readily oxidized to cinnoline with mercuric oxide.

Decarboxylation. It is not usual to treat decarboxylation as a reduction because it is effected by heat, and not reducing agents. However, it formally resembles dehalogenation.

α- and γ-Carboxylic acids, particularly the former, decarboxylate easily on heating; 200° to 250° is a satisfactory range for almost instantaneous decarboxylations of the majority of such substances. Pyridine-3-carboxylic acid (the vitamin, nicotinic acid) has been thus prepared by heating pyridine 2:3-dicarboxylic acid (quinolinic acid).

Nitro-, nitroso-, and azo-derivatives of π-deficient N-heterocycles are reduced by the same methods as their benzene analogues.

Disproportionation. Several examples are known where oxidation and reduction go on simultaneously, two molecules of the starting material yielding one at a higher, and one at a lower oxidative level. For example, N-methylacridinium chloride when treated with alkali gives N-methyl-5-hydroxy-5:10-dihydroacridine (see p. 70 above) and this disproportionates on warming with alkali to give N-methyl-5:10-dihydroacridine, and the N-methyl-derivative of 5-hydroxyacridine (Pictet and Patry, 1902). A quite different type of alkali-induced disproportionation is the conversion of 6-hydroxypteridine to 7:8-dihydro-6-hydroxypteridine plus 6:7-dihydroxypteridine (Albert, 1955, b).

(j) Homolytic, or Free-radical Reactions

Homolytic bromination (i.e. with bromine atoms) has already been mentioned (p. 63), and homolytic hydrogenation on p. 90. It is still often a matter of dispute whether some particular reaction is homolytic or heterolytic. However, it is agreed that the phenylation of heteroaromatic substances with benzoyl peroxide, lead tetrabenzoate, or benzene-diazonium salts is due entirely to the free phenyl radical.

In homolytic substitution, the radicals are neutral and hence are not influenced by the charge at various points on the ring. On the other hand, the fraction of an electron available at any position for free-valency (see Chapter II) should be highly relevant, but atom localization energies provide more reliable material for calculations (R. D. Brown, 1956). Yet, so far, the agreement between such calculations and the experimental results is only fair for heteroaromatic substances (cf. Hey and Williams, 1953). These authors found the following partial rate factors (relative to benzene = 1) for the reaction between pyridine and the phenyl radical (derived from benzoyl peroxide at 80°):

Position attacked	Partial rate factor
2-	1·91
3-	0·86
4-	1·01

The yields of phenylpyridines, when the phenyl-radical was derived from five different sources, are approximately 50, 30 and 15 % of the 2-, 3- and 4-isomers respectively (Hey, Stirling and Williams, 1955). When diazotized *p*-nitroaniline was added to pyrimidine, 2- and 4-*p*-nitrophenyl-derivatives were formed (Lythgoe and Rayner, 1951).

(*k*) *Side-chain Reactions*

Reactions of a methyl-group. We have seen that amino-, hydroxy-, chloro- and carboxylic acid groups all behave differently when α- or γ- to a ring-nitrogen atom. This is also true of the methyl-group, which is activated by the same mechanism that makes the methyl-group in 2:4-dinitrotoluene so active, viz. loss of electron density to an electron-attracting atom.

| LXXVI | LXXVII | LXXVIII |

It is generally believed that the electron-attracting property of the ring-nitrogen atom causes a minute amount of the α- and γ-methyl-derivatives to ionize as anions (e.g. LXXVI), which are nucleophilic reagents, readily adding across the double-bond of aldehydes to give aldols (e.g. LXXVII), which in turn split off water under severer conditions (Ingold, 1953). Acetic anhydride, or zinc chloride, is a suitable catalyst for this sequence of reactions. The sodium salt of (LXXVI), obtained by the action of sodamide, is well known. It was thought at one time that the first step in the aldol reaction was a tautomerism, because substances like (LXXVIII) have been isolated from the reaction between aldehydes and quaternary salts (Taylor and Baker, 1937). As would be expected, quaternary salts react with aldehydes with greater vigour than the tertiary amines: a lower temperature suffices, and piperidine acetate is a sufficient catalyst. Similarly, the introduction of extra ring-nitrogen atoms enhances the effect, e.g. 4-methylpyrimidine reacts much more energetically with aldehydes than 4-methylpyridine. For this type of reaction, it has been stated that each ring-nitrogen is 1·5 times as activating as a *p*-nitro-group in benzene (Khromov-Borisov, 1955). The 3-methyl-group is only slightly activated in *iso*quinoline for reasons given in (*g*) above.

Substances with an α- or γ-hydroxy-group *as well as* a γ- or α-methyl-group will not condense with aldehydes, but the condensation can be carried out if the hydroxy- is changed to methoxy- (through chloro-) (e.g. Albert, Brown and Duewell, 1948).

Substances with active methyl-groups also condense with *p*-nitrosodimethylaniline to a nitrone, which is hydrolysed by acid to the corresponding aldehyde (cf. Perrine and Sargent, 1949).

The condensation of the methiodide of 2-iodopyridine with that of 2-methylquinoline gives the cyanine (LXXIX). Many hundreds of cyanines have been prepared by the photographic industry in the search for substances which will extend the range of photographic silver-gelatin emulsions which normally are sensitive only to light of short wave-lengths. The first cyanine to achieve widespread use for this purpose was pinacyanol, obtained by condensing 2-methylquinoline methiodide with formaldehyde. This is an analogue of (LXXIX) in which two quinoline nuclei are joined by =CH·CH:CH −, which permits the N to N'- conjugation found in all cyanines. By conferring sensitivity to light of various wave-lengths, the cyanines have made possible the true rendering of colour in monochrome, and have greatly increased the speed of films and plates. In addition they play an important part in colour photography. By lengthening the conjugated chain between the heterocyclic nuclei, emulsions have been made sensitive to infrared rays. Many of the finest achievements of modern photography are due to the cyanines (Hamer, 1950).

In 1926, it was found that the symmetrical attachment of three quinoline nuclei to a five-carbon conjugated chain would give improved sensitization at longer wave-lengths and such a substance, neocyanine, was introduced with great success. The 1920's are also noted for the introduction of cyanines having other nuclei than quinoline; indolenine and benzothiazole were particularly successful. For the correlation of spectra with constitution in cyanines, see Brooker *et al.* (1941).

The highly activated methyl-group of 2-methylquinoxaline readily reacts with another molecule of 2-methylquinoxaline, in the presence of air, to give the red substance (LXXX) (Landor and Rydon, 1955). For similar nucleophilic reactions in the pteridine series see Russell *et al.* (1949).

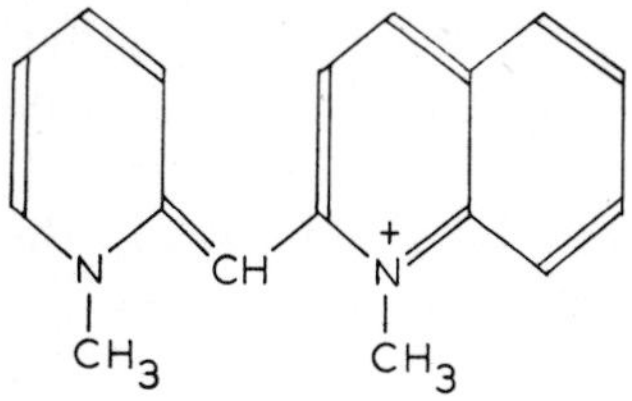

LXXIX 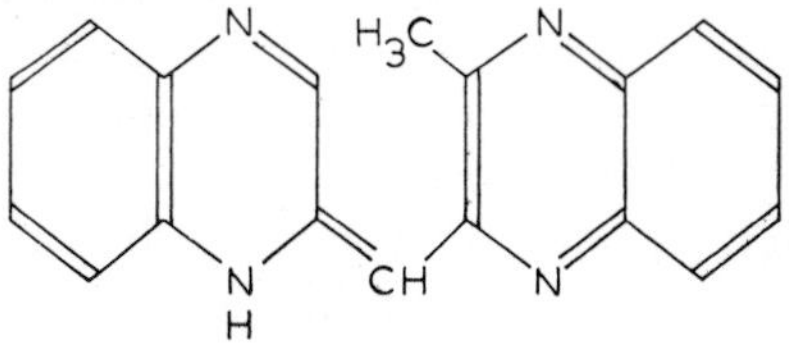   LXXX

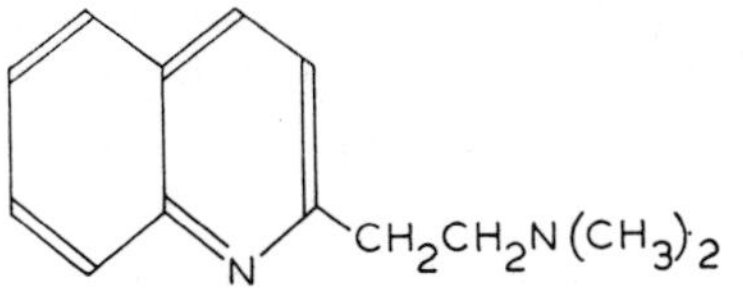

LXXXI

All three methylpyridines can be oxidized to the corresponding acids in about 60% yield by alkaline potassium permanganates. If the α- and γ-methylpyridines are first condensed with benzaldehyde to give styrenes, the oxidation with permanganate gives higher yields, especially if an amino-group is also present (Royer, 1949).

Activated methyl-groups can be oxidized to aldehydes with selenium dioxide. This is successful with 2- and 4-methylquinoline and 1- (and even 3-) methyl*iso*quinoline (Teague and Roe, 1951); but the yields with methylpyridines are not good, for the reaction produces the acids as well as the aldehydes. However, the three pyridine aldehydes are suitably made by oxidizing the corresponding primary alcohols with lead tetracetate (Mićović and Mihailović, 1952). α- and γ-Methyl-derivatives brominate readily in the side-chain, and the bromomethyl-derivatives produced in this way easily give the

H

hydroxymethyl-derivatives just mentioned, and also amino-methyl-derivatives. The latter are also easily converted to aldehydes, namely by the Sommelet reaction with hexamine (Angyal, Barlin and Wailes, 1953).

Active methyl-derivatives give products of the type (LXXXI) by a Mannich reaction with formaldehyde and a primary or secondary amine (Kermack and Muir, 1931); they also undergo Claisen condensations with ethyl oxalate to give e.g. 2-quinolyl-pyruvic acid. Finally the side-chains in the active methyl-derivatives can be lengthened, and this compensates for the complete failure of Friedel-Crafts reactions in π-deficient N-heterocycles. Thus 2-methylpyridine and butyl chloride, in the presence of sodamide at room temperature, give 2-n-amyl-pyridine (Tschichibabin, 1938).

Carboxylic acids. These form esters, amides and nitriles similarly to their aromatic analogues. Sulphuric acid is usually a better catalyst than hydrogen chloride for forming esters. Many of the amides undergo the Hofmann degradation (but only reluctantly in the pyrimidine series). For decarboxylation, see p. 95.

3. MONOGRAPHS

The following short summaries of physical properties, occurrence, uses, and syntheses are to supplement the systematic account of properties in Section 2 of this chapter.

A. Systems with One Ring-Nitrogen Atom

Pyridine is a hygroscopic, colourless liquid with a garlic-like odour. It is miscible with water and forms an azeotrope, b.p. 92°, which corresponds to the formula $C_5H_5N,3H_2O$. Table 8 compares some properties of pyridine with those of its azalogues.

Pyridine is used in chemical industry in large quantities. It forms part of more complex molecules: drugs such as the antitubercular drug, *iso*nicotinic hydrazide, and the antihistamic drug, tripelenna-mine (pyribenzamine, N:N-dimethyl-N'-benzyl-N'-2-pyridylethyl-enediamine); the vitamins nicotinic acid and pyridoxin; also in wetting and waterproofing agents for the textile industry. Pyridine is used as a solvent and proton-acceptor in the manufacture of sul-phonamides and in many other acylations where it improves the yields. Pyridine enters also into the composition of analytical reagents for the determination of moisture, and of unsaturation.

Until a practicable synthesis was found in 1957,[1] the world was dependent on the high-temperature (1000°–1300°) pyrolysis of coal, bone and petroleum. Of these, coal is the most important, yet low-temperature carbonization gives little pyridine. Even in high-temperature pyrolysis, only one pound of pyridine bases is won from 15 tons of coal, and from this only 150 c.c. of pure pyridine is obtained. The lowest boiling fraction of pyridine bases is a mixture of pyridine (b.p. 116°) and 2-methylpyridine (b.p. 129°), with small amounts of sulphur-containing materials. It is commercial practice to sell this mixture as 'purified pyridine', 'fractionated pyridine', 'redistilled pyridine', and it is a valuable solvent, although useless as a starting-material for syntheses. Chemically pure pyridine, prepared from this fraction, is an expensive material, and is used sparingly.

TABLE 8. Pyridine and its Azalogues
(Compiled mainly from Hückel and Jahnentz, 1942; and Grundmann and Kreutzberger, 1954)

Azabenzene	Trivial name	b.p./760 mm.	m.p.	Dipole Moment (D)
1-Mono-	Pyridine	116°	−42°	2·2
1:2-Di-	Pyridazine	207	−6	3·9
1:3-Di	Pyrimidine	124	22	2·4
1:4-Di-	Pyrazine	121	54	0
1:3:5-Tri-	*Sym*-Triazine	114	85	0
1:2:4:5-Tetra-	*Sym*-Tetrazine	—	99	0

The next fraction (up to 144°) of pyridine bases contains 3- and 4-methyl-, and 2:6-dimethyl-pyridine. The last named is removed as the urea complex, from which it is easily regenerated. 3- and 4-Methylpyridine boil within one degree; but azeotropy with acetic acid, azeotropy with water, or fractional freezing and melting, enable them to be separated (Coulson and Jones, 1946). Fractionation of the N-oxides is also suitable for separating the three constituents of the 140–144° fraction (Ochiai *et al.*, 1951; Albert, 1958). For the preparation of pyridine, 2-, 3- and 4-methylpyridine and 2:6-dimethylpyridine of purity greater than 99·7 moles per cent, and the constants of these five substances, see Biddiscombe *et al.* (1954).

The monomethyl-derivatives of pyridine are sometimes called picolines; the dimethyl-, lutidines; and the trimethyl-, collidines. Pyridine 2-, 3- and 4-carboxylic acids are known, respectively, as

---

[1] Reilly Tar and Chemical Corporation, by the combination of acetylene and ammonia.

picolinic, nicotinic and *iso*nicotinic acid. Quinolinic acid is pyridine-2:3-dicarboxylic acid.

The more complex pyridines used in medicine and industry are obtained (i) from coal-tar pyridine and its homologues by the processes described in Section 2 (*f, g, h, i, j* and *k*), above; (ii) from the nicotinic acid produced by the oxidation of nicotine (Chapter XI) from tobacco; (iii) from the pyridine 2:3-dicarboxylic acid obtained by oxidizing quinoline and 8-hydroxyquinoline; or (iv) by synthesis from aliphatic substances.

The aliphatic syntheses proceed mainly from derivatives of glutaconic dialdehyde or the corresponding acid, or from simpler molecules which unite to form these derivatives. Glutaconic aldehyde, which is believed to be the semi-enol (LXXXII), can be obtained in quantity only from pyridine, so that the synthesis of pyridine, by heating this aldehyde with ammonia, is of interest only in confirming the structure.

LXXXII   LXXXIII   LXXXIV

LXXXV

In the Hantzsch synthesis, two molecules of a β-keto-ester, such as acetoacetic ester, are heated with ammonia and an aldehyde (R·CHO), to give dihydropyridines such as (LXXXIV), which can be oxidized to pyridines with nitric acid. The intermediate is believed to be (LXXXIII), a dihydro-glutaconic diketone, fully enolized. The yields in the Hantzsch synthesis are excellent, and the reaction versatile. 1:5-Diketones can be used instead of the β-keto-esters, and the nitrogenous component can be organic. Thus ethoxymethyleneformylacetone and cyanoacetamide give a 75% yield of the nitrile (LXXXV) (Wenner and Plati, 1946).

Acetone dicarboxylic acid (LXXXVI), which is a derivative of glutaconic acid, reacts with ammonia to give 4-amino-2:6-dihydroxy-pyridine; and citric acid triamide (LXXXVII), heated with 70% sulphuric acid, gives 2:6-dihydroxypyridine-4-carboxylic acid.

LXXXVI   LXXXVII   LXXXVIII

LXXXIX   XC

Ethyl β-aminocrotonate and propargylic aldehyde give 2-methyl-pyridine-3-carboxylic acid in 90% yield (Bohlmann and Rahtz, 1957).

A very large number of syntheses are known which produce pyridines from still simpler molecules. In almost all cases the yields are poor, an outstanding exception being the condensation of four molecules of acetaldehyde with one of ammonia at 250° to give 2-methyl-5-ethylpyridine in 70% yield (Frank et al., 1946) (this reaction apparently begins as an aldol condensation). When this mixture is passed over alumina at 330°, 2- and 4-picolines are produced also. Acetone, benzaldehyde and ammonia give 2:6-dimethyl-4-phenylpyridine.

Some syntheses of pyridines initially involve the opening of rings belonging to other systems, e.g. the formation of 3-chloropyridine by heating pyrrole with chloroform. The most practicable syntheses of this kind are those where a γ- or α-pyrone is heated with ammonia, a reaction much assisted by the presence of electron-attracting substituents. Thus γ-pyrone-2:6-dicarboxylic acid (LXXXVIII; chelidonic acid, made from ethyl oxalate and acetone), when heated with ammonia, gives the glutaconic-derivative (LXXXIX) 4-hydroxypyridine-2:6-dicarboxylic acid (XC). This is the penultimate stage in a practicable synthesis of 4-hydroxy-pyridine, the alternative being the alkaline hydrolysis of 4-pyridyl-pyridinium chloride (XCI) (Königs and Greiner, 1931), which is made by the action of thionyl chloride on pyridine at 20°.

Similarly, α-pyrone-5-carboxylic acid (coumalic acid, XCII), made by the action of sulphuric acid on malic acid, gives 2-hydroxy-pyridine-5-carboxylic acid with ammonia.

XCI   XCII   XCIII

For further reading, see Mosher (1950).

Quinoline (II) is a colourless, hygroscopic liquid, b.p. 239° and m.p. −23°, which darkens readily on exposure to light. Its solubility in water at 20° is only 1 in 150 (Albert, 1955, c). The odour is characteristic, sweetish and persistent, and is disliked by most people.

Several important drugs incorporate the quinoline nucleus, notably the antimalarial, chloroquine (7-chloro-4-(4'-diethylamino-1'-methylbutyl)aminoquinoline), and cinchophen (2-phenyl-quinoline-4-carboxylic acid, *atophan*), which is used in gout. Several quinoline alkaloids, of which quinine is the best known, occur in nature. Quinoline cyanines (see p. 99) are important sensitizers for photographic emulsions.

Quinoline and several of its homologues occur in coal-tar and Californian petroleum. Quite unlike pyridine, quinoline is readily synthesized. This is most readily effected by the Skraup reaction, which is essentially the heating of aniline and acrolein. This reaction goes well in the presence of phosphoric acid (Yale and Bernstein, 1948), but the usual practice is to heat aniline, glycerol, sulphuric acid and an oxidizing agent at about 130°. The first intermediate is the aldehyde (XCIII), which cyclizes to 1:2-dihydroquinoline which the oxidizing agent at once converts to quinoline. The best oxidizing agents are freshly-prepared arsenic acid, or m-nitrobenzenesulphonic acid.[1] When a substituent is present *meta* to the amino-group, a mixture of 7- and 5-substituted quinolines is produced; the orientation of these products was ascertained (Bradford, Elliott and Rowe, 1947) after many years of speculation. All aminoquinolines except the 2- and 4-isomers can themselves undergo the Skraup reaction (see below under 'phenanthrolines'). The Skraup reaction has been the subject of a review (Manske and Kulka, 1953).

A variant of the Skraup reaction (the Doebner-Miller reaction) uses crotonaldehyde (or two molecules of acetaldehyde) instead of acrolein, and zinc chloride instead of sulphuric acid (no added oxidizing agent). The product is 2-methylquinoline (sometimes called quinaldine), and by varying the aldehyde, or using a mixture of two aldehydes, quinolines are produced with various alkyl-groups in the 2- and 3-positions. When a substituent is present *meta* to the amino-group, 5-substituted quinaldines predominate contrary to Doebner and Miller's original statement (Elderfield, 1950). Substitution of pyruvic acid for one molecule of acetaldehyde gives a 2-alkylquinoline-4-carboxylic acid (Doebner reaction). Quinoline-4-carboxylic acids are known as cinchoninic acids.

Crotonaldehyde gives good yields of quinaldine under the conditions of the Skraup reaction also (Utermohlen, 1943).

In a further modification of the Skraup reaction, aniline is condensed with methyl vinyl ketone, or a precursor of this substance, to give 4-methylquinoline, sometimes known as lepidine (Campbell and Schaffner, 1945). The best oxidizing agent, ferric chloride, gives a yield of 70%.

A somewhat related group of reactions furnish quinolines with hydroxy-groups in the α- or γ-positions. One of the most important is the Conrad-Limpach reaction, which is the first stage in the preparation of the 4-aminoquinoline antimalarials, and provides a convenient synthesis of 4-hydroxyquinoline as follows. Ethyl oxaloacetate is allowed to stand with aniline, and the product (XCIV) is cyclized by dropping into a great excess of an inert solvent about 250° (cf. Surrey and Hammer, 1946). The resulting ester

---

[1] Made by heating nitrobenzene (3 g.) and 17% oleum (13 g.) at 100° until a drop gives only a faint turbidity on dilution.

(XCV) readily undergoes alkaline hydrolysis to the free acid, and this is easily decarboxylated to 4-hydroxyquinoline in an inert solvent, again at about 250°. The whole sequence of reactions involves surprisingly little work, and the yields are excellent. When a *meta* substituent is present, the relative proportion of the isomers depends on the dilution in ring-closure (Lisk and Stacy, 1946).

XCIV   XCV   XCVI

XCVII

When ethyl acetoacetate is used instead of oxalacetic ester, 4-hydroxy-2-methylquinoline is obtained in place of (XCV). For smooth removal of the methyl-group by oxidation, condensation with benzaldehyde is desirable, and this can proceed only after the hydroxy-group is exchanged (through the 4-chloro-analogue) for a methoxy-, or acetamido-group (cf. Albert, Brown and Duewell, 1948). In another variant, aniline is condensed with ethyl ethoxy-methylenemalonate (XCVI), made from ethyl orthoformate and ethyl malonate, giving (XCVII) (Gould and Jacobs reaction). This product is cyclized at about 250° to 4-hydroxyquinoline-3-carboxylic ester, which is hydrolysed and decarboxylated as was its isomer (see above). The yields are again very good (Price and Roberts, 1946).

4-Hydroxyquinolines, and through them 4-aminoquinolines (including the antimalarial, chloroquine), are conveniently prepared in bulk by either the oxaloacetic or the ethoxymethylene-malonic methods. The only other attractive method is from quinoline, through the N-oxide (see 2 (*h*) above).

2:4-Dihydroxyquinolines are formed by a related reaction, in which aniline is condensed with ethyl malonate (e.g. Baker, Lappin and Riegel, 1946).

Ethyl acetoacetate and aniline can be combined in a way which differs from the Conrad-Limpach reaction, so that 2-hydroxy-4-methylquinoline is formed instead of 4-hydroxy-2-methylquinoline. This reaction, discovered by Knorr, proceeds through the anilide (XCVIII). To force the reaction to take this direction, a higher temperature is used, and a trace of acid as catalyst (cf. Coffey, Thompson and Wilson, 1936). The (often accidental) presence of a trace of copper seems important in some cases. Ring-closure of (XCVIII) is commonly effected with concentrated sulphuric acid, but hydrochloric acid is often advantageous (cf. Albert, Brown and Duewell, 1948).

XCVIII   XCIX   C

CI

A quite different series of quinoline syntheses starts with an *ortho*-substituted aniline, which is condensed with a reagent capable of reacting with both the substituents. For example Friedländer heated o-aminobenzaldehyde with acetaldehyde, to give (XCIX) which he cyclized to quinoline. Reactions of this kind are of value when a substituent is present *meta* to the amino-group, because only one isomer can be produced on ring-closure, in contrast to all the reactions described above. Unfortunately very few substituted anthranilic aldehydes are yet known. This reaction has another virtue; it enables all kinds of groups, even electron-attracting groups such as $-NO_2$, $-SO_3H$, $-COOH$, $-CN$, to be easily introduced into the 3-position. Thus methazonic acid (the oxime of nitro-acetaldehyde), which is readily prepared by mixing nitromethane and alkali, gives 3-nitroquinoline.

Pfitzinger's modification of this reaction, using isatic acid (C), is much more useful. The product from (C) and acetone, for example, is 2-methylquinoline-4-carboxylic acid, when pyruvic acid replaces acetone, quinoline-2:4-dicarboxylic acid is produced (Work, 1942). These acids are readily decarboxylated if necessary. Isatic acid is obtained by basifying isatin (CI), and a large range of substituted isatins are easily prepared by the action of hydroxylamine and chloral on substituted anilines (Sandmeyer, 1919; Martinet and Coisset, 1921; Marvel and Hiers, 1941). Several other reactions are known whereby indoles can be converted into quinolines, but they are not of such general usefulness.

In a further modification, anthranilic acid is condensed with methazonic acid (described above) to give 4-hydroxy-3-nitroquinoline in excellent yield. This is a key substance for the preparation of 3-substituted quinolines (e.g. Clemo and Swan, 1945). The reaction of anthranilic acid with other aldehydes is not satisfactory, but it gives good results with ketones. A related reaction, due to Chiozza, is the reduction of o-nitrocinnamic acid and elimination of water from the product to give 2-hydroxyquinoline.

Many other reactions which produce quinolines are known, but they have not the general applicability of the above. Many quinolines are prepared by stepwise alteration of other quinolines (i.e. metathesis).

For further reading, see Elderfield (1952).

*Iso***quinoline** (IV) is a colourless solid, m.p. 24°, b.p. 240°, and has a more fragrant odour than quinoline, somewhat reminiscent of anisaldehyde. It, and several homologues, occur in coal-tar, but not in economic quantities. Very little use has yet been made of *iso*quinoline and its simple derivatives, some of which constitute the alkaloids of the cactus, and the papaverine series of poppy-alkaloids. However, the poppy also contains annelated, and even cross-linked, *iso*quinoline alkaloids in the berberine, apomorphine and morphine series, the last-named being of greatest economic importance.

In the most direct *iso*quinoline synthesis, due to Pomeranz and Fritsch, benzaldehyde is condensed with aminoacetal. Alternatively, benzylamine is condensed with glyoxal hemiacetal (Schlittler and Müller's modification), yielding the same intermediate (CII), which is cyclized with sulphuric acid to *iso*quinoline. Various substituents may be introduced, and *meta*-groups give a mixture of 5- and 7-substituted *iso*quinolines (see review of this synthesis by Gensler, 1951).

In a somewhat related synthesis (Bischler and Napieralski's),

N-formyl-β-phenylethylamine (CIII) is heated with zinc chloride, or phosphorus pentoxide, to give 3:4-dihydro*iso*quinoline. *Meta*-substituted amines furnish only the 6-derivative. Alternatively, β-phenylethylamine can be condensed with aldehydes to give tetrahydro*iso*quinolines. Both series can be easily dehydrogenated to *iso*quinolines with palladium (cf. review of these syntheses by Whaley and Govindachari, 1951).

CII   CIII   CIV

When an *iso*coumarin (CIV) is heated with ammonia, the ring opens, oxygen is exchanged for the imino-group, and a 1-hydroxy-*iso*quinoline is formed. A similar reaction in the pyridine series will be recalled (see p. 103).

Several other reactions, of more limited application, are known, such as those involving homophthalic acid. It should be noted that many simple mono-substituted *iso*quinolines are still unknown, and that *iso*quinoline chemistry is not so advanced as that of quinoline.

For further reading, see Gensler (1952).

Quinolizine (Pyridocoline), in which a nitrogen atom is shared between two six-membered rings, has a few π-deficient hetero-aromatic derivatives. Consideration of these is deferred to Chapter VII, as quinolizine is neither π-deficient, nor aromatic.

Acridine (III) is a faintly yellow solid, m.p. 110–111°, b.p. 345°, with a faint sweat-like odour. Inhalation of the crystals causes sneezing, but it is not really injurious to mucous membranes. It is soluble in 20,000 parts of cold water, and only slightly volatile in steam. Acridine and dihydroacridine occur in coal-tar, and some of the commercial material has this origin. A series of acridine alkaloids has been found in the *Rutaceae* (Price, 1952). Several synthetic acridines are used in medicine: the antimalarial, atebrin (mepacrine); and the antibacterials aminacrin (5-aminoacridine), proflavine, and acriflavine. Nitroacridines are among the very few substances which exert a chemotherapeutic effect on infections caused by small viruses (Hurst, 1956). Some simple aminoacridines are used as leather dyes, and some more complex acridines as vat dyes for high-grade cotton goods.

The most direct synthesis of acridine is by gently warming diphenylamine-2-aldehyde (CV) with acid (Albert, 1948). The yield is quantitative. A few substituted acridines have been formed similarly, and the reaction deserves further exploration. At present, the similar ring-closure of diphenylamine-2-carboxylic acids is probably the most versatile and widely used synthesis. It leads to 5-hydroxyacridines ('acridones'), which can be reduced (an unusual reaction, even for a γ-hydroxy-group) to dihydro-acridines ('acridans') with sodium amalgam, and the product oxidized with ferric chloride, or potassium dichromate. Alternatively the diphenylamine-2-carboxylic acids can be converted to 5-chloroacridines with phosphorus oxychloride. This chlorine can be readily replaced by alkoxy-, or amino-groups, or else eliminated with *p*-toluenesulphonhydrazide (see p. 95), a method which conserves any nitro- or cyano-groups which may be present. Alternatively, the chlorine may be removed by catalytic hydrogenation. Diphenylamines with a *meta*-substituent give mixtures of 2- and 4- substituted acridines (Gleu and Nitzsche, 1939; Lehmstedt and Schrader, 1937).

CV   CVI

Acridine has also been prepared, but in only 7% yield, by heating diphenylamine with formic acid. This reaction is more successful with acetic and benzoic acid. Conversely, 3-aminodiphenylamine condenses with formic acid to give a good yield of 2-aminoacridine (this synthesis is the best approach to 2-aminoacridines as no isomers are formed), but does not react with acetic or benzoic acids (Albert, 1948). It would seem that two different types of reaction are concerned.

Acridines substituted by amino-groups in both the 2- and 8-positions, a pattern much required for both dyes and antibacterials, are best produced by two methods which have almost no other applicability. In the better of these, *m*-phenylenediamine (substituted, or otherwise) is heated with formic acid (e.g. Albert, 1947); in the other a substituted *m*-phenylenediamine is heated with formaldehyde, and the resulting product, e.g. (CVI), cyclized with acid to a dihydroacridine, which can then be oxidized with ferric chloride. Many syntheses of limited applicability are also known. *For further reading*, see Albert (1951), Elderfield (1950).

Phenanthridine (V) is a colourless and almost odourless solid, m.p. 108°, b.p. > 360°. It is not commercially available in any quantity. Some quaternary aminophenanthridines, such as dimidium bromide, are used in the treatment of bovine trypanosomiasis, in Africa. A few phenanthridine alkaloids occur in nature, notably in *narcissus*. 9-Hydroxyphenanthridine has been isolated in traces from coal-tar pitch.

The simplest and most useful synthesis of phenanthridines is by heating 2-acylamidodiphenyls (CVII) with zinc chloride (Pictet and Hubert's synthesis). In many cases phosphorus oxychloride gives better yields (Morgan and Walls, 1931), and for phenanthridine itself polyphosphoric acid at 150° is preferable (Taylor and Kalenda, 1954). When that ring which is not carrying the acylamido-group bears electron-attracting substituents, ring-closure is difficult (Ritchie, 1945), but usually takes place under severer conditions, e.g. with phosphorus oxychloride in hot nitrobenzene (Walls, 1945). 9-Hydroxyfluorene and hydrazoic acid give phenanthridine (Arcus and Mesley, 1953; Arcus and Coombs, 1954). For kinetics and mechanism see Arcus and Evans, 1958.

CVII   CVIII   CIX

The best synthesis of 9-hydroxyphenanthridine[1] ('phenanthridone') (CVIII) is by heating o-diphenyl *iso*cyanate with polyphosphoric acid (Taylor and Kalenda, 1954). In another useful synthesis, fluorenone (CIX) is stirred at 20° with hydrazoic and sulphuric acids (Walls, 1935). This conversion is thought to pass through a diphenyl-2-carboxylic acid derivative. Diphenyl-2:2'-dicarboxylic acid (diphenic acid), treated similarly, also gives phenanthridone

[1] For syntheses of other hydroxyphenanthridines, see Arcus and Coombs (1954).

(Caronna, 1941). Diphenic acid, converted to the amide, and then submitted to the Hofmann reaction, also gives phenanthridone. When the starting-material, in any of these reactions, is unsymmetrically substituted, a mixture of phenanthridones arises.

Phenanthridones are converted to phenanthridines by treatment with phosphorus oxybromide, followed by hydrogenation over Raney-nickel (Albert, Brown and Duewell, 1948). The action of sodium amalgam on phenanthridone is uncontrollable, but lithium aluminium hydride may be used (de Mayo and Rigby, 1950).

For further reading, see Walls (1952).

Benzoquinolines. There are three families of benzoquinolines, all isomeric with acridine, namely 5:6-, 6:7-, and 7:8-benzoquinolines. These are solids melting at 93°, 118°, and 52° respectively. They are all colourless, but the 6:7-isomer fluoresces and has yellow salts. Thus this series follows the rule that linear isomers melt higher than angular ones, and are more likely to be coloured. The two angular isomers are synthesized by methods commonly used for quinolines, starting from naphthylamines instead of anilines. In their properties, they closely resemble the quinolines, and will not be further dealt with here.

The linear isomer requires special syntheses, for the annelation of 2-naphthylamines almost always takes the angular, rather than the linear, direction because of the higher reactivity of the 1-position. This stricture does not apply to 5:6:7:8-tetrahydro-2-naphthylamine, where a mixture of both 5:6- and 6:7-(tetrahydro)benzoquinolines arises from a Skraup reaction (v. Braun and Gruber, 1922; Albert, Brown and Duewell, 1948). Dehydrogenation of the products has been accomplished, but only in poor yield.

Naphthalenes bearing two reactive substituents, i.e. in the 2- and 3-positions, are more convenient starting-materials. Thus 2-amino-naphthalene-3-carboxylic acid and methazonic acid (nitroacet-aldehyde oxime) give 4-hydroxy-3-nitro-6:7-benzoquinoline, the hydroxy-group of which can be removed in two steps (Albert, Brown and Duewell, 1948). Similarly, the ethyl ester of 3-acetamido-2-naphthoic acid, treated in turn with phosphorus oxychloride and sulphuric acid, gives 4-hydroxy-2-methyl-6:7-benzoquinoline, and from this 4-amino-6:7-benzoquinoline is obtainable by two methods (Albert, Brown and Duewell, 1948).

Finally 2-naphthylamines, if blocked in the 1-position and submitted to the Skraup and similar reactions, either expel the 1-sub-stituent (and so give 5:6-benzoquinoline), or (retaining it) give 10-substituted 6:7-benzoquinolines (Clemo and Driver, 1945: Huis-gen, 1948: Albert, Brown and Duewell, 1948).

The linear benzoquinolines differ from their angular isomers in being less completely aromatic, just as anthracene differs in this way from phenanthrene. Thus they are easily oxidized to 1-azanthraquinone, and easily sulphonated, whereas the angular isomers resist these reactions. For the chemistry of 6:7-benzoquinoline itself, see Etienne (1946). A linear benzoquinoline, phomazarin, has been found in a fungus that causes root-disease in onions.

In all three benzoquinoline series, groups, placed α- or γ- to the ring-nitrogen, display the special properties to be expected in π-deficient systems. Electrophilic reagents attack the benzene-, and avoid the pyridine-, rings.

For further reading, see Walls (1952).

Benzo*iso*quinolines. Apart from phenanthridine, three benzo-*iso*quinoline series are possible, but have been little investigated.

B. Systems with Two Ring-Nitrogen Atoms

The **diazabenzenes** will be dealt with first. Some of their physical properties are summarized in Table 8 (p. 101).

Pyridazine (VI) is a liquid which smells like pyridine. It would seem, from molecular-weight determinations and from the high b.p. (Table 8), to be largely in the form of a dimer, readily dissociable in aqueous solution, and kept together by dipolar bonds. No pyridazines are known to occur in nature; indeed very few substances with two neighbouring nitrogen atoms have been found in nature, none of them heterocyclic. Maleic hydrazide (CX) is a highly effective weed-killer and 'Lederkyn' (6-methoxy-3-sulphanilamidopyridazine) is a valuable, long-acting sulphonamide.

CX

Pyridazines are made by the condensation of hydrazine with 1:4-dialdehydes or -diketones, and allowing the 1:2-dihydropyridazines to oxidize in the air (or with nitrous acid or bromine). Ethyl maleate similarly gives (CX), and the chlorination and reduction of this constitutes the best synthesis of pyridazine itself (Missoni and Spoerri, 1951). Alternatively phthalazine (see below), which is benzopyridazine, is oxidized to pyridazine-3:4-dicarboxylic acid.

2-Alkyfurans, treated with bromine followed by hydrazine, give 3-alkylpyridazines (Levisalles, 1957).

For further reading, see Jacobs (1957); Eichenberger, Staehlin and Druey (1954); and Druey (1958).

Pyrimidine (VII) is a low-melting solid (see Table 8, p. 101), with an odour like the homologues of pyridine. It is soluble in less than its own volume of water. Although pyrimidine has a carbon atom flanked by two nitrogens, it has nothing in common with the amidines because it has a plane of symmetry (contrast with iminazole, in Chapter V).

Several pyrimidines occur in nature, and many play vital roles in the metabolism of living cells. Nucleic acids contain uracil, thymine and cytosine, which are 2:4-dihydroxy-, 5-methyl-2:4-dihydroxy-, and 4-amino-2-hydroxy-pyrimidine, respectively. 5-Hydroxymethyl-cytosine has also been found in the nucleic acid of some micro-organisms, and orotic acid (uracil-6-carboxylic acid), and dihydro-orotic acid, are known to be intermediates in the biosynthesis of uracil. The naturally-occurring pyrimidines form the subject of a review (Bendich, 1955). The chemistry of the nucleic acids is highly complex, and much has yet to be revealed. In particular, little is known as to how many different kinds of nucleic acids there are, nor in what sequences the pyrimidines and purines are arranged. However, the bold pioneering work of Todd and his colleagues in Cambridge has laid durable foundations for further investigations; in particular they have established the mode of linkage of pyrimidines (or purines) to the ribose (or deoxyribose), and of the resultant riboside to the phosphoric acid (giving ribotides), and the way in which these ribotides are interconnected (Brown and Todd, 1955). Thiamine, or vitamin B_1, is discussed in Chapter VI under thiazole.

2:4:6-Trihydroxypyrimidine, known as barbituric acid, gives reactions (with aldehydes, etc.) characteristic of a methylene-group, and hence would appear to be in equilibrium with a little of the tautomer (CXI). As far as is known, this type of tautomerism is not common in π-deficient N-heterocycles. Ionization studies preclude that it consists mainly of this tautomer, because the 5:5-dialkyl-derivatives of (CXI), so much used as hypnotics,[1] are far weaker

[1] E.g. 5:5-Diethyl- (barbitone, Veronal); phenyl-, ethyl- (phenobarbitone, Luminal); ethyl-, *cyclo*hexenyl- (cyclobarbitone, Phandorm); allyl- (1′-methyl)-butyl- (quinalbarbitone, Seconal); ethyl- (1′-methylbut-1′-enyl)- (vinbarbitone, Delvinal); allyl-, *cyclo*hex-2′-enyl-[2-thio-] (thialbarbitone, Kemithal); *cyclo*hex-1′-enyl-, methyl- [1(N)-methyl-] (hexobarbitone, Evipan); ethyl-, 1-methylbutyl-(pentobarbitone, Nembutal); ethyl-, 1-methylbutyl-[2-thio-] (thiopentone, Pentothal); ethyl-, 5-*iso*amyl- (amylobarbitone, Amytal).

acids, and have quite different spectra. Alloxan, obtained by oxidizing uric acid, is 2:4-dihydroxy-5:6-dioxopyrimidine. It causes diabetes in experimental animals. For a review of barbituric acid chemistry see Whiteley and Thorpe (1937), and for alloxan see Whiteley (1937).

2-Thiouracil, and its 6-alkyl-derivatives, are much used to over-come thyrotoxicosis, brought on by over-activity of the thyroid gland. The highly successful antimalarial, pyrimethamine (Dara-prim) is 2:4-diamino-6-ethyl-5-*p*-chlorophenylpyrimidine (Russell and Hitchings, 1951), and the powerful oral diuretic, aminome-tradine (Mictine) is 1-allyl-3-ethyl-6-aminouracil. *p*-Aminophenyl-sulphonamido-2-aminopyrimidine (Sulphadiazine) and its C-methyl-derivatives are much used as antibacterials.

CXI   CXII   CXIII

In the most generally useful synthesis of pyrimidines (Pinner and Traube's method), an amidine (or guanidine, urea or thiourea) is made to combine with a three-carbon reagent which has a central methylene-group, flanked by two aldehyde, carboxylic acid, or nitrile groups. These are usually condensed together in sodium methoxide solution. Pinner used an amidine to introduce an alkyl-group in the 2-position (formamidine is used to introduce hydrogen in that position), and Traube used guanidine, urea and thiourea to introduce a 2-amino-, hydroxy- or mercapto-group (respectively). When the methylene-group in the other reagent is flanked by alde-hyde-groups, only hydrogens appear in the 4- and 6-positions. Flanking by carboxy-groups (or their esters) introduces hydroxy-groups there; by nitriles, amino-groups; and by ketones, alkyl-groups. Unsymmetrical three-carbon intermediates may also be used: thus ethyl cyanoacetate (CXII) and thiourea give 4-amino-6-hydroxy-2-mercaptopyrimidine (CXIII). Furthermore, ethyl oxaloacetate and ethyl ethoxymethylenemalonate are used to introduce the carboxyl-group into the 4- and 5-position respectively, and ethyl γ-diethoxy-acetoacetate to introduce the aldehyde-group into the 4-position. The products of these reactions usually react with nitrous acid to give 5-nitroso-derivatives, easily reduced to 5-aminopyrimidines.

I

When a 4-amino-group is already present, 4:5-diaminopyrimidines are produced and these are valuable intermediates for the synthesis of purines and pteridines. Alternatively a 5-amino-group can be introduced by nitration, by diazo-coupling followed by reduction, and by the use of a nitromalonic-, or a phenylazomalonic-derivative.

It is characteristic of pyrimidine chemistry that usually the most economical approach is to synthesize highly substituted pyrimidines and then remove unwanted groups. Thus, pyrimidine could obviously be prepared according to the above method from malonic dialdehyde and formamidine. These have until recently been two rare chemicals. Fortunately malonic dialdehyde has recently become commercially available as its tetra-acetal, but is expensive; however the new synthesis of formamidine from thiourea (Brown, 1952, a) makes this amidine readily available. Meanwhile, useful syntheses of pyrimidine have been effected by dehalogenating the polychloropyrimidines (from polyhydroxypyrimidines) (see 2 (i), above).

Of recent years, the widespread use of thiouracil in medicine has led to its industrial preparation (from ethyl formylacetate and thiourea) thus presenting pyrimidine chemists with an inexpensive, and highly flexible, new intermediate (Brown, 1950). Thus hydrolysis (to uracil) followed by nitration (5-position), chlorination, partial amination (4-position), and a combined resulphurization (2-position) and reduction gives the very useful intermediate 4:5-diaminopyrimidine, not yet obtainable by any simpler process (Brown, 1952, b). The preparation of 4-amino-5-methylaminopyrimidine is interesting because it involves the reduction of a formamido- to a methylamino-group with lithium aluminium hydride (Brown, 1955). 4:5-Diaminopyrimidines acylate preferentially in the 5-position (Wilson, 1948).

Related to the Traube synthesis is that of Hull (1951) in which the diamide of malonic acid is condensed with ethyl formate, giving 4:6-dihydroxypyrimidine. Esters of higher acids introduce alkyl-groups in the 2-position, whereas substituents (such as CH_3NH-) on the central carbon of malondiamide introduce groups in the 5-position (Brown, 1956). Similarly, malondiamidine and ethyl formate give 4:6-diaminopyrimidine (Kenner et al., 1943).

The use of ethyl ethoxymethylenemalonate (XCVI), mentioned above, is a development of the Traube synthesis due to Wheeler, Johnson and Johns and has been technically improved by Whitehead (1952). It was claimed that unsymmetrical N-methylureas give only the 3-alkyl-isomer (e.g. CXIV) which can be hydrolysed and decarboxylated to 3-methyluracil.

Ethyl ethoxymethylenemalonate is the product of ethyl orthoformate and ethyl malonate. Whitehead generalized his reaction by
mixing ethyl orthoformate with other reactive-methylene substances
(e.g. ethyl cyanoacetate), and an N-alkyl-urea (Whitehead, 1953).
To make certain that these reactions give only 3-methyl-derivatives,
Brown, Hoerger and Mason (1955, a), using a general reaction discovered by Evans and Johnson (1930), refluxed methyl β-methylaminopropionate (CXV) with sodium cyanate, giving 5:6-dihydro-
1-methyluracil (CXVI), which was dehydrogenated with bromine
to 1-methyluracil. This differed in melting-point, spectra, and
chromatography from the substance known as 3-methyluracil, thus
providing the first rigorous proof of the constitutions tentatively
assigned by Johnson and Heyl in 1907. These methyluracils are
important reference-substances for orientating other N-mono-
methylated pyrimidines.

CXIV   CXV   CXVI

The condensation of malononitrile with amidines (or with
iminoethers) does not follow the Pinner-Traube reaction. For
example benzamidine and malononitrile give not 4:6-diamino-2-
phenylpyrimidine but 4-amino-5-cyano-2:6-diphenylpyrimidine
(Baddiley, Lythgoe and Todd, 1943).

2-Hydroxypyrimidine has a curious history. Originally said to be
yellow, amorphous, sparingly soluble in water, and infusible at 320°
(Johnson and Joyce, 1915), it was later found to be colourless,
highly crystalline, soluble in less than two parts of cold water, and
melting at 180° (Brown, 1950). The original material was not
analysed and may well have been ferric oxide. Renewed interest in
5-hydroxypyrimidines has led recently to the discovery of the elusive
5-hydroxypyrimidine itself (McOmie and Chesterfield, 1956).

For further reading on pyrimidines, see Kenner and Todd (1957),
also D. J. Brown's review of monosubstituted pyrimidines and their
metathetical interconversion (Brown, 1953).

Pyrazine (VIII) is a solid with a faint, not unpleasant odour (see Table 8, p. 101 for properties). It is the most difficult to prepare of the three diazines, but its derivatives have been a little more intensively studied than those of pyridazine. It is very soluble in cold water. The only naturally-occurring pyrazine is the antibiotic aspergillic acid (2-hydroxy-3-*iso*butyl-6-*sec*butylpyrazine-N-oxide), but methyl- and ethyl-pyrazines have been isolated from fusel oil. Few technical applications of pyrazines have yet been attempted. Pyrazine-2-carboxamide has a small beneficial action in human tuberculosis.

Pyrazine is best made, in not very good yield, by combining ammonia and chloroacetal to give tetraethoxy-diethylamine (CXVII), which gives 2:6-dihydroxymorpholine (CXVIII) when heated with acid. Hydroxylamine converts (CXVIII) into pyrazine. A complex mixture of pyrazine and its homologues results from the action of ammonia on glucose. Pyrazine can also be prepared by the dehydrogenation of its hexahydro-derivative (piperazine) over a copper chromite catalyst at high temperatures (Dixon, 1946).

CXVII   CXVIII

Pyrazine homologues are made by the self-condensation of α-aminocarbonyl compounds in the presence of an oxidizing agent. Thus aminoacetone, treated with sodium hydroxide, gives 3:6-dihydro-2:5-dimethylpyrazine, which mercuric chloride oxidizes to 2:5-dimethylpyrazine. These alkylpyrazines are oxidized by potassium permanganate to pyrazine-carboxylic acids, which are easily decarboxylated. Pyrazine 2:3-dicarboxylic acid is made by the oxidation of quinoxaline (the benzologue of pyrazine, see below).

2-Aminopyrazine-3-carboxylic acid is readily obtained by the action of alkali on 2:4-dihydroxypteridine (Weijlard, Tishler and Erickson, 1945) and this has been the starting-material for preparing many simple pyrazines, e.g. 2-aminopyrazine by decarboxylation, from which in turn 2-hydroxy- (Erickson and Spoerri, 1946), 2-chloro- and 2-methoxy-pyrazines can be made (Albert and Phillips, 1956). A few other pyrazine-forming reactions are known, the most generally useful being one in which 1:2-dicarbonyl-compounds are condensed with the amides of α-amino-acids (Jones, 1949; Muehlman and Day, 1956). For example, glyoxal and glycine amide give 2-hydroxypyrazine; glyoxal and aminomalonamide give 2-hydroxypyrazine-3-carboxamide (methylglyoxal gives the 5-methyl-homologue according to Jones, but the 6-methyl-homologue according to Dick and Wood, 1955). Sodium hydrogen sulphite is a good catalyst of this reaction.

For further reading, see Pratt (1957), Krems and Spoerri (1947).

The **diazanaphthalenes** will now be dealt with. Ten isomers are possible, and they are all numbered as in naphthalene, e.g. cinnoline (CXIX) and phthalazine (CXX); the nitrogens are always given the lowest numbers possible.

CXIX   CXX

Cinnoline (CXIX), a pale-yellow, bitter-tasting solid, m.p. 39°, has a geranium-like odour. It is very soluble in water and organic solvents. It turns green in air and liquefies, but without undergoing severe decomposition. It is also sensitive to heat. No cinnolines are known to occur in nature. The reduction of a quaternary salt of 4-amino-6-nitrocinnoline gives a substance of unknown constitution which is active against trypanosomiasis (Atkinson and Taylor, 1955). Apart from this, no application has yet been found for cinnolines.

The best preparation of cinnoline is the decarboxylation of the 4-carboxylic acid, a very stable substance prepared by the oxidation of 4-styrylcinnoline made from 4-methylcinnoline and benzaldehyde (Jacobs *et al.*, 1946). The 4-methylcinnoline is prepared by a general method for cinnolines, discovered by Widman and Stoermer, viz. the diazotization of o-aminoarylethylenes (CXXI). R may be methyl or aryl (but not hydrogen), and will appear in the 4-position; R′ may be any alkyl or aryl radical and will appear in the 3-position. This reaction is quite rapid, and 2-aminoarylethylenes are easily prepared from the corresponding methyl anthranilates (Grignard reaction) or o-aminoacetophenones.

The other general method is to diazotize 2-aminoacetophenone: the product (CXXII) slowly cyclizes on standing, to give 4-hydroxy-cinnolines (Borsche and Herbert, 1941). Electron-attracting substituents in the 3- or 5-positions of 2-aminoacetophenone accelerate the reaction. Diazotized *o*-aminobenzaldehyde couples with nitromethane (or acetoacetic ester) to 3-nitro- (or 3-acetyl-) cinnoline (Baumgarten and Anderson, 1958).

4-Methyl-, 4-hydroxy- and 4-amino-cinnoline methylate on $N_{(1)}$, 3-hydroxy- and 3-amino-cinnoline methylate on $N_{(2)}$ (Alford and Schofield, 1953). By far the best way to prepare 4-amino-derivatives is to fuse the 4-phenoxy-analogue (from the 4-chloro-analogue) with ammonium acetate at 210° (Schofield and Theobald, 1949).

CXXI   CXXII   CXXIII

For further reading, see Simpson (1953), Jacobs (1957).

Phthalazine (CXX) is a yellow solid, m.p. 90–91°, and b.p. 175°/17 mm., with a faint quinoline-like odour. It is very soluble in water, and in organic solvents. No occurrence of a phthalazine in nature has been recorded, and very few uses for phthalazines have yet been found. 1-Hydrazinophthalazine has been used to lower high blood-pressure in man.

The best preparation of phthalazine is to heat phthalaldehydic acid (CXXIII) with hydrazine which gives 1-hydroxyphthalazine. This is converted (with phosphorus oxychloride) to 1-chlorophthalazine which is then dechlorinated by catalytic dehydrogenation (Stephenson, 1957). Alternatively ω-tetrabromo-*o*-xylene is hydrolysed to *o*-phthalaldehyde, which is condensed with hydrazine to give a good yield of phthalazine. Phthalic acid and hydrazine give 1:4-dihydroxyphthalazine (cf. Drew and Hatt, 1937) which may prove to be a more convenient intermediate for phthalazine.

Among other less general phthalazine syntheses is the preparation of 1-arylphthalazines by condensing an aromatic aldehyde with benzoylhydrazine.

The stability of phthalazine to acid and alkali has not been sufficiently examined. 1-Hydroxy-4-phenyl-, and 5- (also 6-) nitro-1:4-dihydroxy-phthalazine are hydrolysed by acid or alkali, but 1:4-dihydroxyphthalazine is stable (see 2 (*d*), above). Phthalazines, as a class, are unstable to boiling aromatic aldehydes, and to hot acetic anhydride. 5-Amino-1:4-dihydroxyphthalazine has been much examined because of the chemiluminescence seen on oxidation.

Many monosubstituted phthalazines have yet to be prepared. A satisfactory method for 1-aminophthalazine has only recently been published (Atkinson, Brown and Simpson, 1956; Rodda, 1956). *For further reading*, see Simpson (1953), Elderfield and Wythe (1957).

Quinazoline (XI) is a colourless solid, m.p. 48°, b.p. 242°, with an odour like quinoline. It is very soluble in water and organic solvents. A few quinazoline alkaloids are known, notably vasicine and febrifugine. The latter, from *Dichroa febrifuga*, is antimalarial in man.

Quinazoline is best prepared by the action of zinc and acetic acid on 2-nitrobenzal-*bis*-formamide, which is the condensation product of 2-nitrobenzaldehyde and formamide (Riedel, 1905; Bogert and McColm, 1927). *Bz*-Substituted quinazolines can be similarly prepared (e.g. Albert and Hampton, 1952). When oxidized with potassium permanganate, quinazoline gives pyrimidine-4:5-dicarboxylic acid.

The chemistry of quinazoline bristles with apparent anomalies. The ultraviolet spectrum of the neutral molecule is like that of other diazanaphthalenes, but acidification causes the long-wave peak to retreat a considerable distance into the ultraviolet, an effect not given by the known isomers (Schofield, 1955). Again 4-methylquinazoline is a weaker base than quinazoline (Albert, Brown and Wood, 1954) although methyl-groups are electron-releasing and increase basic strength in other heteroaromatic substances, even in 2-methylquinazoline. Also 8-hydroxy-4-methylquinazoline is a weaker base than 8-hydroxyquinazoline (Albert and Hampton, 1954). Again, 4-methoxyquinazoline is a weaker base than quinazoline, although a γ-methoxy-group is base-strengthening in the pyridine, quinoline, acridine and cinnoline series. Finally the basic strength of many aminoquinazolines are far too low (Schofield, 1955).

These phenomena could be explained if it were assumed that the cation of quinazoline is (CXXIV), derived from a covalently hydrated form of quinazoline, which is hydrated in the 3:4-position (Albert, 1955, a), and existing only in traces in the neutral molecule (see also p. 85). It is evident that this cation will be stabilized by resonance, as the charge can be sited on either nitrogen atom. If it is assumed that a methyl-group in the 4-position offers steric hindrance to this hydration, it becomes understandable why 4-methylquinazoline is a weaker base than the parent substance.

Pyrimidine shows none of the anomalies of quinazoline, but pteridine shares the base-weakening effect of methyl-groups in certain positions (Albert, Brown and Wood, 1954).

Quinazoline methylates partly or even entirely in the 3-position; the 4-hydroxy and 4-phenoxy-derivatives in the 3- and 1-positions, respectively.

The homologues of quinazoline are best made by Bischler's method, as modified by Schofield, Swain and Theobald (1952): e.g. 2-formamido-acetophenone gives 4-methylquinazoline when ammonia is passed through its solution in molten ammonium acetate at 160°. Likewise 2-methylquinazoline is obtained from 2-acetamidobenzaldehyde and ammonia; *o*-aminobenzaldehyde gives 2-hydroxyquinazoline with urea, and 2-aminoquinazoline with guanidine (Rodda, 1956). Anthranilic acid gives 4-hydroxyquinazoline with formamide, and 2:4-dihydroxyquinazoline with urea or potassium cyanate. The best preparation of 4-aminoquinazoline is from the 4-chloro-analogue and ammonia at 20° (Morley and Simpson, 1949; Rodda, 1956).

CXXIV   CXXV   CXXVI

In a Hofmann reaction with hypobromous acid, phthalamide (CXXV) gives the *iso*cyanate (CXXVI), and this cyclizes to 2:4-dihydroxyquinazoline. Dihydroquinazolines, obtained by the action of formic acid on *o*-aminobenzylamines, are easily oxidized to quinazolines with potassium ferricyanide.

2-Hydroxyquinazoline is almost insoluble in boiling water, but dissolves on prolonged boiling, an uninvestigated chemical change from which it is regenerated by acid (Albert and Phillips, 1956).

For further reading, see Williamson (1957).

Quinoxaline (1:4-diazanaphthalene is a colourless solid, m.p. 28°, b.p. 229°, with a quinoline-like odour. It forms a stable monohydrate, m.p. 28°, and is very soluble in water and organic solvents. Quinoxaline is formed by warming *o*-phenylenediamine with glyoxal (cf. Cavagnol and Wiselogle, 1947). Similarly, diacetyl, cyanogen, glyoxylic acid, and oxalic acid give 2:3-dimethyl-, 2:3-diamino-, 2-hydroxy-, and 2:3-dihydroxy-quinoxaline respectively. An alternative synthesis condenses *o*-nitrosoanilines with cyanoacetic ester: thus 2:4-diaminonitrosobenzene gives 3:6-diaminoquinoxaline-2-carboxylic acid (Osdene and Timmis, 1955, a). This method is recommended when ambiguity would otherwise arise from unsymmetrically-substituted reagents.

Diazomethane causes C-methylation in this series (Cheeseman, 1952). Quinoxalines have not yet been found in nature. 2-(*p*-Aminobenzene)sulphonamidoquinoxaline is much used in the treatment of coccidiosis, a protozoal infection in poultry.

For further reading, see Simpson (1953), Pratt (1957).

Naphthyridines is the collective name given to the 1:5-, 1:6-, 1:7-, 1:8-, 2:6-, and 2:7-diazanaphthalenes. Naphthyridines have not yet been found in nature, but a 1:6-naphthyridine is obtained by degrading the lupin alkaloid, matrine.

The synthetic methods used for naphthyridines are principally those used in the quinoline and *iso*quinoline series, but employ pyridine-, instead of benzene-, intermediates. However, 2-aminopyridine is not a suitable starting material for 1:8-naphthyridines: the Skraup, Conrad-Limpach and related reactions with this substance give two-ring systems sharing a nitrogen atom. Nevertheless, a 1:8-naphthyridine is obtainable from 2:6-diaminopyridine.

1:5-Naphthyridine (XII), a pale yellow substance of m.p. 72°, is best prepared by a Skraup reaction on 3-aminopyridine (Hart, 1954), none of the 1:7-isomer being formed. In fact, 3-amino-2-chloropyridine also gives 1:5-naphthyridine, the chlorine atom being expelled. However 3-amino-2-hydroxypyridine gives 8-hydroxy-1:7-naphthyridine (Albert and Hampton, 1952). Few other 1:7-naphthyridines are known. Hence it is interesting that 3-aminopyridine-N-oxide and ethyl ethoxymethylenemalonate (XCVI) give, after the usual operations (see p. 106), 4-hydroxy-1:7-naphthyridine, whereas 3-aminopyridine, similarly treated, gives 4-hydroxy-1:5-naphthyridine (Murray and Hauser, 1954).

Not many 1:6-naphthyridines are known, and these come from pyridine-2:3-carboxylic acid and glycine by a series of reactions (Ochiai *et al.*, 1945; Albert and Hampton, 1952), from 4-nitropyridine-3-aldehyde (Baumgarten and Krieger, 1955), or from 4-aminopyridine (Hauser and Reynolds, 1950).

1:8-Naphthyridine is a colourless solid, m.p. 99°, obtained by replacing the chlorine in the 2:4-dichloro-derivative (Koller, 1927), the source of which is the condensation of methyl 2-aminopyridine-

3-carboxylate with ethyl malonate to give 2:4-dihydroxy-1:8-naph-thyridine-3-carboxylic ester. About a dozen 1:8-naphthyridines are known, but these must be distinguished from numerous derivatives of 2-aminopyridine incorrectly described in the literature as 1:8-naphthyridines (see above).

2:6-Naphthyridines are unknown, but a few derivatives of 2:7-naphthyridine have been described, and are derived from the condensation of pyridine 3:4-dicarboxylic acid with glycine (cf. also Birkover and Kaiser, 1957).

Metal-binding naphthyridines, designed as aza-derivatives of 8-hydroxyquinoline, have been described, and physico-chemically investigated (Albert and Hampton, 1952, 1954).

For further reading on the naphthyridines, see Allen (1950). This series offers many opportunities for systematic exploration.

Phenazine (XIV) is 9:10-diaza-anthracene. It is a yellow solid, m.p. 172°, conveniently prepared by the ferric chloride oxidation of 2:2'-diaminodiphenylamine (Tomlinson, 1939). Distillation in super-heated steam is the best means of purification. Tomlinson's synthesis is suitable for substituted phenazines (cf. also Elderfield, Gensler and Birstein, 1946). Phenazine can also be made by heating o-nitro-diphenylamine and iron filings at 280° (Waterman and Vivian, 1949), a method also suitable for 1-substituted derivatives (Vivian, 1956). Phenazine and its 2-derivatives can be made by the Aue-Wohl synthesis in which aniline and nitrobenzene are refluxed with alkali (Maffei, Pietra and Cattaneo, 1953), similarly aniline and o-nitroaniline give 2-aminophenazine. In all cases, part of the product is in the form of an N-oxide, so that a final reduction is necessary (followed sometimes by a mild oxidation to remove hydrophenazines). Phenazine and its derivatives are also con-veniently made by condensing an o-phenylenediamine with 1:2-*cyclo*hexandione, and dehydrogenating the resultant tetrahydro-phenazine with iodine (Clemo and McIlwain, 1934); or more simply by condensing o-quinone (i.e. catechol + silver oxide) with an o-phenylenediamine in ether (Kehrmann and Mermod, 1927).

Phenazine is soluble in fifty parts of alcohol at 20°, but only slightly soluble in water, ether or benzene. It is di-basic, and has yellow mono-salts whereas the red di-cation can be seen in concen-trated sulphuric acid. It is one of the few substances known to photo-reduce,[1] and the product is a blue complex of phenazine and dihydrophenazine (see Chapter VII) which rapidly reoxidizes in the air (Dufraisse *et al.*, 1952). This complex is also obtained on mild

[1] Pteridines also photo-reduce.

chemical reduction and is believed to have no free radical character (Fellion, 1957).

Three phenazines have been found in nature. Pyocyanin (CXXVII), 1-oxo-5-methyl-1:5-dihydrophenazine (blue), is the anhydride of 1-hydroxyphenazine-5-methochloride (red), and occurs in the bacterium *Pseudomonas pyocyanea* (see below for synthesis). Chlororaphine, monohydrophenazine-1-carboxamide, occurs in various species of *Pseudomonas*. Iodinin, which occurs in one of the chromobacteria, is 1:6-dihydroxyphenazine-5:10-dioxide (CXXVIII) (Clemo, 1955).

Neutral red (CXXIX), a common E_H indicator, is 2-amino-8-dimethylamino-3-methylphenazine, made by oxidizing a mixture of 2:4-diaminotoluene and *p*-aminodimethylaniline. Safranine, a commonly used basic dye, is (CXXX, R = NH_2), obtained by oxidizing a mixture of *p*-phenylenediamine and aniline.

CXXVII   CXXVIII

CXXIX   CXXX

When phenazine is nitrated, it gives a mixture of 1-nitrophenazine, 1:6- and 1:9-dinitrophenazine (Albert and Duewell, 1947; Otomasu, 1958). Phenazine-N-oxide gives 2-nitro-, 2:6- and 2:8-dinitrophenazine-N-oxide (Otomasu, 1958). Chlorination of phenazine gives 1- and 1:4-derivatives (Maffei *et al.*, 1953). Chlorine in the 2-position of phenazine is mobile enough to react with ammonia at 220° (Vivian, 1956).

When the mono-methochloride of phenazine is exposed to sunlight (in sodium carbonate solution) it is changed to formaldehyde and phenazine (plus N-methyldihydrophenazine if air is excluded). In the absence of light, pyocyanin (CXXVII) is produced in 45% yield, and this is the best synthesis of this substance (McIlwain, 1937).

N-phenyl-phenazinium chloride and aqueous ammonia give aposafranine (CXXX, R = H) on acidification. This is reminiscent of the formation of a secondary amine by the action of ammonia on quinoline methochloride (see 2 (*g*), above). The points of interest here are that the amino-group has travelled to a benzene-ring, and that loss of two hydrogens has occurred. Repetition of this cycle gives safranine (CXXX, R = NH$_2$). Safranine, treated with nitrous acid in alcohol, gives aposafranine.

Indanthrone, a more complex phenazine dyestuff, is obtained by heating 2-aminoanthraquinone with alkali at 200°. Discovered in 1902, it marked an important advance in the dyeing of cotton, giving a bright blue colour, resistant to boiling. It was the first of a whole series of anthraquinone vat dyes which soon surpassed the indigo series in the range of colours (vat dyes are those which require reduction to bring them into solution before application to the fibre; the reduced form is then reoxidized on the fibre). For the new light which infrared spectra shed on its constitution, see Wyman (1956).

For further reading on phenazines, see Pearson (1957), Swan and Felton (1957).

Other **diaza-anthracene** families are known, e.g. Ruggli and Staub (1937), Ruggli and Preiswerk (1939).

The **Phenanthrolines** are diazaphenanthrenes. The commonest examples, *o*, *m*, and *p*-phenanthroline, can be prepared by a double Skraup reaction on *o*-, *m*-, and *p*-phenylenediamine, respectively: hence their names. Numbered as phenanthrene (CXXXI), they are 1:10-, 1:7-, and 4:7-diazaphenanthrene, respectively, only *angular* ring-closure occurring. The other isomers have been little investigated: for 3:8-phenanthroline, see Ruggli and Schetty (1940); for 1:8-phenanthrolines, see Misani and Bogert (1945). No phenanthrolines have been found in nature. *o*-Phenanthroline, and its derivatives, are much used in the estimation of ferrous iron and cuprous copper.

o-Phenanthroline, m.p. 117°, is obtainable from *o*-phenylenediamine in 45% yield (Halcrow and Kermack, 1946); *m*- and *p*-phenanthrolines, m.p. 78° and 177° respectively, are obtained in even better yields from the relevant diamines (Smith, 1930).

CXXXI

These three phenanthrolines are colourless, form stable hydrates, and are conveniently purified through their dichromates. They resist all attempts at nitration, chlorination and sulphonation (Linsker and Evans, 1946).

Substituted phenanthrolines are made by the action of oxalacetic, ethoxymethylenemalonic, or acetoacetic esters, etc., on phenylenediamines. For unsymmetrical phenanthrolines, the operation is carried out in two stages: nitroanilines are converted' to nitroquinolines, by one reagent; these are then reduced and combined with an alternative reagent. Examples of *o*-phenanthrolines made by these methods will be found in Hazelwood, Hughes and Lions (1938), Snyder and Freer (1946), Richter and Smith (1944); *m*-phenanthrolines in Kermack and Tebrich (1945), Kermack and Webster (1942), Haworth and Sykes (1944); *p*-phenanthrolines in Jacini (1940) and Kermack and Weatherhead (1940).

C. Systems with Three Ring-Nitrogen Atoms

Three families of triazines are possible: 1:2:3-, 1:2:4-, and 1:3:5- (symmetrical) triazines. The only known parent substance is 1:3:5-triazine (IX), best prepared by the action of bases on formamidine (Grundmann, Schröder and Ruske, 1954). It is hydrolysed by cold water to formamide with great rapidity. This triazine had been known for many years as a trimer of hydrocyanic acid, but its true chemical nature was not realized until Grundmann investigated it.

2:4:6-Trichloro-*sym*-triazine, obtained by the polymerization of cyanogen chloride, is an important intermediate in producing direct-dyeing colours for cotton which have great durability, e.g. Ciba's

'Chlorantine Fast' series. The stepwise replacement of chlorines in trichlorotriazine was discussed under 2 (*g*) above (see p. 74).

2:4:6-Triamino-1:3:5-triazine (melamine) is an important industrial bulk chemical, and the annual production now exceeds 1,000 tons. Although it was recognized as early as 1939 that melamine-formaldehyde resins were colourless, durable, excellent electrical insulators, and less affected by water than urea-formaldehyde and phenol-formaldehyde types, their widespread use has been hindered by the (until recently) high cost of melamine. One of the more familiar uses of melamine resins is in making plates, cups and saucers, similar in appearance to genuine china, and of greater durability. Melamine is usually made by heating dicyandiamide (CN·NH·C(:NH)NH₂) with ammonia. 2-Aminotriazine has been prepared, in poor yield, from 2-amino-4:6-dichlorotriazine; and 2:4-diaminotriazine by heating biguanide (H₂N·C(NH₂):N·C(:NH)NH₂) with formic acid (other fatty acids give homologues, formerly known as 'guanamines').

2:4:6-Trihydroxy-1:3:5-triazine (cyanuric acid) is obtained by polymerizing cyanic acid; and 2:4-dihydroxy-1:3:5-triazine by the oxidation of uric acid with hydrogen peroxide (Brandenberger and Brandenberger, 1954). 2-Hydroxytriazine is unknown.

Other 1:3:5-triazines have been made by heating nitriles (or amidines) with acid anhydrides, or acid chlorides (even with phosgene).

1:2:4-Triazine is unknown. The 3-amino-derivative is prepared from glyoxal and aminoguanidine in cold water (Erickson, 1952). 3:5-Dihydroxy-1:2:4-triazine ('aza-uracil') is obtained by heating ethyl ketomalonate with thiosemicarbazide; the resultant 3-mercapto-5-hydroxy-1:2:4-triazine-6-carboxylic acid is then hydrolysed and decarboxylated (Barlow and Welch, 1956). Several other azalogues of biologically-active pyrimidines have been prepared (Falco, Pappas and Hitchings, 1956).

No 1:2:3-triazines are known. These and the 1:2:4-triazines deserve further exploration. Syntheses of the parent substances and mono-derivatives would be worthwhile, also some physico-chemical exploration. For a review, see Erickson, Wiley and Wystrach, 1956.

Triazanaphthalenes. These substances have attracted attention because of their relationship to pteridines (see below). 1:4:5-Triazanaphthalene (3-de-azapteridine) is a stable, pale yellow solid, m.p. 146°, made by the action of glyoxal on 2:3-diaminopyridine (Leese and Rydon, 1955). Several derivatives are known (*idem*; Osdene and Timmis, 1955, b). 1:4:6-Triazanaphthalene (1-de-azapteridine), m.p. 97°, is similarly made from 3:4-diaminopyridine. It is very unstable to acid: the pyrazine ring opens during titration but does not close on neutralization unless first made alkaline (Albert and Pedersen, 1956). Derivatives of 1:3:5- and 1:3:8-triazanaphthalene are also known, but attempts to prepare the parent substances have not succeeded (Oakes, Pascoe and Rydon, 1956). 1:3:7-Triazanaphthalene (copazoline), m.p. 144°, has been known since 1902. Triazanaphthalenes, designed as diaza-derivatives of 8-hydroxyquinoline, have been prepared and their metal-binding avidities measured (Albert and Hampton, 1952, 1954).

D. Systems with more than Three Ring-Nitrogen Atoms

Tetrazines. Only the 1:2:4:5-isomer is known. The parent substance (X) is readily obtained by dimerizing ethyl diazoacetate with alkali, oxidizing the resultant 1:2-dihydrotetrazinedicarboxylic acid, and decarboxylating the product. *sym*-Tetrazine is a bluish-red solid, m.p. 99°. Other *sym*-tetrazines are obtained by the action of hydrazine on nitriles. 1:2:3:4-Tetrazines are known only as hydrogenated derivatives, and 1:2:3:5-tetrazines are entirely unknown (Erickson, Wiley and Wystrach, 1956).

No **pentazines** are known.

Pteridines. The pteridines have been referred to in Section 2 (*d*) above as the best-known examples of a high N:C-ratio in a two-ring π-deficient system. They are also of great importance in biology.

Pteridine (CXXXIII) is an odourless yellow solid, m.p. 139°, somewhat volatile in steam and highly soluble in water and organic solvents. It was first made in 1948, by the condensation of 4:5-diaminopyrimidine (CXXXII) (see p. 116) and glyoxal (Jones, 1948), a particular case of Isay's reaction. Thirty-five monosubstituted pteridines have been made similarly (Albert, Brown and Wood, 1954), and innumerable poly-substituted derivatives. When the non-pyrimidine reactant is not symmetrical, a mixture of 6- and 7-substituted pteridines results. For example glyoxylic acid and 4:5-diaminopyrimidine give 6- and 7-hydroxypteridine, the former being favoured in 2N-sulphuric acid, the latter in 2N-sodium carbonate. However, where a methyl-group is being introduced with methylglyoxal, control of orientation is obtained not by varying the pH, but by the use of sodium hydrogen sulphite (or other ketobinder) which usually forces the methyl-group into the 6-position.

Pteridines were discovered in the wings of butterflies by Gowland Hopkins in 1891, but their chemical nature remained a mystery for fifty years until it was solved by Purrmann (1940). Xanthopterin (which is also the yellow pigment of bees and wasps) was then shown to be 2-amino-4:6-dihydroxypteridine; *iso*xanthopterin, 2-amino-4:7-dihydroxypteridine; and leucopterin, 2-amino-4:6:7-trihydroxypteridine. Related pteridines have also been isolated from the eyes of insects (where they are believed to play a part in the visual process), and the skin of fish, snakes and amphibians. There is a bound-form of xanthopterin in human urine, as well as other pteridine derivatives: biopterin, uropterin, and some folic acids.

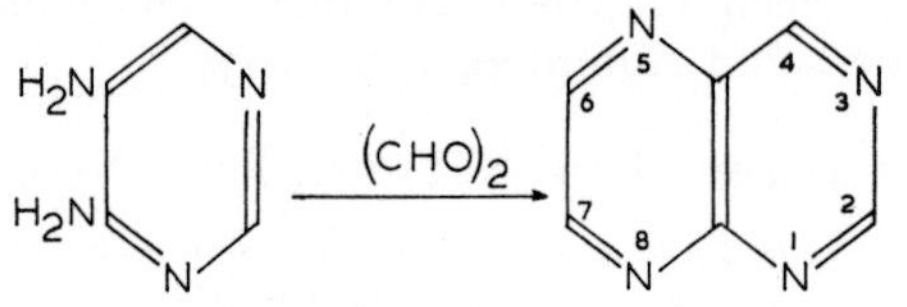

CXXXII   CXXXIII

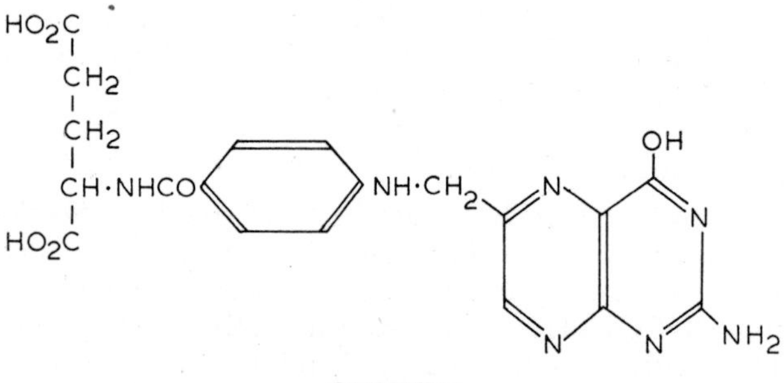

CXXXIV

The name 'folic acid' was coined in 1944 for a class of substances present in leaves and liver, which cures experimental anaemia in animals and stimulates the growth of certain bacteria. In 1946, one such substance was shown by degradation and synthesis to be (CXXXIV), now called pteroylglutamic acid (PGA). This is the principal bound-form of *p*-aminobenzoic acid in nature, and sulphonamides injure bacteria solely by preventing formation of PGA. It has since been shown that pteroylglutamic acid is essential for the multiplication of all mammalian cells (Jacobson, 1952). Mammals, however, do not synthesize their PGA, but absorb it from the intestines. Guanine, and related purines, appear to be the starting materials for the biosynthesis of pteridines (Albert, 1957).

Other folic acids, all derivatives of PGA, occur in nature. In some the pyrazine-ring is reduced, and a formyl group is then sometimes present in the 5-position, or on the anilino-nitrogen atom of the side-chain. Such substances are coenzymes assisting the transfer of one-carbon fragments in biosynthesis and degradation, employing formic acid (but in some cases formaldehyde). Other folic acids have more than one glutamic acid residue, and other amino-acids are sometimes present (Wright, 1955).

Analogues of these pteridines, particularly those where the 4-hydroxy-group has been replaced by a 4-amino-group, are biological antagonists of the folic acids, and are used to prolong life in some types of leukaemia (cancer of bone-marrow). Even 2:4-diaminopteridine shows this effect. Almost all naturally-occurring pteridines are metal-binding (Albert, 1953).

Other syntheses of pteridines include the oxidation of alloxazines (see below); heating 2-aminopyrazine-3-carboxyamide (CXXXV) (or carboxythioamide) with formic acid and acetic anhydride to give 4-hydroxy- (or 4-mercapto-) pteridine (Albert, Brown and Cheeseman, 1951); the condensation of 4-chloro-5-nitropyrimidines with glycine (or aminoacetone) followed by reduction, ring-closure and dehydrogenation of the resulting 6-hydroxy- (or methyl)-7:8-dihydropteridines (Boon, Jones and Ramage, 1951; Boon and Jones, 1951); and the condensation of 4-amino-5-nitrosopyrimidines with ketones or acids containing adjacent active methylene groups (e.g. cyanoacetic acid), for example 4:6-diamino-5-nitrosopyrimidine (CXXXVI) and cyanoacetic acid gave 4:7-diaminopteridine-6-carboxylic acid (Osdene and Timmis, 1955, c).

The great decrease in aqueous solubility observed when hydrogen-bonding groups are introduced into pteridines has been dealt with under Section 2 (a), above (see p. 43).

For further reading see reviews by Albert (1952) and (1954), the latter dealing with the natural products.

CXXXV   CXXXVI   CXXXVII

Benzopteridine (CXXXVII) is unknown, but alloxazine, the 2:4-dihydroxy-derivative, is prepared from alloxan (p. 115) and o-phenylenediamine. Riboflavine, a yellow vitamin, poorly soluble

K

in water, is 6:7-dimethyl-9-(D-1'-ribityl) *iso*alloxazine, the hydrogen on 9, replaced by the ribityl radical, having been borrowed from the hydroxy-group on 2 (hence the prefix, 'iso'). The function of riboflavine in cells is to take hydrogen from the reduced form of the phosphopyridine nucleotides (see Figure 2, p. 92), and pass it on either to the oxygen of air, or (more usually) to the cytochromes (see Chapter V). Riboflavine is reduced in two distinct one-electron steps, and the semiquinone intermediate (a paramagnetic free-radical) is fairly long-lived, although it eventually dimerizes (Beinert, 1956). Riboflavine is metal-binding (Albert, 1953), the hydroxy-group in the 4-position being placed as in 8-hydroxyquinoline. The coenzyme functions of riboflavine depend on the presence of heavy metals such as iron or molybdenum.

The biosynthesis of riboflavine starts with a purine, and has a 2:4-dihydroxypteridine as an intermediate (Masuda, 1956).

π-Excessive N-Heteroaromatics

(i.e. Completely unsaturated heterocycles, having nitrogen as
the sole hetero-element, and an excess of π-electrons elsewhere)

Introduction

π-Excessive N-heteroaromatics have at least one five-membered ring. Whereas the π-deficient rings in Chapter IV embodied a nitrogen atom in a setting that made it electron-attracting ($=CH-N=CH-$), the rings now to be dealt with have nitrogen in an electron-releasing setting ($=CH-NH-CH=$). Considerations of valence impose a six-membered ring on the former and a five-membered ring on the latter. When both systems are built into the same five-membered ring, the influence of the electron-releasing system predominates.

Pyrrole (I) is a typical example of a π-excessive N-hetero-cycle. As was explained in Chapter III, the nitrogen atom in such a ring adds its lone pair of electrons to the four electrons furnished by the two 'double-bonds', and thus makes an aromatic sextet (Armit and Robinson, 1925; Bamberger, 1891). Thus pyrrole (I) has a high degree of aromatic character, whereas cyclopentadiene (II) has almost none. This is reflected in (a) the higher resonance energy of pyrrole compared to that of cyclopentadiene, viz. 24[1] versus 3 Kcal./Mole (Wheland, 1944); and (b) the ease of substitution in pyrrole, which under-goes very few addition reactions.

Pyrrole is a planar pentagon, as found from microwave spectrometry (Wilcox and Goldstein, 1952). The sides vary from 1·35 to 1·45 Å and the nitrogen atom is hybridized sp². The contribution of electrons from the nitrogen atom of pyrrole to the π-layer gives the ring a strongly polar character (dipole moment = 1·8 D). As a consequence, all of the carbon atoms have high electron densities (see Chapter III), and hence pyrrole is more readily substituted by electrophilic reagents than benzene, in fact even more readily than aniline. As would be expected, nucleophilic reactions are rare in this series. The electrophilic reactions will be discussed below (see 2 (f)).

1. THE PARENT SUBSTANCES

None of the parent substances in this chapter is manufactured on a large scale, but several are available in small quantities for laboratory purposes, notably pyrrole, indole, carbazole, imina-zole, benziminazole and benztriazole. The remainder are highly uncommon substances, but some derivatives of pyrazole and purine are readily obtainable.

The formula of pyrrole is best represented as (I) (Ingold, 1933; Pauling and Sherman, 1933) and not as one of the isomeric pyrrolenines (III) and (IV), which are unknown except as derivatives in which both hydrogen atoms of the

---

[1] Other estimates have been 23, 25 and 31 Kcal.; Dewar (1949) prefers 25 Kcal. and discusses the difficulties of determination.

methylene-group are substituted. The preference for formula
(I) over (III) or (IV) is based on infrared and Raman measurements (Zumwalt and Badger, 1939; Lord and Miller, 1942);
also on the dipole moment (which would be reversed in (III)
and (IV); and on the aromatic properties (substitution is preferred to addition). Thus the high resonance energy is derived
from resonance between five canonical forms: (I), (V), (VI),
reversed (V), and reversed (VI). In the remainder of this
chapter, (I) will be used as a simplified formula for this hybrid.
The reactions of pyrrole suggest that minute amounts of the
pyrrolenine tautomers (IV) and possibly (III) are present in
pyrrole, and that these traces continue to be formed when a
specific reagent removes them.

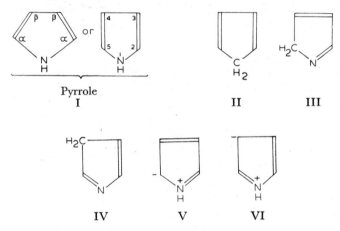

Pyrrole
I

II   III

IV   V   VI

In the disposition of its charges pyrrole resembles aniline: the
nitrogen atom in each is already quaternized without addition
of a proton, and has liberated electrons to the π-layer from
which they are partly re-localized on to the carbon atoms. In
contrast to aniline, *all* the carbon atoms in pyrrole are enriched
by this re-localization. Like aniline and its derivatives, the
pyrroles and indoles are very prone to oxidative destruction
unless electron-attracting groups are inserted to lessen the
negative charges on the carbon atoms.

Using pyrrole as a (theoretical) progenitor, indole (VII) and
carbazole (VIII) are formed by adding one and two benzene

rings. *Iso*indole (IX) is still unknown, but since 1951 a few simple derivatives, e.g. 2-methyl*iso*indole, have been obtained and more complex derivatives have been known for some time.

Indolenine, a tautomer of indole containing the 3-pyrrolenine nucleus (IV), is believed to be present in traces, at equilibrium. In a very few reactions indoles yield indolenines which are stable if both hydrogens in the 3-position are substituted. Thanks to the possibilities of nitrogen-sharing there exists another isomer of indole, viz. indolizine (X), and many derived shared-nitrogen types are known. However, two six-membered rings cannot be combined in this way without considerable loss of aromatic character (see quinolizine in Chapter VII).

Four molecules of some pyrroles having a 1-carbon substituent readily rearrange to give derivatives of the macrocyclic substance porphin (XI), with its central sixteen-membered ring. The side-to-side fusion of two pyrrole rings, e.g. (XII), is also known, but not common.

Any of the $=CH-$ groups in the above substances can theoretically be substituted by $=N-$, leading to azalogues. Thus pyrrole has two mono-azalogues, pyrazole (XIII) and iminazole (XIV); the latter is also known as imidazole and glyoxaline. The insertion of such doubly-bound nitrogen atoms into pyrrole naturally reduces the π-excessive nature of the substances. But the electron-releasing power of nitrogen in $=CH-NH-CH=$ greatly exceeds the electron-attracting power of nitrogen in $=CH-N=CH-$, because pyrazole and iminazole behave as π-excessive substances, although less so than pyrrole. Further addition of doubly-bound nitrogen atoms must further diminish the electron-excessive character of five-membered rings, but information is too scanty to pronounce on the extent. The following evidence suggests that the triazoles are a little more π-electron excessive than benzene. 1:2:4-Triazole undergoes the indophenine reaction (with isatin) which appears to be a mild electrophilic substitution, and 1:2:3-triazole (XVI) readily brominates to the 4:5-dibromo-derivative (Hüttel and Gebhardt, 1947). Confirmatory evidence that these ring-systems are not appreciably electron-deficient is to be found in the stability of the chlorine atom in 3-chloro-1:2:4-tetrazole to attack by amines, and in the ready diazotizing-

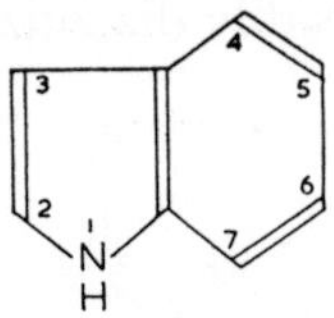

Indole
VII

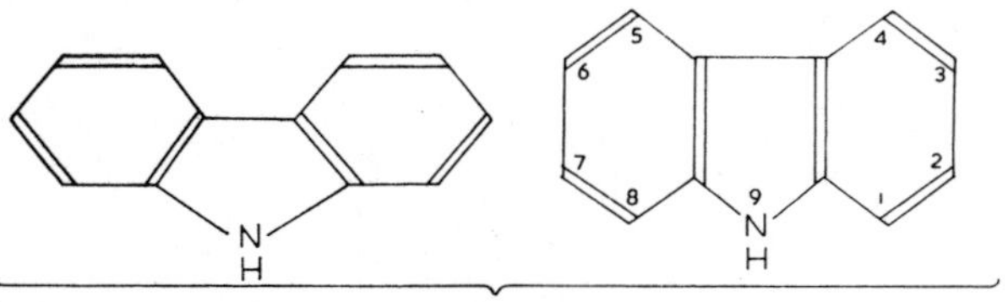

Carbazole
VIII

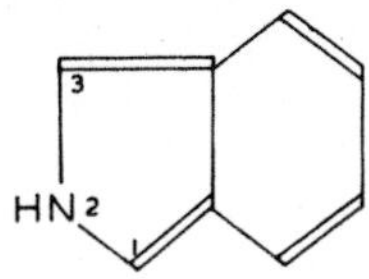

*Iso*indole
IX

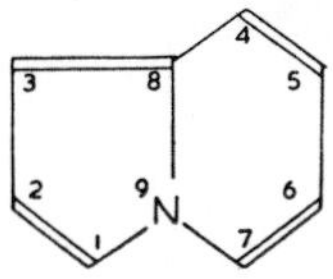

Indolizine[1]
(Pyrrocoline)
X

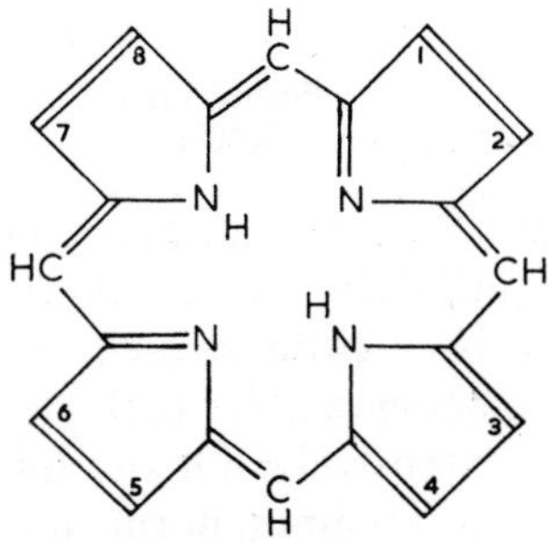

Porphin
XI

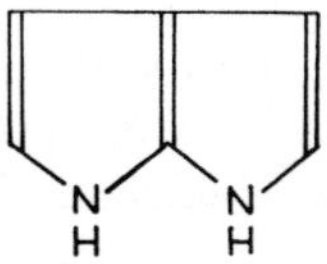

2:3:2':3'-Pyrrolopyrrole
XII

[1] In another nomenclature, the carbon next to nitrogen in the five-membered ring is numbered 3.

and-coupling reactions of α-amino-derivatives of both triazoles. 5-Aminotetrazole also readily diazotizes and couples.

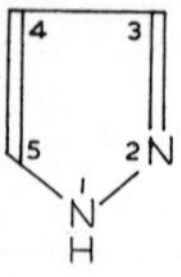

Pyrazole   Iminazole   1:2:4-Triazole 1:2:3-Triazole   Tetrazole
XIII   XIV   XV   XVI   XVII

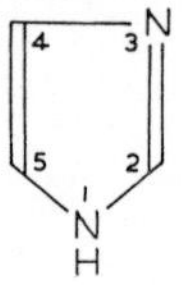

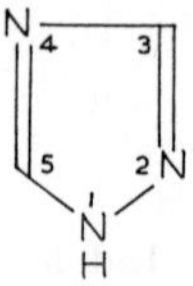

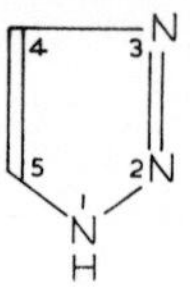

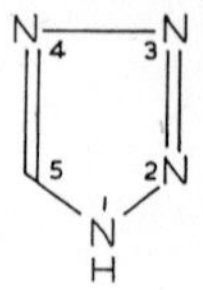

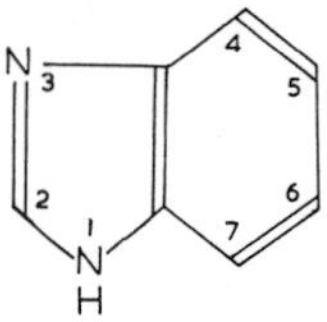

Benziminazole   Indazole   Purine
XVIII   XIX   XX

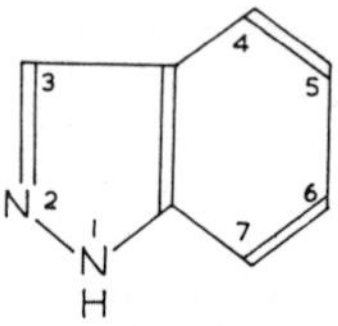

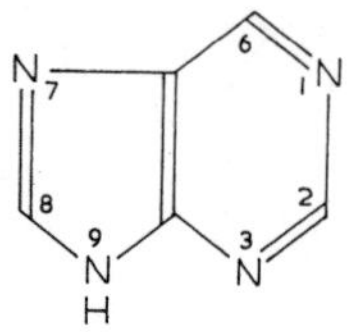

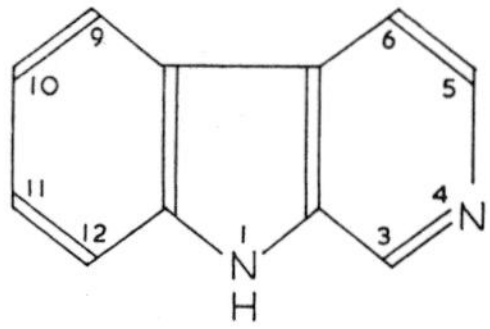

Norharman   Perimidine
XXI   XXII

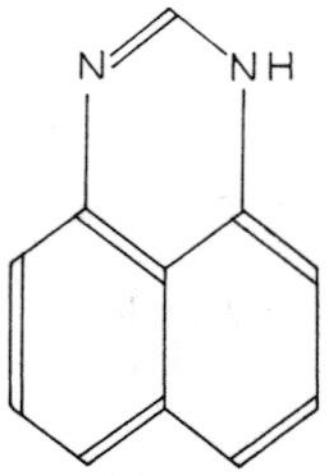

Among the mono-azalogues of indole, the most studied are benziminazole (XVIII), and indazole (XIX). Azalogues involving the benzene ring have been little studied, apart from purine (XX) whose derivatives, being of great biological importance, have been investigated extensively. Of the four mono-azalogues of carbazole, known as carbolines, norharman (XXI) is the best known. Analogous to these carbolines, which have an indole nucleus fused to pyridine, there are quindolines having indole fused to quinoline. Finally, there is a curious substance perimidine (XXII), which has the =CH−NH−CH= system of pyrrole, but in a six-membered ring. It is a typical π-excessive substance.

2. CORRELATION OF STRUCTURE AND PROPERTIES

The presence of the −NH-group in these π-excessive substances introduces features not encountered with their π-deficient analogues. It can ionize as an anion, allow substitution (as opposed to quaternization) on the nitrogen atom, and introduces tautomeric possibilities in unsymmetrical molecules if a tertiary nitrogen atom is also present, e.g. in triazole (XVI) or purine (XX).

To facilitate comparison between the divisions of this section and the corresponding ones in Chapters IV and VI, the same index letters will be used.

(a) Solubility

Whereas the nitrogen atom of pyridine has a lone pair of electrons available for hydrogen-bonding with water, with which it is in consequence completely miscible, the lone pair on the nitrogen atom of pyrrole is utilized in forming the aromatic sextet, and hence is not available for effecting solubility in water. As would be expected pyrrole is poorly soluble in water (about 1–800 at 20°?) but no exact figures are available. In fact, quite in contrast to the π-deficient N-heterocycles, very few solubility data exist for the π-excessive N-heterocycles. Thus, it is recorded of indole, indolizine and carbazole only that they are 'sparingly soluble' in cold water.

The introduction of a doubly-bound nitrogen atom, as in pyrazole (XIII) and iminazole (XIV), would be expected to increase solubility because the lone pair on a tertiary nitrogen is disengaged. In conformity with this idea, it is recorded that pyrazole is soluble 1 in 1, at 20° in water, and iminazole is more soluble than 1 in 1 (Hückel, Datow and Simmersbach, 1940). Annelation of these substances to give indazole (XIX) and benziminazole (XVIII) should decrease solubility (cf. naphthalene with benzene), and this agrees with the literature which states, 'poorly soluble in cold, but soluble in boiling water'. The insolubilizing effect of the benzene ring can be countered by inserting more doubly-bound nitrogen atoms, e.g. purine (XX) is soluble 1 in 2 (at 20°).

Pyrrole and indole boil only slightly higher than their N-methyl-derivatives. Thus self-bonding through $N-H \cdots N$ bonds is unlikely, apart from being improbable on theoretical grounds (see above).

The effect of hydrogen-bonding substituents will now be considered. The insertion of hydroxy-groups into these substances should not depress solubility as happens with π-deficient substances, but increase it. Unfortunately no data are available.

TABLE 9. Solubilities of Purines in Water at 20°

Purine	1 in
(Unsubstituted)	2
2-Hydroxy-	380
6-Hydroxy- (hypoxanthine)	1,400
8-Hydroxy-	240
2:6-Dihydroxy- (xanthine)	2,000
2:8-Dihydroxy-	26,000
6:8-Dihydroxy-	6,000
2:6:8-Trihydroxy- (uric acid)	39,500
2-Methoxy-	200
6-Methoxy-	225
2-Amino-	120
6-Amino- (adenine)	1,100
8-Amino-	2,000
2:6-Diamino-	420
2:6:8-Triamino-	200
6-Dimethylamino-	120
8-Methyl-	18
8-Hydroxymethyl-	220[a]
8-Carboxylic Acid	(very sparingly soluble)

a. From Albert (1955, c); other values from Albert and Brown (1954).

On the other hand, when a doubly-bound nitrogen atom is also present (as in iminazole), the solubility should be depressed by a hydrogen-bonding substituent, just as in the pyridine and pyrimidine series. Thus iminazole-4-carboxylic acid is soluble only 1–20 in water at 100°, and 2:4-dihydroxyiminazole is 'soluble in hot but not in cold water'. In fact, iminazole is itself chain-associated by hydrogen bonds to the extent of a tetramer in naphthalene and in boiling benzene, it boils 58° (and melts 96°) higher than its N-methyl-derivative, and is only one-fortieth as soluble in benzene. Iminazole is not associated in water, even at 0°. Pyrazole is associated as a cyclic dimer, by a pair of hydrogen bonds, completely in benzene, less in dioxane and but little in water (Hückel, Datow and Simmersbach, 1940; Hückel and Jahnentz, 1942).

Fortunately a good deal of solubility data exists for the purines. It was observed by Emil Fischer (1899) that insertion of hydroxyl-groups progressively decreased the solubility of purine. He also suggested that the addition of amino-groups should have the same effect, but this is now known not to be the case when more than one amino-group is inserted. These effects are demonstrated in Table 9, and also the increase in solubility that follows when a bondable hydrogen is suppressed by methylation. The insolubilizing effect of even an aliphatic hydroxyl-group, as in 8-hydroxymethylpurine, is also noteworthy.

(b) Acidic and Basic Strength

The ionizing properties of the π-excessive N-heterocycles cannot be summarized so briefly as those of their π-deficient analogues: firstly, because they possess acidic as well as basic properties, and secondly because the introduction of a further ring-nitrogen atom opposes the polarity of the first one, as was explained above. However, the picture which emerges from this complex situation is orderly.

Acidic properties. Pyrrole, as the pK of $\sim$15 indicates (Table 10), is a very weak acid, weaker than glucose or hydrogen peroxide. However it is a far stronger acid than ammonia ($pK = \sim$33, Branch and Calvin, 1941). It is not difficult for workers to comprehend what an acidic pK of $\sim$15 implies in the case of pyrrole. Thus potassium pyrrole can be made from pyrrole and potassium hydroxide (the metal is not required), but only under anhydrous conditions, and it must be stored and used under anhydrous conditions.[1] It is an important intermediate in the preparation of substituted pyrroles (see (*f*) below). The acidic strengths of indole and carbazole have not been determined, but appear to be of the same order as that of pyrrole. The acid strength of indole is not increased by a substituent in

---

[1] Sodium pyrrole is most conveniently made by the action of sodamide on pyrrole in liquid ammonia.

the 3-position bearing doubly-bound carbon (or nitrogen) conjugated with the nucleus.

The insertion of a doubly-bound nitrogen into the ring of pyrrole, as in iminazole (XIV) and benziminazole (XVIII), increases the acid strength (see Table 10): this is because it is an electron-attracting group, comparable in inductive power to the nitro-group, as was explained in Chapter IV. In addition, more resonance is possible in the anion than in the neutral molecule, thanks to the equivalence of the nitrogens in the anion, as seen in (XXIII) and (XXIV). In tetrazole (triazapyrrole) the combined inductive effect of three tertiary nitrogen atoms has produced an acid as strong as the aliphatic carboxylic acids.

Table 10 also demonstrates the effect of adding increasing numbers of doubly-bound nitrogen atoms to indole. The acid-strengthening effect is naturally greatest when they are in the same ring as the ionizable hydrogen. When, eventually, four tertiary nitrogen atoms are inserted, quite a strong acid ('8-azapurine') is produced.

XXIII   XXIV   XXV   XXVI   XXVII   XXVIII

Basic properties. The weakness of pyrrole as a base is expected, because the lone pair of electrons is not free to anchor a hydrogen ion as it is involved in maintaining the aromatic sextet (see above). Looked at from another viewpoint, the positive charge on the nitrogen atom must repel protons by a coulombic effect. The C-alkyl pyrroles give stable crystalline salts with hydrogen bromide in dry ether (Stedman and MacDonald, 1955, cf. Treibe and Kolm, 1957), but these undergo further chemical change in water (see (*d*) below). As near as can be judged in such a difficult case, the basic pK_a of pyrrole is ~0·4, which is a low figure indeed. No data exist for indole, indolizine, or carbazole, but they appear to be of the same order.

The insertion of a doubly-bound nitrogen atom into the ring

of pyrrole, e.g. as in iminazole (XIV), might be expected to have a base-weakening (inductive) effect on the singly-bound nitrogen. The doubly-bound nitrogen should thus be for the more basic of the two. It may be that the two nitrogen atoms act in concert through the extra resonance possible in the cation, as compared with the neutral molecule. This resonance arises from the equivalence of both nitrogen atoms in the cation, as in (XXV) and (XXVI). The base-strengthening effect is not so marked in pyrazole as in iminazole. Hence it cannot definitely be said that extra resonance is available in the cation from the canonical forms (XXVII) and (XXVIII).

TABLE 10. Ionization of π-Excessive N-Heterocycles (in Water at 20°)

Substance	Acidic pK_a (the higher the figure, the weaker the acid)	Basic pK_a (the higher the figure, the stronger the base)
Pyrrole (I)	~15[a]	~0·4[b]
Pyrazole (XIII)	14[k]	2·53[c]
1-Methyl-	—	2·09[c]
Iminazole (XIV)	14·5[d]	7·16[c]
1-Methyl-	—	7·41[c]
1:2:4-Triazole (XV)	10·1[k]	2·30[c]
Tetrazole (XVII)	4·9[e]	?
Indazole (XIX) (2-aza-indole)	?	1·3[f]
Benziminazole (XVIII) (3-aza-indole)	12·3[f]	5·53[f]
Benzotriazole (2:3-diaza-indole)	8·57[f]	1·6[f]
3:4-Diaza-indole	11·08[g]	3·95[g]
3:6-Diaza-indole	10·88[h]	6·10[h]
Purine (XX) (3:4:6-triaza-indole)	8·93[i]	2·39[i]
8-Azapurine (2:3:4:6-tetra-aza-indole)	4·9[j]	2·1[j]

a. Branch and Calvin (1941).
b. Hall (1930).
c. Dedichen (1906).
d. Walba and Isensee (1956).
e. Lieber, Patinkin and Tao (1951).
f. Albert, Goldacre and Phillips (1948).
g. Mason (1954).
h. Albert and Pedersen (1956).
i. Albert and Brown (1954).
j. Felton (1955).
k. Dr. S. F. Mason, personal communication.

An earlier explanation, that pyrazole is weaker than iminazole because the neutral molecules of pyrazole may be hydrogen-bonded in pairs (in water), cannot be sustained because 1-methylpyrazole is not stronger than pyrazole.

The insertion of a doubly-bound nitrogen atom into indole is base-strengthening if in the pyrrole ring, as is seen for indazole and benziminazole (Table 10). But further insertions can be base-weakening (due to the inductive effect) if they occur in positions where resonance is not aided, or where cross-resonances can occur. The rather high basic strength of 3:6-diaza-indole must be due to increased resonance in the cation through the canonical forms (XXIX) and (XXX): this is like the base-strengthening already discussed for 4-amino-pyridine (see p. 47).

XXIX   XXX   XXXI

The α:α'-dipyrrylmethanes (see (f) below, p. 157) are necessarily as weak bases as pyrrole, but the dipyrrylmethenes formed from them by oxidation (see (k) below, p. 177) should be stronger because the cation has extra resonance possibilities. However, this base-strengthening effect is opposed by a base-weakening effect shown in (XXXI), namely the sharing of a hydrogen atom by both nitrogen atoms in the neutral molecule. The dipyrrylmethenes behave as if somewhat weaker than aniline, but no precise figures are available.

The basic strength of porphin (XI) and its derivatives has excited speculation, but experimental difficulties are formidable because of the sparing solubility of the neutral molecules. A pK_a of 7 has been suggested (Neuberger and Scott, 1952), but the esters seem to be much weaker bases than this (Phillips, 1958).

The py-methochloride (XXXII) of norharman (XXI) (synonyms 4-carboline; 2-azacarbazole) gives a pK_a of about 11 on titration with alkali (Gray, 1955). The substance obtained, known as the 'anhydronium base', is a resonance hybrid of the zwitterion (XXXIII) and the neutral molecule (XXXIV) (Armit and Robinson, 1925; Spenser, 1956). This pK_a is best regarded as the ionization, as an anion, of the indolic nitrogen atom, aided by the electron-attracting quaternary nitrogen atom, and by the extra resonance in the anion. Alternatively it can be thought of as a composite of two constants: one for the ionization of the quaternary nitrogen atom and another for the final dehydration to a much weaker base (see Goldacre and Phillips, 1949, for the development of this concept in the triphenylmethane series). The change from the *py*-methochlorides to the 'anhydronium bases' is accompanied by a colour change from white to orange and the appearance of a large dipole moment, sometimes as great as 8D. An earlier concept that this change involves ring-opening has been refuted (Spenser, 1956).

XXXII   XXXIII

XXXIV

(c) Ultraviolet Spectra

The spectra of the π-deficient N-heterocycles were shown in Chapter IV to be almost identical with those of the corresponding hydrocarbons (e.g. acridine with anthracene). The π-excessive N-heterocycles have ultraviolet spectra related to the same hydrocarbons, although the connexion is not so close (Badger and Christie, 1956).

Thus the spectrum of carbazole (VIII) is comparable with that of phenanthrene (see Figure 18 in Chapter VIII: carbazole, a V-shaped molecule, is not to be compared with anthracene). The intensity of the 320–340 mμ absorption is much greater for carbazole than for phenanthrene. No useful comparison can be made with fluorene (XXXV), the central ring of which is not aromatic. In fact fluorene does not absorb at wavelengths longer than 300 mμ.

XXXV

As would be expected, the spectrum of indole resembles that of naphthalene. An outlying (isolated) peak at 288 mμ in indole seems to correspond to the one about 310 in naphthalene, but is more intense (see Figure 20, Chapter VIII).

The spectrum of pyrrole (see Figure 23 in Chapter VIII) is lacking in detail compared to that of benzene, but both substances have their λ_{max} in the same region. Very little more can be recorded for iminazole (XIV) on the usual quartz prism instruments, than a little 'end absorption' (see Figure 23 in Chapter VIII). This is also the case with tetrazole (XVII).

Studies of the ultraviolet spectra of methylated derivatives reveal that benzotriazole has the mobile hydrogen atom principally in the 1-position, and purine (XX) has it principally in the 9-position (Specker and Gawrosch, 1942; Bendich, Russell and Fox, 1954, respectively).

Non-tautomerizable substituents (e.g. $-Cl$, $-CH_3$, $-OCH_3$) slightly displace the spectra of π-excessive N-heterocycles to longer wavelengths. This behaviour resembles that of non-heterocyclic aromatic substances (Jones, 1948). As an example, 5- and 6-methoxyindole have spectra similar to that of indole, but displaced to slightly longer wavelengths (Pruckner and Witkop, 1943). This displacement is specially revealing in the pyrrole series where the peak of the parent substance is not entirely resolvable by the usual quartz prism instrument, but ethyl 3:5-dimethylpyrrole-2-carboxylate has a well-defined peak at 276 mμ (Cookson, 1953). Similarly, iminazole (XIV) shows little ultraviolet absorption with the quartz prism, but iminazole-4-carboxaldehyde has a well-defined peak at 256 mμ, and iminazole-4-carboxylic acid has two peaks at 271 and 277 mμ

(Turner, 1949). Pyrazole (XIII) behaves similarly (e.g. Noyce, Ryder and Walker, 1955).

The porphyrins are notable for the fine structure of their spectra in the visible region, and rules connecting spectra and structure have been evolved by porphyrin chemists (cf. Lemberg and Falk, 1951; Aronoff, 1950). When the $-CH=$ groups which connect the pyrrole rings in porphyrins are changed to $-N=$ atoms, radically different spectra are obtained, and this has been attributed to a distortion, by the nitrogen-bridges, of the originally symmetrical sixteen-membered ring (Pruckner, 1941).

The spectrum of N-phenylpyrroles reveals conjugation between the rings, by the shifting of the peak to longer wavelengths. This conjugation is sterically hindered when methylgroups occupy both the 2- and 5-positions (Davoll, 1953).

(d) Action of Acids and Alkali

Action of acids. Any reaction which causes the ring-nitrogen atom of pyrrole to withdraw its lone pair of electrons from the aromatic sextet must inevitably deprive the product of aromatic character. This happens when pyrrole is placed in mineral acids. Although pyrrole is a very weak base, some cation is formed. This is highly unstable and undergoes several simultaneous reactions, of which polymerization has been the most studied. This tendency to polymerize is reminiscent of the behaviour of *cyclo*pentadiene (II) which also lacks aromatic stabilization (see the introduction to this chapter) and whose polymerization involves mutual 1:4-addition (Alder and Stein, 1932). The most easily crystallized of the many acid-decomposition products of pyrrole is 'tripyrrole', $C_{12}H_{15}N_3$. It is a low-melting colourless trimer and it has been assigned the constitution, 2:5-dipyrrolylpyrrolidine (Potts and Smith, 1957). Less is known of the other products of acid-decomposition. An orange, amorphous product, 'pyrrole red', has also been isolated but has been little studied. N-Methylpyrrole also undergoes acid-catalysed polymerization. The C-alkylpyrroles, thanks to steric hindrance, are somewhat less prone to polymerization, and give crystalline hydrobromides (Stedman and MacDonald, 1955). Dimers are obtained if one free α- and one free β-position are adjacent and

L

the structure of these 'dipyrroles' has been investigated (Allen, Gilbert and Young, 1937). If no free α- and β-positions are adjacent, pyrroles usually survive boiling 25% sulphuric acid.

Indole resembles pyrrole in sensitivity to acid, and the structures (XXXVI) and (XXXVII) have been proposed for the dimer and trimer respectively (Smith, 1954). In (XXXVI), one molecule of indole has added across the 2:3-double-bond of another.

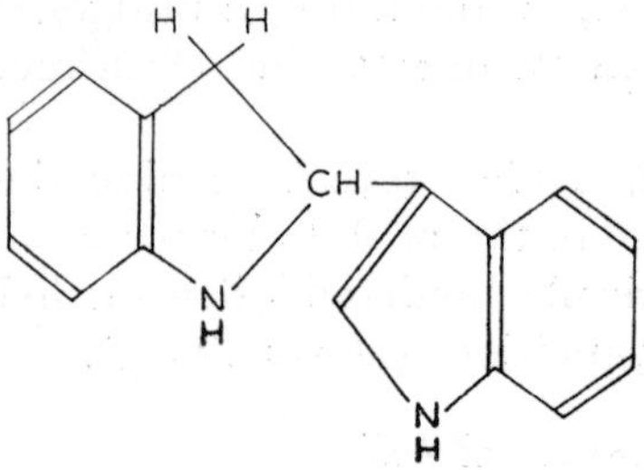

'Di-indole'
XXXVI

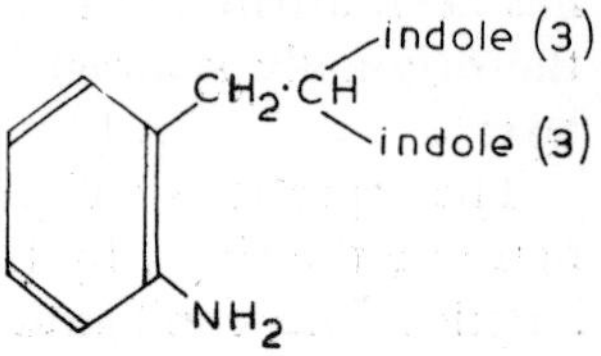

'Tri-indole'
XXXVII

*Iso*indoles are resinified by acid (Wittig *et al.*, 1951), but indolizine (X) is only slowly destroyed by boiling 10 N-sulphuric acid.

Carbazole is unaffected by acid, because the positions which would be involved are sterically protected by the two annelated benzene rings, and these preserve their aromatic character (see p. 162).

The insertion of a doubly-bound nitrogen atom into any position in pyrrole or indole brings increased stability to acid. Thus iminazole is stable to boiling 60% hydriodic acid, to chromic-sulphuric acid. Similarly 1:2:4-triazole survives 10 N-hydrochloric acid at 150°. 7-Aza-indole can safely be refluxed with concentrated hydrochloric acid, and benziminazole (XVIII) is unchanged by heating with 10 N-hydrochloric acid at 270°. Similarly, indazole (XIX) is unchanged by 20% sulphuric acid at 250°. Purine (XX) is also highly stable to acid.

This stabilization by the tertiary nitrogen atom may owe much to the high resonance energy of the cations that it makes possible, as has been explained in (*b*) above (see p. 142). This resonance may not be so great when the two nitrogen atoms are in different rings. But even here the doubly-bound nitrogen atom, by far the more basic, is the first to unite with a proton and thus, by the coulombic effect, protects the secondary nitrogen from protonation. In this way, the molecule is saved from destruction even under severe acidic conditions.

The porphyrins also are very stable to acids, thanks to the high resonance energy of the porphin nucleus (XI).

Action of alkali. Pyrrole is remarkably stable to alkali, because it can be synthesized from succinic dialdehyde and ammonia. However the equilibrium position can be shifted if an aldehyde-binding agent is added. Hydroxylamine at pH 8 serves this purpose and gives an excellent yield of succinic dialdoxime (Findlay, 1956). 2:5-Dimethylpyrrole similarly gives acetonyl-acetone dioxime. Pyrrole-2:5-dipropionic acid is split by alkali (to di-laevulinic acid) even in the absence of ketone-binders (Diels and Alder, 1931). Indole is unaffected by aqueous or alcoholic alkali, even in the presence of hydroxylamine, but potassium hydroxide attacks it at 200°, and some o-toluidine is produced. Iminazole and purine are highly stable to alkali.

(e) The Nature of Hydroxy- and Amino-derivatives

The hydroxy- and amino-derivatives of π-excessive substances have not been so well studied as those of their π-deficient analogues.

That the hydroxy-derivatives are tautomeric has long been recognized because under some circumstances they react like normal hydroxy-compounds (e.g. they give O-acetyl-derivatives) but under others the carbon atom adjacent to that bearing the oxygen reacts as though it were part of a methylene-group. Thus the tautomerism of 2-hydroxypyrrole lies between the normal structure and 2-oxo-Δ^4-pyrroline (XXXVIII). It should be noted that considerations of valency rule out any transfer of the proton to the ring-nitrogen atom, and the hydroxypyrrolenine structure (XL) is thought unlikely because N-alkyl derivatives of some substituted hydroxypyrroles have been investigated and found to have the same ultraviolet spectra as the examples not alkylated on nitrogen (this is, of course, not a rigid proof and more work is needed).

Because 2-hydroxypyrrole is rather unstable, its tautomerism has not been investigated. In its place Grob and Ankli
(1949) studied 2-hydroxy-4-carboethoxypyrrole. This has enolic
properties, for it dissolves in aqueous alkali, as does its N-ethyl-
derivative. It also acetylates on the oxygen atom, as is shown by
the identity of the spectrum with that of the acetylation product
of the N-ethyl derivative, and the ready hydrolysis of both
acetyl-derivatives to their respective starting-materials. It also
has pyrrolenine-type properties, e.g. benzaldehyde gives the
3-benzylidene derivative, the sign of an activated methylene
group. As chemical evidence is notoriously misleading in
deciding tautomeric equilibria (see corresponding section in
Chapter IV, p. 53), recourse was had to ultraviolet spectra. It
was found that the spectrum of 2-hydroxy-4-carboethoxy-
pyrrole and its O-acetyl-derivative were totally unlike. From
this somewhat meagre but fairly convincing evidence, it was
concluded that equilibrium greatly favoured the pyrroline form,
as (XXXVIII).

XXXVIII   XXXIX   XL

XLI   XLII

One must be careful not to generalize from this finding,
because the elimination of the ester-group, or the insertion of an
electron-releasing group in its place, could alter the position
of equilibrium. However it is evident that the structure
(XXXVIII) would be stabilized by resonance with the dipolar
structure (XXXIX). Hence the tautomerism of these π-excessive hydroxy-derivatives, at first sight so unlike that of their

π-deficient analogues, owes its equilibrium position to the same principle, viz. the compensation that amide resonance gives for the loss of some of the resonance derived from the aromatic sextet. It is because they are essentially amides and not ketones that the 2-hydroxypyrroles give no reaction with semicarbazide and other ketone-reagents.

3-Hydroxypyrrole is unknown, but substituted 3-hydroxy-pyrroles are clearly tautomeric giving O-acetyl-derivatives, but also reacting as though an active methylene group were present in the 2-position. A spectrographic comparison has been made between 3-hydroxy-4-carbomethoxy-5-methylpyrrole and its O-methyl- and O-acetyl-derivatives; also of 3-hydroxy-2:5-dimethyl-1-phenylpyrrole and its O-methyl-derivative (Davoll, 1953). It was concluded that the substances with a free hydroxyl-group were, at equilibrium, mainly in the 3-oxo-Δ^4-pyrroline form, as (XLI), because the spectra were so different from those of the O-methyl- and O-acetyl-derivatives.

2:5-Dimethyl-3-hydroxy-1-phenylpyrrole is insoluble in dilute alkali, a further indication that the equilibrium strongly favours the oxopyrroline form. Just as (XXXVIII) is a cyclic amide, so (XLI) is a cyclic *vinylogous* amide, and no reaction takes place with semicarbazide.

It may seem equally logical to place the 2- and 3-hydroxy-pyrroles in Chapter VII with the dihydropyrroles, i.e. among the hetero-ethylenics. However, there is no evidence, such as halogenation might afford, that they have an ethylenic double-bond. A more difficult decision is the logical allocation of 2:5-dihydroxypyrrole, better known as succinimide (XLII). This seems to be a typical dibasic acid-imide, although it gives some reactions characteristic of a hydroxypyrrole, e.g. with Grignard reagents. It has already been dealt with alongside the other cyclic acid imides in Chapter II (p. 27), but a case could be made for its inclusion in this chapter.

2- and 3-Aminopyrrole are unknown, but Grob and Utzinger (1954) have examined 1-(β:β-diethoxyethyl)-2-amino-4-cyano-pyrrole (XLIII) in the infrared and concluded that it has a primary amino-group. This is so far the only evidence of the nature of amino-groups in a pyrrole, and may prove not to be typical.

The nature of the tautomerism of 2-hydroxyindole (better known as oxindole) has been investigated by infrared spectra which show that equilibrium favours the amide form (XLIV) in chloroform solution (Kellie, O'Sullivan and Sadler, 1956). Conscientious exploration of ultraviolet spectra of oxindole by comparison with those of derivatives held by methylation in the *three* possible tautomeric positions, has not been done in spite of several partial attacks on the problem (summarized by Julian, Meyer and Printy, 1952). Thus it is still unknown which tautomer is preferred in aqueous solution. The tautomerism of 3-hydroxyindole (indoxyl) has been even less investigated, doubtless because it oxidizes so easily. It is thought to be a stronger acid than the 2-isomer.

XLIII   XLIV

2-Aminoindole has been investigated more fully (Kebrle and Hoffmann, 1956). For the monomethyl-derivative, methylated on the ring nitrogen, only two structures are possible, (XLV) and (XLVI, R and R' = H). As the spectrum differs in shape from, and exceeds in λ_{max}, that of 1:3:3-trimethyl-2-iminoindoline (XLVI, R and R' = CH$_3$), it was concluded that the monomethyl-derivative has the orthodox formula (XLV). The authors then considered that the spectrum of unsubstituted 2-aminoindole differed sufficiently from both of these methyl-derivatives to require a third structure, and concluded that equilibrium (in ether) favoured 1-aminoindolenine (XLVII). The hydrochlorides of the three substances gave identical spectra in water, showing that the methyl-groups do not greatly interfere with the interpretation, and also that resonance produces a similar cation (XLVIII R, R' or R″ = H or CH$_3$) from all three substances.

In conformity with these findings, infrared spectra revealed a strong C=N band at 6·05μ for '2-aminoindole' and for the trimethyl-derivative (XLVI, R and R' = CH₃), but this band was absent in the monomethyl-derivative (XLV).

As all three possible tautomers of 2-aminoindole can form the same highly resonant cation (XLVIII, R, R' and R" all = H), this substance should be a strong base. This is indeed so: the pK_a is 8·2.

XLV   XLVI   XLVII

XLVIII   XLIX

3-Aminoindole has not been investigated. There is nothing in the literature to suggest that indoles carrying an amino- or hydroxy-group in the benzene ring show tautomeric behaviour. However they are easily oxidized in air, and have been little examined. The hydroxy- and amino-carbazoles are more stable, and there is no evidence in the literature of tautomeric behaviour. 1-Hydroxyisoindole (phthalimidine) is mainly in the − CONH − form in chloroform solution, from infrared evidence (Kellie, O'Sullivan and Sadler, 1956).

Little is known about the tautomeric equilibria of hydroxy- and amino-derivatives of those π-excessive N-heterocycles which have more than one ring-nitrogen atom. Many speak of 4-hydroxypyrazole as 'pyrazolol', and of 3-hydroxypyrazole as 'pyrazolone', but these distinctions are based only on chemical reactions, always an unreliable criterion. 2:4-Dihydroxyimina-zole is commonly referred to as 'hydantoin', and the formula written as (XLIX), but without appropriate physico-chemical evidence. 3-Aminopyrazole and 4-aminoiminazole diazotize and couple, whereas 2-aminoiminazole does not, but this is not to be taken as evidence of a =NH structure (see Chapter IV, p. 52).

In the tetrazole (XVII) series, the 5-amino-derivative has been shown by ultraviolet and infrared investigation to have a primary amino-group (Murphy and Picard, 1954).

The hydroxy- and amino-derivatives of purine (XX) have been examined by ultraviolet and infrared spectroscopy in comparison with N- and O-methylated-derivatives (Mason, 1954; Elion, 1956; Brown and Mason, 1957). In most cases it was possible to reach definite conclusions, viz. that the amino-derivatives have NH_2-groups and the hydroxy-derivatives have the =O structure.

In concluding this section, it is worth pointing out how much of the spadework yet remains to be done on π-excessive material, qualitatively and quantitatively, to bring it into line with the results recorded for the π-deficient analogues in Chapter IV.

(f) Substitution by Electrophilic Reagents

Electrophilic substitution is as characteristic a feature of π-excessive substances as nucleophilic substitution is of the π-deficient N-heterocycles. The electrophilic substitution of pyrrole will now be dealt with, then substitution of its benzologues, and finally of its azalogues.

Pyrrole. Pyrrole readily undergoes electrophilic substitution. Sulphonation, halogenation, and the Friedel-Crafts reactions proceed with great vigour; so do a number of reactions given by phenol but not by benzene such as diazo-coupling, and the reactions whereby the aldehyde or carboxylic acid group is introduced.

Ciamician, a pioneer worker in pyrrole chemistry, pointed out analogies between pyrrole and phenol. However laboratory experience indicates that the carbon-atoms of pyrrole (L) are more electron-rich than those of phenol (pyrrole, although combining with the same type of reagents as phenol and aniline, reacts much more vigorously). Electron density calculations suggest that electrons are more evenly distributed on the carbon atoms in pyrrole than in phenol. According to the diagram (L), electron density is higher in the 2- than the 3-position, and this accords with the experimental evidence that substitution favours the 2- (and 5-) positions; when these are blocked, the 3- (and 4-) positions are favoured. Electron-releasing groups (e.g. methyl) increase the velocity of electrophilic substitution, and electron-attracting groups (e.g. $-COOEt$) considerably diminish the velocity. Electrophilic reactions occur on the nitrogen atom provided that this is first converted to the anion, and hence is negatively charged (the anionic pK is believed to be ~ 15). The electron-density on the carbon atoms of pyrrole is so high that no nucleophilic replacements of hydrogen have been demonstrated (sodamide merely gives the sodium salt of pyrrole).

L[1]   LI   LII

Just as nucleophilic reagents displace substituents other than hydrogen in π-deficient substances, electrophilic reagents displace substituents other than hydrogen in these π-excessive substances (see below).

It was formerly thought that substitution was preceded by tautomerism, e.g. to the (unknown) pyrrolenines (III) and (IV). However, the readier substitution of N-alkylpyrroles, which cannot tautomerize, speaks against this (cf. Doak and Corwin, 1949). For further evidence against the pyrrolenine hypothesis see Corwin (1950, p. 291). However, pyrrolenine tautomerism is believed to precede the nitration and nitrosation of pyrrole, which occurs in the 3-position (see below). These two reactions have never been observed in the pyrrole series unless a hydrogen atom can first be borrowed (from $-NH$, or from $-OH$) to make a methylene group.

[1] From Longuet-Higgins and Coulson (1947). These figures are compatible with all those given in this chapter and in Chapter III.

The alkylation of pyrrole can be carried out by leading the vapour, plus that of an alcohol, over heated zinc dust (2:5-diethylpyrrole is made thus), or by leading N-alkylpyrroles through a glowing tube whereby the alkyl-carbonium ion moves to the electron-richer 2-position. The N-alkylpyrroles cannot be formed by direct alkylation but the potassium salt of pyrrole readily reacts with alkyl halides at the temperature of boiling ether giving, e.g. N-methylpyrrole. By heating potassium pyrrole with alkyl iodides, both stages of the synthesis of 2-alkylpyrroles can be combined. The Friedel-Crafts reaction, so much used for making acylpyrroles, is not effective for alkylation.

2:3:4:5-Tetramethylpyrrole, heated with methyl iodide and magnesium oxide in ether, gives 2:2:3:4:5-pentamethyl-pyrrolenine (LI), which is distinctly basic, quite unlike a pyrrole. On further alkylation, this forms a N-methyl-derivative.

Chloroform reacts vigorously with pyrrole at 550° to give 3-chloropyridine in 33% yield (Rice and Londergan, 1955). A C-dichloromethylated pyrrole seems to be an intermediate.

Pyrrole readily reacts with Grignard reagents, giving, at low temperatures, N-derivatives such as (LII). Water regenerates the original pyrrole, but with other reagents some useful reactions can be effected. Alkyl and acyl halides give N-alkyl- and N-acyl-pyrroles in the cold, or 2- (or 2:5-)-substituted alkyl- or acyl-pyrroles at about 150°. Ethyl formate gives the 2-aldehydes, ethyl chloroformate similarly gives 2-carboxylic esters and carbon dioxide forms the carboxylic acid. The two stages of all these reactions are often unified by the early application of heat.

Pyrrole does not N-acetylate directly but requires the action of acid chlorides (or anhydrides) on the potassium salt. Heating N-acetylpyrrole to 250° gives 2-acetylpyrrole, i.e. pyrryl methyl ketone. Here, as usual, the N-potassium and N-halomagnesium derivatives of pyrrole give similar products, but the Grignard reactions are preferred for their higher yields.

Pyrrole ketones can be produced in other ways, the Friedel-Crafts reaction being particularly useful. This reaction goes so vigorously that the aluminium chloride can often be omitted, e.g. pyrrole and acetic anhydride give 2-acetylpyrrole. Ketones are obtainable also by the Houben-Hoesch synthesis, i.e. by heating pyrrole with alkyl cyanides and hydrogen chloride. Pyrrole-2-aldehydes are similarly obtained by the Gattermann-Adams method (HCN + HCl) (Corwin and Andrews, 1936); or by heating a pyrrole with phosphoryl chloride and dimethyl-formamide (Silverstein *et al.*, 1955). The Tiemann-Reimer reaction, in which the pyrrole is heated with chloroform and alkali, gives low yields as by-products are copiously formed (see above).

Pyrrole, treated with carbon tetrachloride and potassium ethoxide, gives pyrrole-2-carboxylic acid. A better yield of the same product is obtained when pyrrole is heated with ammonium carbonate solution at 130°, or potassium carbonate solution at 100°. These are the conditions under which resorcinol is carboxylated, whereas phenol requires 250°. Potassium pyrrole and carbon dioxide at 200° give the isomeric pyrrole-3-carboxylic acid.

Aldehydes react with pyrroles in the 2-position. Formaldehyde apparently gives 2-hydroxymethyl-derivatives, two molecules of which condense at higher temperatures to a dipyrryl-methane (below, p. 177). The much used Ehrlich test for a free 2-position in pyrrole, consists of the development of a red colour with *p*-dimethylaminobenzaldehyde and cold dilute acid. It is thought that the colour is due to the cation (LIII) (Fischer and Orth, 1934). The pine-splinter test for pyrroles (a red colour with a pine-splinter moistened with 10N-hydrochloric acid) is believed to be some type of aldehyde condensation also, but it is given also by carbazole which does not have a free position in the pyrrole ring.

The reactions of pyrrole with halogens are so energetic that they must be carried out at great dilution to prevent destruction. Thus bromine in alcohol gives only the tetrabromo-derivative: when less bromine is used, the same product is obtained, but in decreased yield. The presence of an electron-attracting group (e.g. −COOEt) moderates bromination sufficiently for quantitative yields of monosubstituted products to be obtained.

Studies of the rate of iodination of 3:5-dimethyl-2- (and −4-)

carboethoxypyrrole show that the 2-position is about twenty-five times as easily substituted as the 3-position (Doak and Corwin, 1949). N-methyl-substitution increases the rate in each case.

It has been known since 1905 that the mildest chlorinating agent for pyrrole is sulphuryl chloride (SO_2Cl_2). In ether at 0°, it gives 2-chloropyrrole; further addition of the reagent gives 2:5-dichloro- and 2:3:5-trichloro-pyrrole. The chloro- and bromo-pyrroles are highly unstable to oxygen and light. Potassium pyrrole and iodine give 2:3:3:4:5-tetraiodopyrrole, once used as a not very effective antiseptic under the name 'iodol'.

LIII   LIV

Substitutions using acidic electrophilic reagents, or those which generate acid, are undesirable for pyrroles having adjacent 2- and 3-positions unsubstituted, as polymerization is strongly encouraged (above, p. 147). Thus chlorosulphonic acid has proved suitable for sulphonating trisubstituted pyrroles (Pratesi, 1935), but for pyrrole the neutral pyridine-sulphur trioxide complex must be used, and this gives excellent yield of pyrrole-2-sulphonic acid at 90° (Terentev and Shadkina, 1947).

Pyrrole can be nitrated in the 2-position with nitric acid in acetic anhydride at −10° in 20% yield (Rinkes, 1934). Further nitration gives 2:4-dinitropyrrole. Pyrrole can also be nitrated with ethyl nitrate in the presence of sodium. This gives the sodium salt of pyrrole-3-nitronic acid (LIV), which is converted to 3-nitropyrrole on neutralization. Similarly pyrrole, which is resinified by free nitrous acid, gives 3-nitrosopyrrole with amyl nitrite and sodium ethoxide.

Pyrrole couples readily with diazotized aniline, giving 2-benzeneazo-pyrrole in acidic, and 2:5-*bis*benzeneazopyrrole in neutral or alkaline, media.

Pyrrole chemistry is rich in reactions wherein an electrophilic group displaces a substituent other than hydrogen. Such reactions are not unknown in aromatic chemistry, e.g. bromine displaces the carboxylic-group from *p*-aminobenzoic acid, giving 2:4:6-tribromoaniline. In the pyrrole series, these reactions occur so readily that they are much used in preparative work.

For example, 3-acetyl-2:4-dimethyl-5-carboethoxypyrrole and concentrated nitric acid gives 3-nitro-2:4-dimethyl-5-carboethoxypyrrole. The same reagent converts 2:4-dimethyl-3:5-dicarboethoxypyrrole to 2:4-dinitro-3:5-dicarboethoxypyrrole. Bromine often replaces $-COCH_3$ and $-COOH$ groups (Corwin and Viohl, 1944) and it is said that this reaction accomplishes decarboxylation when all other means fail (Corwin, 1950). Sodium methoxide sometimes replaces a carboethoxy-group in a polyalkylpyrrole by a methyl-group. For displacement of formaldehyde, see p. 177.

LV   LVI

Indole. The electrophilic substitution of indole differs from that of pyrrole in favouring the 3-position; if this is blocked, the 2-position is attacked. The electron-density diagrams (L) and (LV) are in agreement with these long-known facts. The benzene ring of indole is only attacked if positions 2- and 3- are already occupied, and vigorous conditions are required. Indeed, where the electron-density of the pyrrole ring is further increased by a substituent, further attack is made on this ring, rather than on the benzene ring (see next paragraph).

N-Alkylindoles are prepared from sodium indole and an alkyl halide. Indoles are alkylated in the 3-position (and in the

2-position if the 3- is blocked) by heating at 220° with a sodium alkoxide (Oddo and Alberti, 1933; Cornforth and Robinson, 1942). Methyl iodide reacts with indole to give in turn 2-methyl- and 2:3-dimethylindole, but it is difficult to isolate these in quantity as the reaction continues and gives 2:3:3-trimethyl-indolenine (LVI), which then quaternizes to 1:2:3:3-tetra-methylindolenine iodide. Alkyl exchanges between the 2- and 3-positions are common in indolenines at high temperatures, but these are not entirely aromatic substances. 3-Oxo-2:2-dimethylindolenine is produced by the action of methyl iodide on 3-hydroxyindole.

The Grignard reagents are believed to be N-derivatives. 3-Methylindole is obtained upon heating the Grignard reagent with methyl iodide whereas formaldehyde, ethylene oxide, and cyanogen chloride give 3-hydroxymethyl, 3(β-hydroxyethyl)-, and 3-cyano-indole respectively. Ethyl formate gives N-formylindole at −10° and 3-formylindole at 75°. Ethyl acetate gives N-acetyl- and 3-acetyl-indole. Carbon dioxide gives indole 3-carboxylic acid, and sulphur dioxide a mixture of di-indolyl sulphoxide and sulphide.

Indole is best acetylated through the Grignard reaction. N-acetylindole is stable in water for many days, whereas N-acetylbenziminazole has a half-life of only 21 hours, and N-acetylbenzotriazole is readily hydrolysed (Staab, 1957). All these acyl-derivatives are more stable to hydrolysis than their monocyclic analogues (see below under 'iminazole', p. 166).

Indole itself reacts with acetic anhydride to give N-acetyl-indole at 180°, which is easily hydrolysed to indole by alkali. Higher temperatures produce 1:3-diacetylindole which is hydrolysed by boiling water to 3-acetylindole. 3-Methylindole gives 2-acetyl-3-methylindole with acetyl chloride. If both 2- and 3-positions are blocked, acylation favours the 6-position, but the severer conditions of the Friedel-Crafts reaction are required (Borsche and Groth, 1941). The Houben-Hoesch (nitrile) synthesis is also applicable for C-acylindoles.

Indole-3-aldehyde is best made by the action of phosphoryl chloride and N-methylformanilide (or dimethylformamide) on indole (Tyson and Shaw, 1952; Shabica et al., 1946). The Gattermann-Adams (cyanide) synthesis is applicable if the 2-

position is blocked, otherwise polymerization occurs. The Tiemann-Reimer (chloroform) synthesis gives a 30% yield of indole-3-aldehyde, but much 3-chloroquinoline is formed by ring-expansion (Boyd and Robson, 1935). The indole-3-aldehydes give semicarbazones, and similar derivatives. Forty years ago it was suggested that these aldehydes may really be 3-hydroxymethylene-indolenines, but no physico-chemical support has been offered for this hypothesis.

Sodium indole, heated in a stream of carbon dioxide, gives indole-3-carboxylic acid.

Indole, formaldehyde and dimethylamine react to give 3-dimethylaminomethylindole (Kühn and Stein, 1937), which is the alkaloid gramine. Indole gives red Ehrlich and pine-splinter tests (see under pyrrole, p. 157).

Indole condenses readily with aldehydes, the reaction being more controllable if a methyl- or hydroxy-group is in the 2-position. If the proportions are 1:1, benzaldehyde and 2-methylindole give 2-methyl-3-benzylidene-indolenine; when the indole is in excess, substances analogous to triphenylmethanes are produced. 3-Hydroxyindole readily forms benzylidene-derivatives in the 2-position (and in this position also condenses with aromatic nitroso-compounds, and with ketonic acids). Indoles may be chlorinated (to mono-chloro- or 2:3-dichloro-indole) with sulphuryl chloride, brominated with bromine to monobromoindole after prior N-acylation, or iodinated (to mono-iodoindole) by iodine in potassium hydroxide. Whether the position of the mono-halogeno products is 2- or 3- is in dispute, but the 3-position seems most likely. Bromine in carbon tetrachloride acts on oxindole (2-hydroxyindole) to give 3:3-dibromo-2-oxo-indolenine, but in water 5-bromo- (and 5:7:dibromo-)-2-hydroxyindole results, a rather surprising reaction (Sumpter, Miller and Hendrick, 1945).

Benzenediazonium chloride, under mildly acidic conditions, couples with indole in the 3-position.

3-Nitrosoindole is obtained when amyl nitrite and sodium ethoxide act on indole (note that this reaction, and that of nitration, were anomalously orientated in pyrrole). Nitrous acid causes dimerization. If the 3-position is blocked, N-nitroso-indoles are formed, but 3-hydroxyindole gives a 2-nitroso-derivative. It is likely that this reaction proceeds through the indolenine tautomers, as in the pyrrole series. Indole, ethyl nitrate and sodium ethoxide give 3-nitroindole. Nitroindoles are also easily obtained by the oxidation of nitrosoindoles. Nitrations of 2:3-dimethyl- and 2-hydroxy-indole give the 6-nitro- and 5-nitro-derivatives respectively (Plant and Tomlinson, 1933; Sumpter, Miller and Magan, 1945).

Indole sulphonates in the 2-position with the pyridine-sulphur trioxide complex (Terentev and Golubeva, 1946), a more surprising orientation here than in pyrrole.

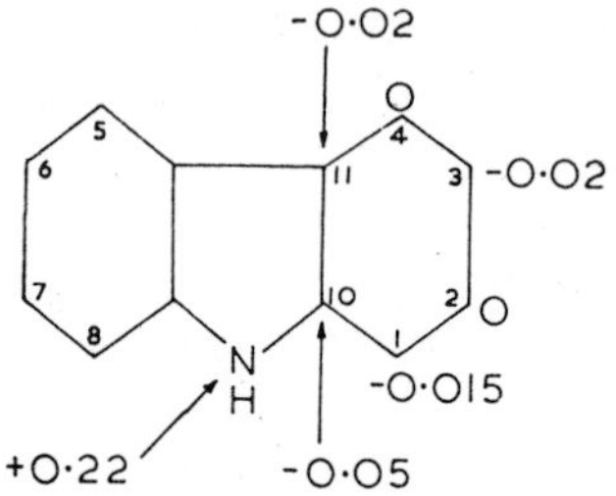

LVII

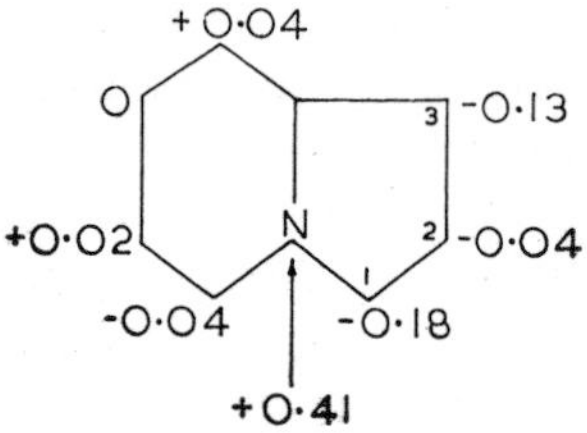

LVIII

Carbazole (VIII) has less avidity for electrophilic substitution than indole or pyrrole, because the electron-rich carbon atoms of the pyrrole ring carry no hydrogen atoms, and only a small fraction of their negative charge is available to the two benzene rings. The electron-density diagram (LVII)[1] is consistent with the experimental facts that carbazole reacts only with electrophilic reagents, that these attack the benzene rings, that they prefer the 3- and 6-positions, followed by the 1- and 8-positions, and that more vigorous conditions are required than in the pyrrole and indole series. Electrophilic reagents also attack the nitrogen of carbazole when this bears a negative charge. Thus potassium carbazole and methyl iodide give N-methylcarbazole. This does not undergo a heat-rearrangement to a C-methylcarbazole (contrast with N-methylpyrrole), but ring-enlargement to phenanthridine takes place.

[1] The electron-density diagrams of pyrrole, indole, carbazole and indolizine used in this chapter are comparable, and are taken from Longuet-Higgins and Coulson (1947).

Carbazole readily N-acylates in the presence of alkali, and the product gives 3-acylcarbazoles on heating. When 9-acetylcarbazole is submitted to a Friedel-Crafts reaction, 2:9-diacetylcarbazole emerges, but carbazole itself gives 3:6-diacetylcarbazole even when the quantity of acyl halide is limited (Plant, Rogers and Williams, 1935). N-methylformanilide and phosphorus oxychloride convert N-methylcarbazole to the 3-aldehyde (Buu-Hoï, 1951), the first aldehyde to be prepared in the carbazole series!

Carbazole, like pyrrole, indole and the *iso*indoles, gives a red pine-splinter test, but does not appear otherwise to react with aldehydes.

Potassium carbazole, or the N-Grignard reagent, gives carbazole-1-carboxylic acid with carbon dioxide at 270°. The 3-isomer is obtained by the action of trichloroacetonitrile and aluminium chloride on carbazole (Dunlop and Tucker, 1939).

Chlorine, bromine and iodine halogenate carbazole in the 3-position; and 3:6-disubstituted carbazoles are formed on further treatment. N-bromosuccinimide has given good yields of 3-bromocarbazole (Schmid and Karrer, 1946).

Carbazole does not couple with diazotized amines, the electron-density on the benzene rings being too low. Hence it would not be expected to C-nitrosate directly. However N-nitrosocarbazole (from carbazole and nitrous acid) rearranges to 3-nitrosocarbazole in acid at 20°.

Nitration of carbazole with concentrated nitric acid gives a mixture of (mainly) 3-nitro- and 3:6-dinitrocarbazole, but nitric acid in acetic acid gives a mixture of 1- and 3-nitrocarbazole (Morgan and Mitchell, 1931). Vigorous nitration yields 1:3:6:8-tetranitrocarbazole. 1-Nitrocarbazole is best prepared by nitrating carbazole-3:6-dicarboxylic acid, or the trisulphonic acid.

Iso*indole* (IX). Very little is yet known about this series. N-methyl*iso*indole turns brown in the air, gives a red pinesplinter test and a blue Ehrlich test (cf. pyrrole, p. 157) (Wittig *et al.*, 1951). An electron-density diagram suggests a somewhat similar distribution of electrons to that of indole, in spite of the non-kekulé appearance of the conventional formula (Longuet-Higgins and Coulson, 1947). The orientation reported for

M

electrophilic substitution in 1-hydroxy*iso*indole (phthalimidine) is so surprising as to deserve further investigation.

Indolizine (X) substitutes (electrophilically) in the 1-position, and if this is blocked, in the 3-position. The electron-density diagram (LVIII) is consistent with this. 2-Methylindolizine and methyl iodide gives first the 1-methyl- (at 20°), and then the 1:3-dimethyl-derivatives (Rossiter and Saxton, 1953). Acetic anhydride similarly gives the 1-acetyl-derivative, and benzenediazonium chloride substitutes in the 1-position. Again, the aldehyde-group is readily introduced in the 1-position by N-methylformanilide and phosphoryl chloride at 10°, and the Tiemann-Reimer reaction with chloroform gives a 50% yield of the 1:3-diformyl-derivative.

The easy alkylation in the 1-position shows that the negative charge on this carbon atom must be exceptionally high, indeed higher than in indole just as the diagram (LVIII) indicates.

Unlike indole, indolizine has no imino-group to form N-acyl-derivatives. But, thanks to the high negative charge on the 1- and 3-carbon atoms, C-formyl- and C-acetyl-groups are easily hydrolysed with boiling 2N-hydrochloric acid, a hydrogen atom taking their place.

Porphyrins, of which porphin (XI) is the parent substance, consist of four pyrrole rings, united by $-CH=$ groups so as to form a sixteen-membered ring with several canonical forms and hence a high degree of stabilization by resonance. As would be expected the reactions are essentially pyrrole-like with the advantage that acidic reagents can be freely used without causing hydrolysis or polymerization. The porphyrins are stable in air, can be N-methylated with methyl iodide (McEwen, 1946) and undergo C-acetylation in a Friedel-Crafts reaction (the iron complexes may be used for this). Nitric acid and bromine substitute the pyrrole rings. Aldehyde groups can be introduced with dichloromethyl ethyl ether (Fischer and Orth, 1934).

Rings with more than one nitrogen atom. The insertion of doubly-bound nitrogen atoms must lessen the accumulation of electrons on the carbon atoms of the pyrrole ring. However, even two such insertions, as in 1:2:3-triazole (XVI), leave the carbon atoms more negatively charged than in benzene, as is shown by the ready bromination to 4:5-dibromo-1:2:3-triazole (Hüttel and Gebhardt, 1947). Finally, three such insertions leave the amino-group of 5-aminotetrazole readily diazotizable, which may imply that tetrazole is less π-deficient than pyridine.

It is regrettable that so little is known of electrophilic substitution in the triazoles and tetrazole. However, their behaviour makes it plain that the mono-azalogues of pyrrole (pyrazole and iminazole) are strongly π-excessive substances, although naturally not so π-excessive as pyrrole. Thus they react with a variety of electrophilic reagents, but require somewhat more vigorous conditions than pyrrole does. The less reactive electrophilic reagents are naturally made more effective if an electron-releasing group is already present or, conversely, are rendered ineffective by an electron-withdrawing group.

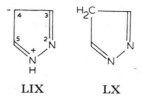

LIX   LX

Rough electron-density diagrams have been worked out for pyrazole, iminazole and both of the triazoles (Orgel *et al.*, 1951). These will not be quoted here as they are not compatible with the diagrams used in this chapter.

Pyrazole. Electrophilic substitution in pyrazole occurs mainly in the 4-position, so that (LIX) may be an important contributor to the resonance hybrid of pyrazole, even in its ground state. Upon heating the silver salt of pyrazole with methyl iodide, the secondary nitrogen atom becomes methylated; at a higher temperature the other nitrogen is quaternized as well. N-acylation is effected with acid chlorides. There is no record of alkyl- or acyl-groups wandering from N to C.

Although the two nitrogen atoms in pyrazole are equivalent, because the hydrogen atom can wander from one to another, they are no longer equivalent when there is a substituent in the 3-position. Different isomers are obtained on methylation of non-symmetrical pyrazoles. The orientation depends more on the nature of the methylating agent than on the substituent (see below under iminazole for a similar phenomenon). Two acyl derivatives are also obtainable in such cases, and one easily isomerizes to the other.

Chlorination with chlorine (in water or carbon tetrachloride) gives 4-chloropyrazole, and bromination 4-bromopyrazole. If bromination is continued in the presence of iron, as catalyst, 3:4-dibromo- and 3:4:5-tribromopyrazole are obtained (Hüttel, Wagner and Jochum, 1955). As in pyridine, the tertiary nitrogen can also form a perbromide under mild conditions.

Thanks to the presence of the doubly-bound nitrogen, the strongest acid reagents can safely be used on pyrazole. Thus the preparation of 4-nitropyrazole requires fuming nitric and fuming sulphuric acids, and the yield is excellent (Hüttel, Büchele and Jochum, 1955). Nitration in acetic anhydride gives N-nitropyrazole, which is changed to 4-nitropyrazole on heating. Sulphonation also occurs in the 4-position.

3-Hydroxypyrazole (known as pyrazolone) has the equivalent of a reactive methylene group in the 4-position, cf. (LX). It condenses there with benzaldehyde, or diazotized aniline; it nitrosates there, and can be alkylated there by heating with sodium alkoxides.

Iminazole (XIV). The two nitrogen atoms of iminazole are equivalent, as the mobility of the hydrogen atom makes the molecule symmetrical. However, if a substituent is inserted in the 4-position, the molecule becomes unsymmetrical. Thus the methylation of 4-methyliminazole gives a mixture of 1:5- and 1:4-dimethyliminazole. When diazomethane or methyl sulphate (alone) is used as the alkylating agent, an electron-attracting group (e.g. NO_2) directs the methyl group to the adjacent nitrogen atom, and hence 1:5-derivatives arise. This reaction is slow, and concerns the neutral molecule. But when methyl sulphate is used with alkali, or when methyl iodide is used on the silver salt, a fast reaction occurs with the anion, and 1:4-derivatives are favoured (Grimison and Ridd, 1956). N-methyliminazole reacts with methyl iodide by quaternization on the other nitrogen atom. These quaternary compounds are unstable to aqueous alkali, complete fission of the ring taking place.

N-acylation of iminazoles is difficult to accomplish, because quaternization leads to a similar decomposition: e.g. 1:2-dibenzoylaminoethylene results from the action of equimolecular quantities of benzoyl chloride and iminazole in sodium hydroxide solution at 0°. However, N-benzoyliminazole can be obtained, provided anhydrous conditions are observed and an excess of iminazole is used instead of the inorganic base. N-acetyliminazole, similarly obtained, is a powerful acetylating agent, easily hydrolysed by water (Staab, 1956), and N-acetyltetrazole is yet more vigorous.

Both 2- and 4-positions in iminazole are subject to electrophilic substitution. N-methyliminazole rearranges to 2-methyliminazole in a red-hot tube. Iminazole-N-magnesium iodide gives 1:2-dimethyliminazole with methyl iodide. Very little use has been made of Grignard reagents in iminazole chemistry. Iminazoles do not undergo the Friedel-Crafts reaction with acid chlorides, a sign of the decreased electron-availability on carbon, as compared with pyrrole.

All other methods for the direct introduction of the aldehyde or ketone group have so far failed. However, the insertion of a hydroxy-group in the 2-position increases the electron availability, and the Friedel-Crafts (C-acylation) reaction then goes readily.

Formaldehyde reacts with iminazole, but no single product has been obtained. However 4-alkyliminazoles give 4-alkyl-5-hydroxymethyliminazoles, whereas 1-alkyliminazoles give the 2-hydroxymethyl-derivatives. Electron-attracting groups hinder these (and other) electrophilic reactions in the iminazole series.

The halogenation of iminazole is very brisk. Even when only one equivalent of bromine is used, 2:4:5-tribromoiminazole is the sole product (at −20°, a little 4:5-dibromoiminazole is detectable). The chlorination of iminazole has been little investigated. Iodination in alkali forms 2-iodo-, 2:4-diiodo- and (principally) 2:4:5-triiodo-iminazole. Iodination of iminazole-4-carboxylic acid gives the same triiodo-iminazole.

Diazotized amines couple with iminazole in the 2-position, in alkaline solution giving orange, red or blue azo-derivatives (the Pauly reaction). If the 2-position is blocked, the azo-group enters the 4-position. Nitroiminazoles do not react because the electron density on carbon is too low. Kinetic studies show that diazo-coupling is a second-order reaction between the iminazole *anion* and the diazonium cation (Brown, Duffin, Maynard and Ridd, 1953).

Nitration so strongly favours the 4-position that nitration does not occur in the 2-position of 4:5-dimethyliminazole. Dinitration is unknown. Iminazole does not react with nitrous acid which always requires a high negative charge on carbon. Sulphonation is also a reaction needing high electron density, and the sulphonation of iminazole requires 50 % oleum at 160°.

Benziminazole (XVIII). Alkylation of benziminazole replaces a hydrogen atom from one nitrogen; under severer conditions, the other nitrogen atom is quaternized. The resultant 1:3-dialkylbenzimidazolium salt is decomposed by alkali to a N:N′dialkyl-*o*-phenylene diamine, and this is the standard method for preparing these substances.

The action of benzoyl chloride on benziminazole in the presence of alkali at 0° produces N:N′-dibenzoyl-*o*-phenylene-diamine, and three intermediate stages have been characterized (Gerngross, 1913). However this chain of reactions can be stopped at N-benzoylbenziminazole by using excess benziminazole in benzene.

Halogenation in this series has been little investigated. 2-Methylbenziminazole gives 2-methyl-4-bromo- (and, on further bromination, 2-methyl-4:6-dibromo-) benziminazole. 2-Aminobenziminazole chlorinates in the 5-position, and benziminazole (as anion) appears to iodinate in the 2-position.

Benziminazole does not couple with diazotized amines, a sign that all negative charges on the carbon atoms are feeble. The insertion of amino- or hydroxy-groups in the benzene ring should rectify this (see purine, below).

Nitration of benziminazole occurs in the 5-position (van der Want, 1948). 2-Hydroxybenziminazole nitrates first in the 5-, then in the 5:6-positions. Sulphonation occurs in the 5-position (Efros, 1953).

Indazole (XIX) is alkylated by alkyl iodides in the 2-position, but in the 1-position if sodium methoxide is present. It acylates on $N_{(2)}$ where electron density is higher than on $N_{(1)}$, but the product is orthoquinonoid and rearranges to the $N_{(1)}$ isomer which has a kekulé-type benzene ring (Angyal, 1952).

Indazole couples in the 3-position with diazotized amines and the product may be reduced to 3-aminoindazole. Indazole on bromination gives 3-bromo- and 3:5-dibromo-derivatives whereas acetylindazole gives 5-halogenated derivatives. Nitration of indazole takes place in the 5-position. Sulphuric acid does not affect indazole at 250°, but oleum produces indazole-5-sulphonic acid.

Purine (XX), which is essentially an iminazole ring attached to a pyrimidine ring, might be expected to substitute electrophilically on nitrogen in the 7- or 9-position. It is also possible that it may substitute on carbon in the 8-position, although the equivalent 2-position in benziminazole is not very active, and the pyrimidine ring in purine makes a greater drain on the iminazole electrons than the benzene ring does in benziminazole. As it happens, purine has been methylated in the 9-position (Bredereck, Ulmer and Waldmann, 1956), but the few examples of electrophilic substitution that have been reported show that an amino- or hydroxy-group must be present in either the 2- or the 6-position for coupling to occur with diazotized aniline in the 8-position. Guanine (2-amino-6-hydroxypurine) is easily brominated in the 8-position, and so are several N-methylated derivatives of xanthine (2:6-dihydroxypurine), but little is known about the halogenation of simple purines.

(g) Substitution by Nucleophilic Reagents

No example of the substitution of hydrogen (on carbon or nitrogen) by a nucleophilic reagent appears to have been recorded for the π-excessive N-heterocycles. Thus sodamide in liquid ammonia forms only sodium salts with pyrrole, iminazole, benziminazole.

Nucleophilic exchange is uncommon in the pyrrole-indole-carbazole series. One of the few examples is the conversion of tetrachloropyrrole to tetraiodopyrrole by potassium iodide in alcohol.

Nucleophilic exchange should be assisted by the presence of doubly-bound nitrogen in the ring. Yet the halogens in 2- or 4-halogenated iminazoles are not displaceable by the usual nucleophilic reagents[1] (however, aqueous sodium sulphite

[1] See p. 73 for available reactions in π-deficient series.

produces sulphonic acids). The insertion of a nitro-group activates halogenated iminazoles. The benzene ring in 2-chlorobenziminazole activates the halogen, but 3-bromoindazole and 3-chloro-1:2:4-triazole are quite unreactive.

Nucleophilic exchange has been much practised in the pyrimidine ring of purine (XX), where it may be regarded as an extension of pyrimidine chemistry. Thus the chlorine in 6-chloropurine may be replaced by primary or secondary amines (Elion, Burgi and Hitchings, 1951; Daly and Christensen, 1956; Robins, Jones and Lin, 1956). The chlorine in the 6-position of 2:6:8-trichloropurine is the first to be replaced by ammonia.

6-Chloropurines are converted to 6-mercaptopurines by thiourea (Bendich, Russell and Fox, 1954), or sodium hydrogen sulphide (Elion, Burgi and Hitchings, 1951), and to 6-iodopurines by hydriodic acid (Elion and Hitchings, 1956). The hydrolysis of 6-chloropurine to 6-hydroxypurine is accomplished in 1 to 4 hours at 100° by 0·1 N-sodium hydroxide or hydrochloric acid (Bendich, Russell and Fox, 1954). 2:6:8-Trichloropurine is hydrolysed first in the 8-position by acids, but in the 6-position by alkalis. Cuprous cyanide converts 6-iodo- to 6-cyanopurine (Mackay and Hitchings, 1956).

A methylmercapto-group in the 2-, 6-, or 8-position of purine is readily replaceable by ammonia, or dimethylamine (Albert and Brown, 1954; Elion, Burgi and Hitchings, 1952). This reaction is most reluctant in the 8-position, but is facilitated if oxidation to a methylsulphonyl-group ($-SO_2CH_3$) is first performed with chlorine (Brown and Mason, 1957).

Replacement of hydroxyl by chlorine. Few examples are known in this series. 4-Hydroxypyrazole gives 4-chloropyrazole with phosphoryl chloride, and 2-hydroxybenziminazole reacts similarly. Phosphorus pentachloride converts both 2:3-dihydroxyindole and 2-hydroxyindole to 2:3-dichloroindole. The preparation of 6-chloro- and 2:6-dichloro-purine (and their bromine analogues) from the corresponding hydroxypurines has been described (Bendich, Russell and Fox, 1954; Elion and Hitchings, 1956). One instance of activation of phosphoryl chloride by prior partial reaction with water is given in the last-named reference.

6-Hydroxypurines are converted to 6-mercaptopurines by phosphorus pentasulphide in pyridine (Elion, Burgi and Hitchings, 1952). 2:6-Dihydroxypurine gives 2-hydroxy-6-mercaptopurine (Beaman, 1954). These mercaptopurines are easily alkylated on sulphur with methyl iodide in cold sodium hydroxide (Elion, Burgi and Hitchings, 1952; Albert and Brown, 1954).

Diazotization. The diazotization of amino-groups in *π-deficient* N-heterocycles occurs readily only when they are not α- or γ- to a ring-nitrogen atom. But almost all of the amino-derivatives of *π-excessive* N-heterocycles diazotize readily in dilute acid (2-aminoiminazole is one of the rare non-diazotizers). In purine, an amino-group in the 8-position (iminazole ring) readily diazotizes and couples, whereas no amino-group in the 2- or 6-position (pyrimidine ring) has been diazotized so far.

The conversion of an amino- to a chloro-substituent with nitrous acid has been carried out on 5-aminotetrazole, and in the 3:7-diazaindole series (Kögl, van der Want and Salemink, 1948), but seems to have been little used elsewhere. Diazotized 5-aminotetrazole gives 5-hydroxytetrazole with cupric hydroxide. Nitrous acid converts 2-aminobenziminazole to the 2-hydroxy-analogue. The 2- and 6-amino-group in a purine is hydrolysed to the hydroxy-group by refluxing with 8N-hydrochloric acid. These amino-groups can also be hydrolysed with nitrous acid, thus 2-aminopurine gives 2-hydroxypurine (Albert and Brown, 1954), but 2:6-diaminopurine gives 6-amino-2-hydroxypurine, although 6-amino-purine gives 6-hydroxypurine in good yield.

(h) Addition Reactions

Because the π-excessive N-heterocycles are truly aromatic, they have practically no tendency to combine with maleic anhydride in the Diels-Alder reaction (the π-deficient N-heterocycles are also unreactive, and for the same reason). Thus pyrrole is merely substituted, giving pyrrole-2-succinic acid (Diels and Alder, 1931). Indole behaves similarly, but in the 3-position. N-methyl*iso*indole reacts with maleic anhydride, but in a manner not known (Wittig *et al.*, 1951).

Some polysubstituted pyrroles combine *covalently* with water which they can take up from the air, and are regenerated when the product is vacuum distilled, even at 60°. For example, 1-methyl-2-hydroxy-5-phenylpyrrole is believed to give (reversibly) 1-methyl-2:5-dihydroxy-5-phenyl-4:5-dihydropyrrole (Lukeš and Prelog, 1926). This phenomenon may have something in common with the well-known ethylenic character of the 4:5-double-bond in 4:5-diphenyliminazole, where the benzene rings appear to set up a cross-resonance which decreases the aromatic nature of the iminazole nucleus. Thus 2-hydroxy-4:5-diphenyliminazole and bromine give 4:5-dibromo-4:5-diphenyliminazolidone (iminazolidone is 4:5-dihydro-2-hydroxyiminazole, or ethylene-urea, see Chapter II).

Purines add two hydroxyl-groups across the 4:5-bond (i.e. the bond shared by both rings) when treated with sodium hypochlorite and thus give glycols.

Indole forms a complex with sodium hydrogen sulphite, which is reconverted to indole by alkali. This phenomenon may be more widespread than has been recorded.

The quaternization of the doubly-bound nitrogen atom in iminazole, pyrazole, benziminazole, indazole, etc., has been dealt with in (f) above.

(i) Oxidations and Reductions

Oxidations. The π-excessive N-heterocycles oxidize readily in the air unless they contain an electron-attracting substituent, such as $-NO_2$, or a doubly-bound nitrogen in the ring, as in iminazole. This is in keeping with Fieser's general rule that the presence of a high negative charge on a carbon atom is conducive to oxidation (Fieser and Fieser, 1935).

Pyrrole turns yellow, then brown in contact with air, and finally forms a black resin. This reaction is accelerated by light, and 2:5-dihydroxypyrrole (succinimide) is one of the products. In addition, a substance of unknown constitution, called Pyrrole Black, is produced as in other oxidations of pyrrole, e.g. with hydrogen peroxide or benzoquinone. Pyrrole Black is oxidized by chromic acid to maleimide, which is also formed directly from pyrrole and chromic acid. Similarly pyrrole and sodium hypochlorite give dichloromaleimide.

Indole is changed by air and light to 3-hydroxyindole (which oxidizes further to indigo (LXI)), di-3-indolyl ether, and an oxygen-containing trimer. Similarly indole and iodine give indigo, as well as 3-iodoindole. 3-Methylindole and peracetic acid give 2-hydroxy-3-methylindole. 1-Hydroxy*iso*indole (phthalimidine) is oxidized by permanganic acid to phthalimide. Carbazole is oxidized by permanganate to 9:9′-dicarbazyl and some C — C linked isomers.

Thus the general pattern of oxidation of π-excessive substances is substitution by oxygen, or oxidative dimerization. The formation of indigo embodies both these processes.

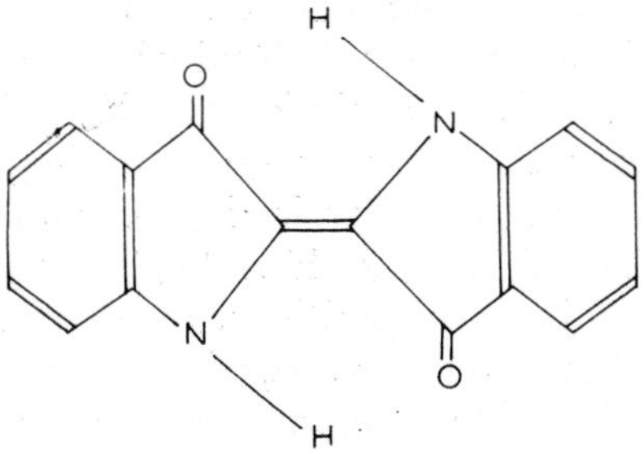

Indigo
LXI

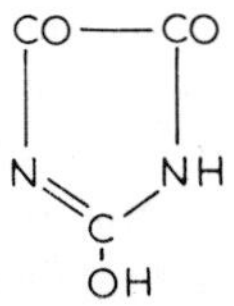

Parabanic acid
LXII

Pyrazole, iminazole, the triazoles, and tetrazole are very stable to oxidation, as would be expected. However, the insertion of electron-releasing groups resensitizes them: thus 2-hydroxyiminazole and chromium trioxide give parabanic acid (LXII). '3-Alkyl-2-pyrazolones' absorb oxygen and give 3-hydroxy-derivatives quantitatively (Veibel and Linholt, 1955).

Drastic permanganate oxidation of benziminazole ruptures the benzene ring, giving iminazole-4:5-dicarboxylic acid.

Reduction. An analytical review of the nature of reductive processes of various kinds was given on p. 90, and will not be repeated here.

Hydrogenations will first be dealt with. Pyrrole gives 2:5-dihydropyrrole (Δ³-pyrroline) with zinc and acid, whereas hydrogen (over platinum) in cold acetic acid reduces pyrrole directly to the tetrahydro-compound. The presence of an N-alkyl-group facilitates these reactions. Indole gives 2:3-dihydroindole (indoline) with zinc, with hydrogen over platinum (or Raney-nickel) at room temperature; or over copper chromite at 180° (250 atmospheres; 80% yield). Hydrogen over nickel at 250° gives octahydroindole, also in 80% yield (Adkins and Coonradt, 1941). Similarly, N-methyl*iso*indole is converted to the dihydro-derivative by cold hydrogenation over Raney-nickel (Wittig *et al.*, 1951).

Carbazole is reduced to 1:2:3:4-tetrahydrocarbazole with sodium in alcohol. Further reduction, with tin and hydrochloric acid, or with hydriodic acid and phosphorus, adds two more hydrogens in the 10:11-positions, so that one benzene ring is completely saturated. Carbazole, hydrogenated at 230° with Raney-nickel or copper chromite, gives dodecahydrocarbazole (Adkins and Coonradt, 1941). N-methylcarbazole, reduced with hydrogen over nickel at 210°, gives octahydro-N-methylcarbazole, both double-bonds of the pyrrole ring remaining.

Porphins are reduced to dihydroporphins ('chlorins'), the hydrogens adding to two adjacent 3-positions. Further reduction gives hexahydroporphins (Whalley, 1955). Porphins are reductively split by hydriodic acid to a mixture of four pyrroles, the methine bridges becoming 2-methyl-groups (an example of hydrogenolysis).

Pyrazole, indazole and iminazole are resistant to reduction. 2-Hydroxyiminazole readily adds a molecule of hydrogen. Benziminazoles add two molecules of hydrogen to the benzene ring upon catalytic hydrogenation, but lithium aluminium hydride gives the 1:2-dihydro-derivative (Bohlmann, 1952). There appears to be no work on reduction of the triazoles, or of tetrazole.

A preliminary investigation of the reduction of purine has been made (Bendich, Russell and Fox, 1954). Substituted purines have been submitted to electrolytic reduction whereupon they add a molecule of hydrogen. Hypoxanthine (6-hydroxypurine) undergoes hydrogenolysis with zinc and N-sulphuric acid at 100°, giving 4-aminoiminazole-5-carboxamide (Friedman and Gots, 1952).

Inverse substitutions will now be dealt with. These are reductions in so far as hydrogen is acquired by the carbon skeleton, although there is no loss of double-bonds.

In pyrroles, a 2- or 3-C-acetyl-group can be replaced by

hydrogen by heating at 100° with 25% sulphuric acid. To avoid polymerization, one member of each pair of adjacent 2- and 3-positions must carry a permanent substituent (see (d) above, p. 148). It is because the carbon atoms of pyrrole carry high negative charges that these C-acyl hydrolyses are as facile as the N-acyl hydrolysis of an amide.

All halogens are easily removed from halogenated pyrroles by catalytic hydrogenation. Also tetraiodopyrrole gives pyrrole with zinc and alkali. The halogens in halogenated iminazoles are replaced by hydrogen upon heating with sodium sulphite (sulphonic acids are intermediates).

3-Hydroxyindole gives indole with sodium amalgam or zinc dust and alkali. 2-Hydroxyindole gives 2:3-dihydroindole on catalytic hydrogenation. Lithium aluminium hydride converts 2-hydroxy-N-methylindole to N-methylindole. 4-Hydroxy-pyrazoles give pyrazoles with phosphorus tribromide, phosphorus pentasulphide, or upon distillation over zinc. 1-Phenyl-3-hydroxy-1:2:4-triazole and phosphorus pentasulphide give 1-phenyl-1:2:4-triazole (this method also converts 2-hydroxy-indoles to indoles (Plieninger and Werst, 1958)).

Mercapto-groups have often been replaced by hydrogen in the iminazole series using such diverse reagents as ferric chloride, hydrogen peroxide, or nitric acid: a sulphinic acid is known to be an intermediate (Hofmann, 1953). Raney-nickel (without external hydrogen) and alkali effectively remove mercapto-groups from purines (Beaman, 1954; Bendich, Russell and Fox, 1954), also methylmercapto-groups (Baker, Joseph and Schaub, 1954). This method has also been used for 2:4-dimercaptoiminazoles (thiohydantoins) (Cook, Downer and Heilbron, 1948).

As in Chapter IV, decarboxylation is treated as an inverse substitution. It usually occurs, in the carboxylic acids of π-excessive N-heterocycles, at various temperatures between 120° and 300°. A few acids are even more readily decarboxylated, e.g. purine-8-carboxylic acid upon warming with water (Albert, unpublished) and tetrazole-5-carboxylic acid upon acidifying a solution of its salts. In general electron-attracting groups, even a second carboxyl-group, make decarboxylation more difficult.

Amino-groups have been removed from 5-aminotetrazole and 3-amino-1:2:4-triazole by diazotization in the presence of hypophosphorus acid (Henry and Finnegan, 1954).

The reduction of nitro-, nitroso- and azo-groups proceeds just as easily with π-excessive N-heterocycles as in the aromatic series.

(j) Homolytic, or Free-radical Reactions

Very few free-radical reactions have been discovered for π-excessive substances, so far. In pyrrole, localization energies and free valences both predict preferential attack in the 2- and 5-positions (Dr. R. D. Brown, personal communication). This agrees with an experimental result in which pyrrole reacted vigorously with the free radical, triphenylmethyl, giving 2:5-*bis*triphenylmethyl-2:5-dihydropyrrole (Conant and Chow, 1933).

(k) Side-chain Reactions

Oxidations. Methyl-groups have been oxidized to aldehydo-groups with lead tetracetate in the pyrrole series. 2-Alkyl-pyrroles and indoles are oxidized to 2-carboxylic acids on fusion with alkali. 3-Acetylcarbazole, fused with potassium hydroxide, gives the 3-carboxylic acid, otherwise difficult to obtain (Plant and Williams, 1934). Porphyrins (e.g. haemin) give pyrrole polycarboxylic acids on cold permanganate oxidation, and this has been helpful in determining their structure. Pyrryl methyl ketones are similarly oxidized to pyrrole carboxylic acids.

4-Hydroxymethyliminazole and hot concentrated nitric acid give iminazole-4-aldehyde. The π-excessive aldehydes, even pyrrole-2-aldehyde, are stable to aerial oxidation.

Reductions. Lithium aluminium hydride converts 3-formyl-indole or -indolizine to the 3-methyl derivative (Rossiter and Saxton, 1953), 2-carboethoxyindole to 2-hydroxymethylindole (Taylor, 1950), and indole-3-acetic acid to 3-hydroxyethyl-indole (Snyder and Pilgrim, 1948).

Aldehyde and ketone groups in the pyrrole series are readily converted to alkyl groups with the same number of carbon atoms by hydrazine in sodium ethoxide at about 150° (the Wolff-Kishner reaction). Decarboxylation has been treated on p. 175.

Other reactions involving carbon. Preferential hydrolysis of pyrrole 2:3- or 2:4-di-esters occurs in the 2-position with alkali, and in the 3-position with concentrated sulphuric acid. This discrimination is much used in preparative work. For the most part the acids, esters and amides of π-excessive N-heterocycles behave like their aromatic analogues, but some amides do not undergo the Hofmann degradation (notably iminazole-4-carboxyamide).

The electronic distribution in π-excessive N-heterocycles is not conducive to activation of methyl-groups. Even in the iminazole series, the 4-methyl-group reacts with aldehydes only if a nitro-group is in the 5-position, but not even under these circumstances will a 2-methyl-group react. However 2-methyl-benziminazole, where the benzene ring drains off some of the surplus negative charge, reacts with aldehydes, giving 2-styrylbenziminazole. However indolenines, e.g. (LVI), when quaternized, condense with ethyl orthoformate to give astraphloxines, cynanines which are both textile dyes and photographic sensitizers (see p. 98).

Two molecules of a 2-hydroxymethylpyrrole condense by evolving one molecule of formaldehyde, giving a 2:2′-dipyrrylmethane, which is readily oxidized to a dipyrrylmethene, e.g. (LXIII).

LXIII   LXIV

Similarly, a 2-bromomethylpyrrole condenses with a 2-bromopyrrole to give a dipyrrylmethene directly; and a 2-aldehydopyrrole can form the same product from a pyrrole unsubstituted in the 2-position. The presence of N-methyl-groups in both components is no barrier to this reaction (Brunings and Corwin, 1942), thus refuting an earlier hypothesis that pyrrolenine tautomers are involved.

An interesting and useful nucleophilic reactivity is shown by gramine (3-dimethylaminomethylindole (LXIV)) and its methiodide. These react with hydrogen cyanide to give 3-indolylacetonitrile (i.e. $-N(CH_3)_2$ is exchanged for $-CN$). Many substances with active methylene groups (e.g. diethyl malonate) react similarly with gramine (e.g. Hausch and Godfrey, 1951).

Chlorination of methyl-groups in the most π-deficient of the N-heterocycles often occurs only after some chlorines have been introduced into the nucleus, notably in the pyrrole series.

3. MONOGRAPHS

The following are summaries of occurrence, uses, and syntheses, to supplement the discussion of properties in Section 2 of this chapter.

A. Systems with One Ring-Nitrogen Atom

Pyrrole (I) is a colourless liquid, b.p. 131°, with a pleasant odour resembling chloroform. It is present in coal-tar, bone oil and shale oil, but is usually made synthetically, by heating ammonium saccharate or mucate (McElvain and Bolliger, 1941).

Apart from the porphins and their precursors (see below), the bacterial pigment prodigiosin, and the antibiotic netropsin (Waller *et al.*, 1957), few pyrroles occur naturally, but pyrrole-2-carboxylic acid is formed (from amino-carbohydrate precursors) during the alkaline hydrolysis of various mucoproteins (Gottschalk, 1955). No industrial use for pyrroles has yet been found.

The most self-evident synthesis of pyrrole, from enolized succinic dialdehyde (LXV) and ammonia, has been referred to in Section 2 (*d*) (p. 149), when discussing the reversal of this reaction. The common laboratory synthesis of pyrrole, by heating ammonium mucate, is a parallel reaction, and so is the formation of pyrrole by heating acetylene, formaldehyde and ammonia (Reppe, 1941), a reaction which proceeds through 2-butyne-1:4-diol (LXVI) and is adaptable to the synthesis of many other pyrroles. The Paal-Knorr synthesis of 1:2:5-trimethylpyrrole from methylamine and acetonylacetone is similar.

The most generally useful pyrrole synthesis, known simply as the Knorr synthesis, is shown in (LXVII). It consists of the alkaline condensation of a ketone (or β-diketone or β-keto ester) with an α-aminoketone. When R_1 in (LXVII) is alkyl or aryl, the yields are low (but this reaction can nevertheless be the most useful approach to the product!). When R_1 is a ketonic or ester group, the yields are very good (R_2 can be varied greatly without detriment to the yields). Thus ethyl acetoacetate and ethyl α-aminoacetoacetate give an excellent yield of 2:4-dimethyl-3:5-dicarboethoxypyrrole. During the Knorr reaction, the self-condensation of α-aminoketones produces pyrazines as by-products. Unsymmetrical β-diketones can give one of two products, depending on the pH.

LXV   LXVI   LXVII

LXVIII

In a new pyrrole synthesis, diethyl hydroxyiminomalonate (LXVIII) is reductively condensed with acetylacetone to 3:5-dimethyl-2-carboethoxypyrrole in good yield. The isomeric 2-methyl-3-oxobutyraldehyde gives the 3:4-dimethyl isomer (Kleinspehn, 1955). If the malonate is replaced by ethyl hydroxyiminocyanoacetate, the nitrile is formed instead of the ester.

The Hantzsch synthesis of pyrroles uses a chloroketone (or chloroaldehyde), a β-ketoester and an amine. Thus chloroacetaldehyde, ethyl acetoacetate and ammonia give 2-methyl-3-carboethoxypyrrole. Furans are by-products (and sometimes major products) of the Hantzsch synthesis.

Furans have been converted to pyrroles by ammonia over alumina at 450° (Bordner, 1952), and succinimide has been reduced to pyrrole in a number of ways, but these reactions appear not yet to have achieved practical importance.

Dipyrrylmethenes, e.g. (LXIII), are important as intermediates in the synthesis of porphyrins. Three methods for producing them have already been given as examples of side-chain reactions, in Section 2 (k) (p. 177). It is also possible to condense two molecules of a pyrrole having a free 2-position. They are usually orange substances

N

with red or blue salts. When both nitrogen atoms are methylated, or where considerable steric hindrance results from substituents, the action of bases on the salts is to introduce a hydroxy- or methoxy-group on the bridging carbon atom. Many dipyrrylmethenes are volatile in steam.

The connexion between constitution and colour has been reviewed (Brooker *et al.*, 1947). Two molecules of dipyrrylmethenes strongly bind one atom of divalent metals to give crystalline blue, green or violet complexes: these lack the highly resolved spectra of their porphyrin analogues. The bile pigments consist of four pyrrole rings joined by three bridges, each a single carbon atom. The bridges are either all methene in type (the pigments are then green or blue) or, more commonly, mixed methane and methene in type (the pigments are then red or yellow). They are formed in nature by the breakdown of porphyrins.

For further reading on pyrroles, see Fischer and Orth (1934–40), and Corwin (1950).

Porphyrins are derivatives of porphin (XI), a system in which four pyrrole rings are linked by four —CH= groups to give a sixteen-membered ring. The porphyrins are essential for three biological functions, (i) oxygen storage and transport, as in haemo-globin, (ii) cellular respiration, as in the cytochromes, peroxidases and catalases, and (iii) photosynthesis, as in the chlorophylls. The terminal role of the cytochromes in dehydrogenation is indicated in Figure 2 (p. 92). All these biologically active substances consist of three parts: the porphyrin, the metal, and the specific protein.

The porphyrins carry side-chains at the eight β-positions of the four pyrrole rings, for example protoporphyrin has four methyl, two vinyl and two propionic acid side-chains. This porphyrin is the prosthetic group of the haemoglobins and myoglobins, and of the following enzymes: the cytochrome *b* family, the catalases and horseradish peroxidase. These various combinations of proto-porphyrin owe their specificity to the different proteins with which they are combined. They all contain iron. Other porphyrins with a C-formyl side-chain are found in cytochrome *a*, and cytochrome oxidase, whereas that present in cytochrome *c* has a hydroxyethyl group.

The porphyrin iron complexes are called haems, and the hydro-porphyrin magnesium complexes are the chlorophylls (the hydro-porphyrins are called chlorins). Haematin is the haem of proto-porphyrin. The metal complexes are formed by the loss of two hydrogens from the nitrogen atoms which combine instead with the metal. Subsidiary links are formed by the remaining two nitrogen atoms, and the four links are hybridized, so that a strongly resonant structure results. This leaves (ferrous) iron still with two free covalencies, which are used in haemoglobin to combine with protein and with oxygen. Thus the iron in oxyhaemoglobin is still ferrous, and the ferric analogue (methaemoglobin) is a pathological (but harmless) product in the blood. On the other hand, the iron in cytochromes, catalases and peroxidases undergoes a valence change as each of these substances runs through its cycle of reaction. It is to histidine in the protein of haemoglobin that the iron of protoporphyrin is attached. Even the (protein-free) adduct of iminazole and ferro-protoporphyrin combines reversibly with oxygen (Corwin and Reyes, 1956).

The iron in the haems is so strongly bound that it does not exchange with radioactive inorganic iron, but is nevertheless expelled by 10N-hydrochloric acid.

The most useful synthesis of porphyrins is a simple extension of the most used dipyrrylmethene synthesis: if one free 2-position in a dipyrrylmethene is substituted by bromomethyl, and the other 2-position (i.e. in the other ring) by bromine, two such molecules can be condensed by heating with acid to give a porphyrin.

The chemistry of porphyrins, handicapped by poor solubility and lack of melting-points, has received great help from the visible spectra, which have a degree of resolution unusual for organic substances. Porphyrin specialists have worked out correlations between structure and spectra which have diagnostic value (Stern and Molvig, 1936; Lemberg and Falk, 1951). Esterification of carboxylic acid groups improves solubility and melting-point characteristics somewhat and so has contributed towards establishing criteria for identity and for purity in this series. Nevertheless such criteria are not always so clear-cut as in most other branches of heterocyclic chemistry. Recent modifications of chromatography have made it applicable to porphyrins; infrared spectra are also useful (Falk and Willis, 1951).

Several syntheses of porphin (XI) the parent substance have been announced, the most recent being the dehydrogenation of chlorin (dihydroporphin) with various quinones (Eisner and Linstead, 1955). The chlorin was prepared by heating 2-dimethylamino-methylpyrrole with ethyl magnesium bromide and subjecting the product to counter-current distribution followed by partition chromatography. The porphin, obtained in this way as deep reddish-brown plates (from benzene), appears to be identical with that of earlier workers. Yet the spectrum is seemingly incompatible with the structural-spectral correlations established by porphyrin spectroscopists. This difficulty may be solved by the hypothesis that porphyrins may exist in two tautomeric forms, i.e. with the mobile hydrogens placed *cis* or *trans* to one another in the sixteen-membered ring (Corwin, 1943), or it may turn out that the above correlations are over-simplified.

The biosynthesis of porphyrins follows this course: glycine → α-amino-β-ketoadipic acid → δ-aminolaevulinic acid (Shemin and Russell, 1953; Neuberger and Scott, 1953). Two molecules of this acid condense to porphobilinogen (LXIX) (Dresel and Falk, 1953). Porphobilinogen (Cookson and Rimington, 1953), which may be regarded as a Mannich base, then self-condenses to porphyrins, but the mechanism is imperfectly known.

Porphobilinogen
LXIX

Cyanocobalamin (Vitamin B_{12}), the red antianaemic principle, contains a fifteen-membered porphyrin-like ring lacking one of the $-CH=$ bridges. The centre of the ring is occupied by tervalent cobalt so tightly bound that it does not exchange with inorganic cobalt. A cyanide radical is attached to this cobalt atom. The macrocyclic ring bears several acidic groups, one of which forms an amide with propanolamine, the oxygen atom of which is esterified with phosphoric acid, which is in turn connected to ribose. This ribose is attached to a nitrogen atom of 5:6-dimethylbenziminazole (Hodgkin, Johnson and Todd, 1955; Hodgkin *et al.*, 1956). X-ray crystallography played an important part in elucidating this structure.

For further reading on porphyrins, see Lemberg and Legge (1949), Lemberg (1955), Rimington (1955, 1956).

Indole (VII) is a colourless solid, m.p. 52°, b.p. 253°, with a pleasant narcissus-like odour when dilute. It is discoloured by light, and readily oxidizes in air to indoxyl which has a faecal odour. Indole is present in jasmine flowers (2·5% of the oil), in coal-tar, in human sweat and faeces. Scatole (3-methylindole), m.p. 95°, has an unpleasant odour resembling α-naphthylamine and occurs in human faeces. Indole, which is used in compounding perfumes and for the manufacture of tryptophane and indoleacetic acid, is now in regular commercial production.

Tryptophane, or β-(3-indolyl)alanine (LXX, R = −CH₂CH (NH₂)COOH), is one of the two dozen amino-acids of which proteins are constituted. Proteins deficient in tryptophane have little nutritive value. Of all the amino-acids, it is the most easily destroyed during acid hydrolysis. The higher plants degrade tryptophane to indole-3-acetic acid (LXX, R = −CH₂·COOH), also known as heteroauxin, which is an important growth hormone for them. Bacteria degrade tryptophane to tryptamine (LXX, R = −CH₂CH₂NH₂) and, in some cases, beyond this to indole-3-acetic acid and indole. Mammals, on the other hand, convert tryptophane to 3-hydroxyanthranilic acid and thence to nicotinic acid (cf. Fruton and Simmonds, 1953).

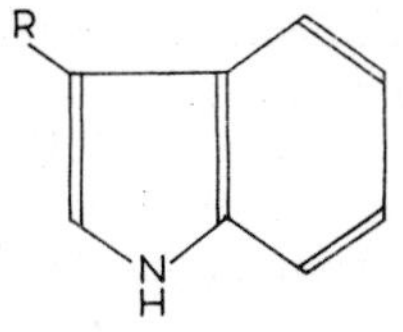

LXX 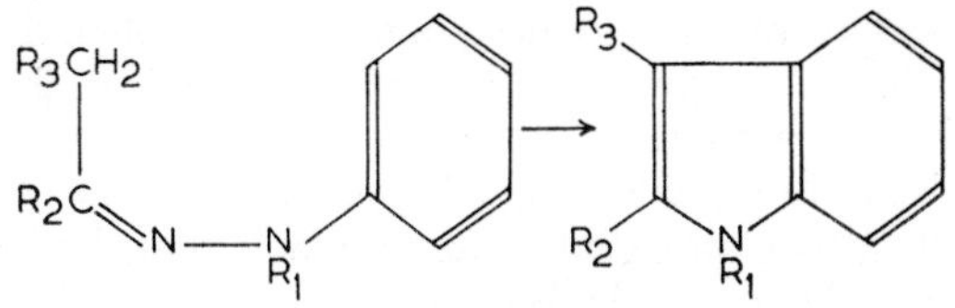   LXXI

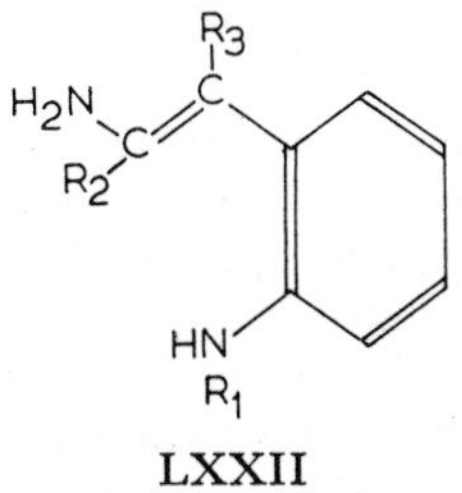

LXXII

Serotonin (5-hydroxytryptamine) is believed to be a hormone, possibly concerned in conducting impulses in the higher central nervous system of man. It is also present in the serum and intestinal wall of mammals, and in many marine creatures. Bufotenine (5-hydroxy-β(3-indolyl)ethyldimethylamine), the tertiary amine analogue of serotonin, occurs in the skin of toads.

Gramine, 3-dimethylaminomethylindole (LXIV), typical of the simpler indole alkaloids, occurs in sprouting barley. Some of the minor alkaloids of cinchona are indole derivatives. The more complex skeletons of physostigmine and the ergot alkaloids contain a fused indole nucleus. Norharman (XXI), which contains an indole nucleus, and the alkaloids derived from norharman will be treated below under 'carbolines'. Indigo (LXI), a blue dye of natural origin, is now entirely produced synthetically (see below).

The Fischer synthesis is most widely used for the preparation of indoles. In this the phenylhydrazone of a ketone is heated with catalytic amounts of zinc chloride: a molecule of ammonia is split out and the reaction goes as illustrated in (LXXI). Indole itself cannot be obtained from acetaldehyde by this reaction. β-Keto-esters, which give pyrazolones, are also unsuitable starting materials. When the benzene ring carries a *meta* substituent, the orientation of the isomers formed was shown by Ockenden and Schofield (1957). Of the many explanations of the Fischer synthesis, that of Robinson and Robinson (1924) is generally accepted, and kinetic confirmation has been obtained (Pausacker and Schubert, 1950). According to this mechanism, the double-bond in the phenylhydrazone, shown in (LXXI), migrates one position further from the benzene ring, which is then attacked by the doubly-bonded carbon, giving (LXXII). Using isotopic nitrogen as a tracer, it has been shown that the nitrogen eliminated as ammonia is that furthest from the benzene ring (Allen and Wilson, 1943).

In the Madelung synthesis, an *o*-acyltoluidide is heated with a base. Thus *o*-acetotoluidide gives 2-methylindole, and the formyl-analogue gives a good yield of indole (Tyson, 1950). In Reissert's synthesis, an *o*-nitrotoluene is condensed with diethyl oxalate. The product (LXXIII), on acidic reduction, cyclizes to indole-2-carboxylic acid which is easily decarboxylated. Indole-2-carboxylic acid can be alkylated in the 3-position prior to decarboxylation (Cornforth and Robinson, 1942).

In the Bischler synthesis an arylamine is condensed with an α-halogenated ketone. Thus 2-phenylindole is obtained by heating phenacyl bromide with aniline, and α-bromoethyl methyl ketone gives 2:3-dimethylindole. The mechanism has been much debated, but studies with isotopic carbon have narrowed the choice of hypotheses (Weygand and Richter, 1955).

There are also several syntheses where *o*-amino-styrenes (ω-substituted) are cyclized. Of these, the most valuable seems to be that of Nenitzescu in which *o*-nitrobenzaldehyde is converted to *o*:ω-dinitrostyrene, which gives indole on reduction, a valuable reaction for preparing *Bz*-hydroxyindoles (Beer *et al.*, 1948). A versatile starting material is *o*-aminobenzyl cyanide which gives 2-aminoindole with sodium ethoxide, 2-hydroxyindole with sodium hydroxide, and 3-cyanoindole with amyl formate and sodium.

The indolenines, e.g. (LVI), may be thought of as indoles in which hydrogen has migrated from N to $C_{(3)}$, and the molecule held in that configuration by substitution in the 3-position. They have no true heteroaromatic ring, and are best regarded as azomethines. Several syntheses of indolenines were mentioned in Section 2 (f) above (p. 160). They are more basic than the isomeric indoles.

All the mono-aminoindoles are now known (Harley-Mason and Jackson, 1954; Plieninger, 1955). They are colourless substances which rapidly become oxidized in air.

LXXIII

Isatin
LXXIV

The mono-hydroxyindoles are also all known, and except for the 2-isomer are unstable in air, although 5- and 7-mono- and 5:6-di-hydroxyindole can be prepared by oxidative procedures (Harley-Mason, 1953; Cromartie and Harley-Mason, 1952). The identification of 5:6-dihydroxyindoles as intermediates in the enzymic oxidation of tyrosine and adrenaline to melanin-like substances, has focused attention on the possibility that melanin, the pigment of skin and hair, may be a poly-indole.

2-Hydroxyindole (oxindole), the lactam of o-aminophenylacetic acid, may be obtained by heating this acid with mineral acid, or by the reduction of isatin (see below). 3-Alkylindoles can be oxidized to oxindoles. In another synthesis, aniline gives oxindole when condensed with chloroacetylchloride (Stollé et al., 1930; Sugasawa, Satoda and Yanagisawa, 1938). Oxindoles are reduced to indoles on heating with zinc (Stollé, Hecht and Becker, 1932).

3-Hydroxyindole (indoxyl) occurs in the plant Indigofera as the glucoside, indican, and in human urine as the O-sulphate which is also called indican. Because alkaline solutions of indoxyl are readily oxidized in the air to indigo (LXI), indoxyl early became the first target for a commercially practicable synthesis of indigo. The most valuable synthesis of indoxyl is that of Heumann who fused N-phenylglycine, or N-phenylglycine-2-carboxylic acid with alkali (sodamide was later found to be the best base to use). The hot alkaline dehydrogenation of β-hydroxyethylaniline is also used commercially for indoxyl. Indoxyls can be reduced to the corresponding indoles by sodium amalgam, or zinc dust in alkali.

Indigo is known from X-ray crystallography to be planar and to have the *trans*-structure (LXI). The internal hydrogen-bonding may not be as complete as suggested in this formula (the m.p. is high (390°), and the solubility in common solvents is slight). Indigo does not give reactions characteristic of a carbonyl-group. It is obviously a resonance hybrid of various forms, some carrying a negative charge on oxygen counterbalanced by a positive charge on nitrogen.

Indigo is insoluble in acid and alkali. Before use as a dye, it is reduced ($+2H$) in alkaline solution to the di-enol ('indigo white'), which is taken up by immersed cotton cloth, and later auto-oxidized to indigo in the air. The halogenated indigos have better fastness to light and washing. Indigo is readily sulphonated or brominated, and under severe conditions four such groups can be introduced (into the 5:5′:7:7′-positions). It can be oxidized to isatin (LXXIV) by nitric or chromic acid.

Unlike indigo, N:N′-dimethylindigo is green, basic and easily hydrolysed by alkali. These differences are attributed to the steric effect of the methyl-groups which force the molecule out of the coplanar structure and decrease the double-bond character of the $C=C$ link (Weinstein and Wyman, 1956).

Isatin (LXXIV) does not contain a heteroaromatic ring, but is essentially aromatic in character (viz. it does not add bromine across the vicinal double-bond, and hence is not heteroethylenic). It is the lactam of 2-aminophenylpyruvic acid ('isatic acid'), and readily gives this acid on warming with alkali. The $-CO$ group in the 2-position has the unreactivity of an amide but that in the 3-position is typically ketonic. Isatin is bright red, and stable to oxidation. Halogenation, nitration and sulphonation occur first in the 5-, and then in the 5:7-positions.

Ultraviolet spectroscopic investigations, to determine if isatin was principally enol or amide (as regards positions 1- and 2-), proved unavailing as both reference substances, the O-methyl- and N-methyl-derivatives, had similar spectra. It was considered that the high dipole moment favoured a preponderance of the $-CO\cdot NH-$ tautomer (Cowley and Partington, 1936), and this has been confirmed by infrared studies (O'Sullivan and Sadler, 1956). X-ray crystallography suggests that the molecule is mainly, but not entirely in the $-CONH-$ (i.e. amide) form (Goldschmidt and Llewellyn, 1950). None of this evidence, of course, is applicable to aqueous solutions, in which the relative proportions of tautomers at equilibrium remains unknown.

Isatins are usually prepared by Sandmeyer's method, in which aniline (or a substituted aniline) is condensed with chloral and hydroxylamine (Marvel and Hiers, 1941). Nitro-groups hinder this reaction. Isatins are active reagents, and have already been mentioned as starting materials for the synthesis of quinolines (see p. 108). The benzisatins, particularly linear benzisatin (Étienne and Staehlin, 1954), are of interest for benzoquinoline synthesis.

For further reading on indoles, see Sumpter and Miller (1954), and Julian, Meyer and Printy (1952).

Isoindole (IX) is still unknown, but N-methyl*iso*indole (m.p. 91°) was discovered in 1951. It was obtained in 70% yield by the action of lithium aluminium hydride on N-methylphthalamide (Wittig, Closs and Mindermann, 1955). It is quite stable, despite some earlier predictions.

Phthalimidine (1-hydroxy*iso*indole), a stable solid, is prepared by warming phthalide (lactone of o-hydroxymethylbenzoic acid) with ammonia, or by reducing phthalimide, or by ring-closure of o-aminomethylbenzoic acid. Some of the older literature on the reactions of phthalimidine would bear reinvestigation.

Phthalimide (3-ketophthalimidine; 1:3-dioxo*iso*indoline) is made by heating phthalic anhydride with ammonia or ammonium carbonate. It is a white solid, m.p. 235°, and a stronger acid than phenol. Although it does not contain a heteroaromatic ring, it does not give heteroethylenic reactions and hence is included here. Infrared spectroscopy in chloroform shows that amide-forms predominate over the enol-forms (Kellie, O'Sullivan and Sadler, 1956), and no simple ketone derivatives are given. Under more vigorous conditions, one —CO-group can be condensed with active methylene groups.

Phthalimide is much used for the preparation of anthranilic acid (with sodium hypochlorite) and primary amines (with alkyl halides, followed by hydrazine: the Gabriel method, as modified by Ing and Manske). The di-imide of phthalimide (1:3-di-imino*iso*indoline) is now easily prepared (Elvidge and Linstead, 1952).

Phthalocyanine (LXXV), first discovered as a contaminant of phthalonitrile (o-dicyanobenzene), is obtained by heating this substance to about 200° with a metal (free or combined) (Linstead and Lowe, 1934). Phthalocyanine differs from porphin (XI) in having =N— linkages instead of =CH— (but mixed types can be made, Linstead, 1937), and in having benzene rings attached to each pyrrole. Tetra-azaporphins (i.e. without these benzene rings) can be made from succinimidine (Elvidge, 1956). Phthalocyanine is greenish-blue and is a highly valued pigment used mainly in printing inks, as is its pure-blue copper compound (they are marketed as Monastral Fast Blue G and B, respectively). Sixteen chlorine atoms can be introduced by halogenation, giving a valuable green pigment. Sulphonation gives a blue direct dye, much used on cotton. The phthalocyanine compounds of heavy metals (lead and manganese excepted) retain the metals even in mineral acids, whereas porphyrins relinquish heavy metals under these conditions. The metallic phthalocyanines are good catalysts of several oxidations, e.g. the autoxidation of benzaldehyde.

For further reading on *iso*indoles, see Elderfield and Dodd (1952); for phthalocyanines see Haddock and Linstead's article in Thorpe's *Dictionary of Applied Chemistry*.

Phthalocyanine
LXXV

Indolizine (X), sometimes called pyrrocoline, is a colourless solid, m.p. 74°, which rapidly becomes brown in air. It is prepared by quaternizing 2-methylpyridine with ethyl bromopyruvate, cyclizing to indolizine 2-carboxylic acid and decarboxylating (Borrows and Holland, 1947; cf. Boekelheide and Feely, 1957). 2-Chloroacetone similarly gives 2-methylindolizine. The high negative charge on $C_{(1)}$ enables indolizine to be acetylated on carbon as readily as amines are acylated on nitrogen; and the product is just as readily hydrolysed as though it were an amide (see p. 175).

For further reading, see Borrows and Holland (1948); Ing (1952); Rossiter and Saxton (1953).

Carbazole (VIII) is a colourless, poorly soluble solid, m.p. 247°, found in the anthracene fraction of coal-tar, but easily purified only if made synthetically. The principal use for carbazole is conversion to the 'sulphur-dye', Hydron Blue, by heating in turn with *p*-nitrosophenol and sodium sulphide (Bernasconi, 1932). (Technically, a sulphur-dye is one that requires sodium sulphide to render it soluble in the dyebath, and then becomes insoluble on the fibre through oxidation.)

Carbazole is prepared by heating 2:2'-diaminodiphenyl with dilute mineral acids at 200°, or diazotizing this diamine and then reducing the solution e.g. with copper. Another useful carbazole synthesis is the palladium dehydrogenation (Horning, Horning and Walker, 1948) of tetrahydrocarbazole obtained by heating *cyclo*-hexanone phenylhydrazone with acid (i.e. by a Fischer indole synthesis). The presence of a *meta*-substituent in the phenylhydrazone gives rise to two isomeric carbazoles. Carbazole can also be prepared by diazotizing 2-aminodiphenylamine.

For further reading, see Freudenberg (1952); Sumpter and Miller (1954).

B. Systems with Two Ring-Nitrogen Atoms

Pyrazole (XIII) is a colourless, highly soluble solid, m.p. 70°. There is a new direct synthesis from hydrazine and malondialdehyde tetracetal, which had not long been commercially available (Noyce, Ryder and Walker, 1955), and another new synthesis from hydrazine and propargylaldehyde ($CH \equiv C \cdot CHO$) also gives good yields (Hüttel, Büchele and Jochum, 1955). Pyrazole has previously been produced by the isomerization of vinyl diazomethane ($CH_2{:}CH \cdot CHN_2$), obtained either from allyl nitrosourethane (Hurd and Lui, 1935) or allyl (acetyl-*t*-butyl) nitrosamine (Adamson and Kenner, 1935). Also dehydrogenation of dihydropyrazole (pyrazoline) with bromine gives pyrazole.

Pyrazoles are unknown in nature, but some important drugs and dyes belong to this series. Phenazone (antipyrine), used for headache and mild fever, is comparable in effect to aspirin, but much more soluble. It is described as 2-phenyl-1:5-dimethyl-3-pyrazolone (LXXVI, R = H), and is prepared by condensing phenylhydrazine with ethyl acetoacetate, and methylating the resulting 2-phenyl-5-methyl-3-pyrazolone[1] ('3-pyrazolone' is the amide tautomer of 3-

---

[1] Also called 1-phenyl-3-methyl-5-pyrazolone or Developer Z, widely used in photography, and the largest commercial outlet for pyrazoles.

hydroxypyrazole). Nitrous acid forms the 4-nitroso-derivative of antipyrine. When this nitroso-compound is reduced and methylated, pyramidon (LXXVI, R $= -N(CH_3)_2$) is formed. This is widely used in Germany as a mild analgesic, but is considered unsafe in the English-speaking countries (some fatalities through agranulocytosis have occurred) and is seldom prescribed there. The most important pyrazole drug is phenylbutazone (butazolidine; 1:2-diphenyl-4-butyl-5-hydroxy-3-pyrazolone), noted for its longer persistence in the blood-stream (four days). It relieves pain in many inflammatory conditions such as arthritis, and occupies a place in therapy intermediate between cortisone and the salicylates.

LXXVI

Histidine
LXXVII

The pyrazolone dyes are the best yellow dyes available for wool (yellow is a key colour to the wool-dyer, being one of the three primaries from which he compounds almost all other colours). Tartrazine, 1-(p-sulphophenyl)-4-(p-sulphobenzeneazo)-5-hydroxy-pyrazine-3-carboxylic acid, is obtained by the action of phenyl-hydrazine-p-sulphonic acid on ethyl oxaloacetate, and treatment of the resulting pyrazolone with diazotized sulphanilic acid. A more durable, though slightly more expensive, yellow dye is Xylene Light Yellow 2G (Lissamine Fast Yellow 2GS), which is 1-(2':5'-dichloro-4'-sulphophenyl)-3-methyl-4-(p-sulphobenzeneazo)-5-hydroxypy-razine, discovered in 1908.

For further reading on pyrazoles, see Jacobs (1957).

Iminazole (XIV), also known as glyoxaline, is a colourless, highly soluble solid, m.p. 90°. It may be prepared by decarboxylating imina-zole-4:5-dicarboxylic acid (Snyder *et al.*, 1942) but the best method is to heat paraldehyde, bromine and glycol; the product, heated with formamide, gives a 60% yield of iminazole (Bredereck *et al.*, 1958). Iminazole and its alkyl-derivatives are used as buffers in the pH 7–8 region.

Histidine (LXXVII) is one of the two dozen amino-acids which, condensed together, constitute the various proteins. Histamine, formed from histidine by simple decarboxylation, is abundantly present in the human body, but appears to be restrained by membranes from general diffusion. Although the normal physiological role of histamine is unknown, its release is the cause of the symptoms in various allergic and anaphylactic states, including serum shock, urticaria (hives) and hay fever. Ergothionine (2-mercaptohistidine betaine, i.e. the nitrogen atom on the side-chain is quaternized with three methyl-groups) is present in blood. 1-Methylimidazole-2-thione and its derivatives are important antithyroid drugs used in thyrotoxicosis. The alkaloid pilocarpine is a 1-methyliminazole with a 5-alkyl side-chain which incorporates a lactone.

4-Aminoiminazole-5-carboxamide, the penultimate stage in the biosynthesis of purines, is prepared by condensing formamidine and aminocyanoacetamide (Cook, Heilbron and Smith, 1949).

2:4-Dihydroxyiminazole (hydantoin) is a colourless solid, m.p. about 220° with decomposition. It occurs in sugar beet. It is a weak acid ($pK_a = 9$), slightly stronger than phenol. The formula is often written as (LXXVIII) or (LXXIX). It reacts with aromatic aldehydes to give 5-benzylidene derivatives, which can be reduced and hydrolysed to α-amino-acids. Thus benzaldehyde and hydantoin give phenylalanine (Boyd and Robson, 1935). It is hydrolysed by alkali to ureidoacetic acid (hydantoic acid) from which it is reformed by evaporation with acid. Hydantoin can also be made by the acid hydrolysis of allantoin (4-ureidohydantoin) which occurs in the allantoic fluid of pregnant cows, and is prepared by the oxidation (quantitative) of uric acid with permanganate. Parabanic acid (LXII), 5-oxohydantoin or oxalylurea, is formed by the action of bromine, chloric acid or nitric acid on uric acid.

LXXVIII   LXXIX

Creatinine (1-methyl-2-amino-4-hydroxyiminazole) is found in milk and urine and is the anhydride of creatine $NH:C(NH_2)\cdot NCH_3\cdot CH_2CO_2H$ (N-methyl-N-guanyl-glycine). Creatinine, obtained from creatine by boiling with acetic acid, is a weak base ($pK_a = 4$), and also has acidic properties. It is more soluble in boiling water than creatine is.

2-Thiohydantoin (2-mercapto-4-hydroxyiminazole) is prepared from glycine and potassium thiocyanate. When phenyl*iso*thiocyanate (PhNHCS) is added to a polypeptide or protein, the terminal amino-acid having the free-COOH can be split off as 3-phenyl-5R-2-thiohydantoin. As many as six amino-acid residues have been split off consecutively in this way and identified (Edman, 1953).

Iminazoles are commonly synthesized by gently warming a 1:2-diketone with ammonia and an aldehyde (Davidson, Weiss and Jelling, 1937). Similarly glyoxal, ammonia and acetaldehyde give 2-methyliminazole. The formation of 4-hydroxymethyliminazole from fructose, ammonia and formaldehyde is a related synthesis. 2-Mercaptoiminazoles are obtained by the reaction of an α-amino-ketone with potassium thiocyanate. The conversion of oxazole-4-carboxylic acids to iminazoles has been achieved by heating with ammonia at 150° (Cornforth and Cornforth, 1947; Cornforth and Huang, 1948).

For further reading on iminazoles see Hofmann (1953), Schipper and Day (1957). For hydantoins see Ware (1950), and for allantoin and creatinine see articles by Whiteley and Thorpe in Thorpe's *Dictionary of Applied Chemistry*.

Benziminazole (XVIII) is a white solid, m.p. 167°, prepared by heating *o*-phenylenediamine with formic acid. Acetic acid similarly gives 2-methylbenziminazole, also obtained by reducing 2-nitro-acetanilide with tin and hydrochloric acid. Benziminazoles are also obtained when *o*-phenylenediamine is treated with an aldehyde and an oxidizing agent, particularly copper acetate (Weidenhagen and Weeden, 1938). The only known occurrence of a benziminazole in nature is the 5:6-dimethyl-derivative which forms part of the molecule of vitamin B_{12} (see p. 182). Many benziminazoles antagonize the action of purines in living cells. Some benziminazoles are antagonistic to some viruses, other inhibit the incorporation of amino-acids into bacteria.

2-Mercaptobenziminazole, used to prevent deterioration of rubber upon storage, is prepared by the action of carbon bisulphide and potassium hydroxide on *o*-phenylenediamine (van Allan and Deacon, 1950). 2-Hydroxy- and 2-amino-benziminazole are formed from *o*-phenylenediamine and urea, or guanidine, respectively. The *Bz*-hydroxybenziminazoles are obtained normally from the methoxy-1:2-diaminobenzenes (e.g. Sorkin, Roth and Erlenmeyer, 1952). Some confusion which arose between 4- and 5-aminobenziminazole has now been solved (van der Want, 1948): the 5-isomer is the sole product in the reduction of mono-nitrated benziminazole.

For further reading, see Wright (1951), Hofmann (1953), Schipper and Day (1957).

Indazole (XIX) is a colourless solid, m.p. 146°, prepared by strongly heating *o*-hydrazinocinnamic acid, acetic acid being split out. Similarly *o*-hydrazinobenzoic acid and phosphorus oxychloride give 3-chloro- or 3-hydroxy-indazole according to the conditions. The most used reaction for preparing indazoles is the diazotization of substituted *o*-toluidines, but the yields are high only when the substituent is electron-attracting. All the *Bz*-monohydroxy- and -monoaminoindazoles have been prepared with a view to their possible value as dyestuff intermediates (Davies, 1955). Indazoles do not occur in nature.

For further reading, see Elderfield (1957).

The **monoazaindoles.** These are the four isomers of benziminazole and indazole, having the doubly-bound nitrogen in the six-membered ring. Of these, the 7-azaindoles have been most studied (Robison and Robison, 1955), and some 6-azaindoles were obtained during the degradation of the harmaline alkaloids (see carbolines, below). Much work remains to be done on the *Bz*-azaindoles.

Carbolines. These are the mono-azacarbazoles, all colourless. Of the four isomers, norharman (XXI) has been most studied. It is obtained by oxidizing the condensation product of tryptophan and formaldehyde. Harmine, the principal alkaloid of *Peganum* seeds, is methylmethoxy-norharman. The alkaloids of *Evodia*, of *Corynanthe yohimbe*, of *Rauwolfia*, and of *Gelsemium* (jasmin) are more complex derivatives in which two further rings are joined to norharman by annelation (Marion, 1952). All these norharman derivatives are believed to arise by biosynthesis from tryptophane.

C. SYSTEMS WITH THREE RING-NITROGEN ATOMS

The **triazoles.** 1:2:3-Triazole (XVI) is a colourless hygroscopic solid, m.p. 23°, b.p. 204°, obtainable by decarboxylating the mono- or di-carboxylic acid. A three-stage preparation, suitable for 200 g., uses benzylazide and acetylene dicarboxylic acid (Wiley, Hussung and Moffat, 1956). It can also be prepared by heating hydrazoic acid with acetylene at 100°. The carboxylic acids are made by the action of hydrazoic acid on acetylene-mono- or -di-carboxylic acid. 4-Hydroxy-1:2:3-triazole is in tautomeric equilibrium with diazo-acetamide. 1:2:3-Triazole analogues of the purine intermediate 4-aminoiminazole-5-carboxamide have been made (Hoover and Day, 1956).

For further reading, see Benson and Savell (1950).

1:2:4-Triazole (XV), m.p. 121°, b.p. 260°, also known as symmetrical triazole, is prepared from formamide and formic hydrazide. 3:5-Dimethyl-1:2:4-triazole is prepared from 1:2-diacetylhydrazine and ammonia, 3-aminotriazole from aminoguanidine and formic acid, 3:5-dihydroxytriazole (urazole) from biuret and hydrazine, and 3:5-diaminotriazole (guanazole) from dicyanamide and hydrazine. 3-Amino-1:2:4-triazole is used to defoliate cotton-plants before mechanical harvesting, and also in weed-control.

Diaza-indoles. Benzotriazole (2:3-diaza-indole), m.p. 98°, is prepared by the action of nitrous acid on *o*-phenylenediamine. It is used in some photographic developers to increase contrast, also as a restrainer and anti-fog.

The following diaza-indoles are of interest as potential blockers of purine metabolism, being in effect 'purine minus one nitrogen atom'. 3:4-Diaza-indole (1-deazapurine) was made from 2:3-diaminopyridine and formic acid by Petrow and Saper (1948) who call it 4-azabenziminazole. Korte (1952) seemed to obtain a different product, but has now confirmed the earlier work (personal communication). For substituted derivatives, see Korte (1952); Kögl, van der Want and Salemink (1948). 3:5-Diaza-indole (3-deazapurine) was similarly prepared from 3:4-diaminopyridine (Albert and Pedersen, 1956). For substituted derivatives, see Salemink and van der Want (1949). 4:6-Diaza-indole (9-deazapurine) derivatives have been made by Tanaka *et al.* (1955); Rose (1954).

D. SYSTEMS WITH FOUR OR MORE RING-NITROGEN ATOMS

Tetrazole (XVII), a colourless solid, m.p. 156°, is obtained by the reaction of hydrazoic and hydrocyanic acids, or better by the action of alcohol on diazotized 5-aminotetrazole. This 5-aminotetrazole is formed by the action of nitrous acid on aminoguanidine, or of aqueous hydrazoic acid on dicyandiamide.

Pentamethylenetetrazole, also known as Cardiazole and Metrazole (LXXX), is used in medicine as an analeptic (stimulant). It is prepared by the action of hydrazoic acid on *cyclo*hexanone. 2:3:5-Triphenyltetrazolium chloride is a colourless substance formed by the oxidation (lead tetracetate) of triphenylformazan (LXXXI) (Kuhn and Jerchel, 1941), which in turn is formed by the action of diazotized aniline on benzalphenylhydrazone. This tetrazolium salt is used to detect areas of active reduction in biological specimens: where reduction occurs, the red formazan is reconstituted. This is one of a rare and useful type of indicators which is more coloured in the reduced than in the oxidized form. Many derivatives have been made, varying in reduction potential and in the colour given.

Although tetrazoles are remarkably stable, in spite of their high content of bound nitrogen, some have found employment in explosives as initiators. Others explode on strong heating. *For further reading* on tetrazoles, see Benson (1947). For the tetrazoliums see Nineham (1955).

Pentazole. Evidence for the existence of N-phenylpentazole has been obtained from kinetic studies of the reaction between lithium azide and benzene diazonium chloride (Huisgen and Ugi, 1957).

LXXX   LXXXI   LXXXII

Purine (LXXXII), m.p. 212°, is a colourless solid, highly soluble in water but poorly soluble in organic solvents. It is prepared by the action of formic acid on 4:5-diaminopyrimidine (Albert and Brown, 1954), by the (nickel) desulphurization of 6-mercapto-, or 2:6-dimercapto-purine, or the catalytic hydrogenation of 6-chloropurine (Bendich, Russell and Fox, 1954; Beaman, 1954). Purine can be made by heating formamide and ammonia at 200°, in a yield (1 %) that would be uninviting were not the starting materials so cheap (Bredereck, Ulmer and Waldmann, 1956). Purine has been found in nature only as the 9-riboside: in a mushroom (Löfgren and Lüning, 1953). However, derivatives of purine are widely distributed in nature, much more so than those of pyrimidine.

Adenine (6-aminopurine) is present in urine, faeces, milk and in many plants. It is a constituent of the living cell's principal phosphorylating agent: adenosine triphosphate. Adenine also forms part of various coenzymes such as di- and tri-phosphopyridine nucleotide and (with pantothenic acid) coenzyme A. Adenine thiomethylriboside forms a sulphonium salt (with homocysteine) which plays an important part in cellular transmethylation reactions (Cantoni, 1952). Cordycepin, a fungal antibiotic, is the adenine-9-nucleoside of a branched 3-deoxypentose (Bentley, Cunningham and Spring, 1951). Puromycin, another fungal antibiotic, gives on hydrolysis 6-dimethylaminopurine, 3-aminoribose, and O-methyltyrosine (Waller et al., 1953). The plant-growth factor, kinetin, is 6-furfurylamino-

o

purine, i.e. an alkylated adenine (Miller *et al.*, 1955). Exceeding all these in complexity are the nucleic acids, compounds in which the purines adenine and guanine are united with various pyrimidines by bridges of pentosephosphoric acids. Much of the detailed structure of these macromolecules has been elucidated (Brown and Todd, 1955). The sequence of the heterocyclic components, and the spatial disposition of the molecules (perhaps in the helices of Watson and Crick, 1953) remain to be determined. Even the number of kinds of nucleic acid is unknown, but the belief that there are only two (ribose- and deoxyribose-nucleic acids) is no longer held. The biosynthesis of adenine and its derivatives proceeds from inosinic acid through the secondary amine: adenylo-succinic acid, which has been synthesized (Hampton, 1957).

Guanine (2-amino-6-hydroxypurine) is found free in milk, in the excreta of mammals, birds and spiders, in the eyes and scales of fish, in the skin of reptiles and amphibia, in the tissues of pigs during a gout-like disease from which they suffer, in molasses, and in some plants. Isoguanine (6-amino-2-hydroxy-purine) has been isolated from butterfly wings, and (as riboside) from the croton bean. Guanine derivatives seem to be the starting materials for the biosynthesis of pteridines (Albert, 1957).

Inosinic acid, the ribotide of hypoxanthine (6-hydroxy-purine), is biosynthesized by the living cell from the ribotide of 4-amino-iminazole-5-carboxamide (Levenberg and Buchanan, 1956), by an enzyme which inserts the $C_{(2)}$ of the purine nucleus. This enzyme has a pteridine coenzyme, as has also a previous stage in the biosynthesis where the $C_{(2)}$ of the iminazole ring was inserted (this becomes the $C_{(8)}$ of the purine). Purines and pteridines thus enjoy a cyclic interrelationship, for not only are pteridines required (in catalytic amounts) to make purines, but purines, in turn, can be bio-transformed to pteridines (Albert, 1957) through 4:5-diaminopyrimidines. The vitamin riboflavine also arises from purine precursors (Brown, Goodwin and Jones, 1956). All of the natural purines appear to be biosynthesized from inosinic acid.

Hypoxanthine also occurs in mammalian tissues as inosine triphosphate, an important agent in transphosphorylation, and is found free in human urine and faeces. 6-Mercaptopurine is used to suppress leukaemia.

Xanthine (2:6-dihydroxypurine) has often been isolated from natural sources where it seems to arise by the enzymic oxidation of hypoxanthine (and inosine), and the enzymic deamination of guanine. It is readily prepared by heating uric acid with formamide

(Bredereck, v. Schuh and Martini, 1950). Caffeine (1:3:7-trimethyl-xanthine) occurs in tea, coffee, cola and maté and exerts the stimulant effect for which these beverages are consumed in great quantity. Theophylline (theocin, 1:3-dimethylxanthine) is present in traces in tea, and is used in medicine as a powerful diuretic. Monomethyl-xanthines have been isolated from human urine. Caffeine and theobromine (3:7-dimethylxanthine) are easily obtained by the methylation of xanthine (Bredereck, v. Schuh and Martini, 1950).

Uric acid, 2:6:8-trihydroxypurine, is the end product of purine metabolism in man and many other animals (but not in the dog), and also occurs in some plants and in the wings of some types of butterfly. Uric acid riboside occurs in human and bovine red blood cells.

New purines are still being found in nature: 6-hydroxy-2-methyl-aminopurine in human urine (Weissmann, Bromberg and Gutman, 1955); 6-methylaminopurine in some bacteria (Dunn and Smith, 1955); 2-methyl-6-hydroxy- and 2-methyl-6-amino-purine (as well as adenine) from the hydrolysis of subsidiary members of the B_{12} group of vitamins where they take the place of the benziminazole (see p. 182); 2-methoxy-6-aminopurine in a nucleoside of a sponge (Bergmann and Burke, 1956).

The synthesis of purines is nearly always accomplished by Traube's method: heating an appropriately substituted 4:5-diaminopyrimidine (see p. 116) with formic acid. The best yields are obtained when conditions are as mild as possible. In preparing hypoxanthine, for example, the temperature need not rise above 100° (Elion, Burgi and Hitchings, 1952). Where this method is ineffective, or where water must be excluded, a mixture of ethyl orthoformate and acetic anhydride is useful (Montgomery, 1956). Where severer conditions are required, the diamine, or its sulphate, is refluxed with formamide (Robins et al., 1953; Beaman, 1954). Sodium dithioformate has also been used, and gives the 5-thioformyl-derivative which is cyclized with a mild base (Todd, Bergel and Karimullah, 1936; Kenner, Rodda and Todd, 1949). When a 4:5:6-triaminopyrimidine bears an alkyl-group on the 4-position, cyclization always occurs on to the substituted nitrogen, so that a 9-alkylpurine results (Lythgoe, 1949). This fact has proved of great value in synthesizing the natural purine nucleosides which have the pentose on $N_{(9)}$, as was first shown spectroscopically (Gulland and Holiday, 1936), and later confirmed by synthesis (Davoll, Lythgoe and Todd, 1948). It is also possible to insert a sugar, or other alkyl, group in the 9-position of a purine by means of the 9-mercuri-derivative which purines readily form with mercuric chloride (Davoll and Lowy, 1952).

When a substituent other than hydrogen is required in the 8-position, formic acid is replaced by guanidine (for $-NH_2$), thiourea (for $-SH$), and urea or ethyl chloroformate (for $-OH$).

Another series of purine syntheses follow the lines of purine bio-synthesis by commencing with an iminazole, and building a pyrimidine ring on to it (Heilbron, 1949; Cook and Heilbron, 1950). So far, these reactions have always introduced a hydroxy- or amino-group in the 6-position. Thus 4-aminoiminazole-5-carboxamide (see p. 191) gives hypoxanthine with formic acid, and xanthine with urea (Shaw, 1950).

More recently a method has been found for creating both rings of purine simultaneously, starting, e.g. from the amidine (LXXXIII) of aminomalonamide which gives 6-hydroxypurine with ethyl ortho-formate (Richter and Taylor, 1955).

LXXXIII   LXXXIV   LXXXV

LXXXVI

For further reading, see Bendich (1955), and Baddiley in Thorpe's *Dictionary of Applied Chemistry.*

Purine isomers. These have been investigated in recent years in a search for purine antagonists, partly with a view to the ultimate control of cancer, but also with the more immediate aim of investigating the metabolism of purines. The 2:5:7-triaza-indoles, e.g. (LXXXIV), have been made from 3-amino-4-carbomethoxypyrazole (Schmidt and Druey, 1956; Robins, 1956), or pyrazole-3:4-dicar-boxamide (Falco and Hitchings, 1956). The isomeric 2:4:6-triaza-indoles have been made similarly from 4-amino-3-carboxypyrazole

(Robins *et al.*, 1956), and also by diazotization and internal coupling of 5-amino-4-methylpyrimidines, as in an indazole synthesis (Rose, 1954).

Purine azalogues have been made for the same purposes as the purine isomers. Nitrous acid and 4-aminoiminazole-5-carboxamide gave 2-aza-6-hydroxypurine (LXXXV), also described as 7-hydroxy-3:4:5:6-tetraza-indole, as 2-azahypoxanthine and as 6-hydroxy-iminazolo-1:2:3-triazine. The amidine corresponding to the above amide gave 2-aza-adenine (Woolley *et al.*, 1951).

Whereas few biochemically interesting results were obtained with these substances, the 8-azapurines (Roblin *et al.*, 1945) have proved to be powerful antagonists of purines. The most important of these is 8-aza-guanine (LXXXVI) (8-aza-2-amino-6-hydroxypurine), a potent inhibitor of guanine throughout nature. This substance is prepared by the action of nitrous acid on 4:5:6-triamino-2-hydroxy-pyrimidine. The parent substance (8-azapurine, 2:3:4:6-tetraaza-indole or triazolopyrimidine) has similarly been prepared from 4:5-diaminopyrimidine (Felton, 1955).

π-Excessive O- and S-Heteroaromatics

[i.e. Completely unsaturated heterocycles having oxygen or
sulphur as a hetero-element (with or without nitrogen), and
an excess of π-electrons elsewhere]

THIS CHAPTER deals with those O- and S-heterocycles in which
the hetero-elements are in a five-membered ring. The six-
membered rings containing oxygen or sulphur will be described
along with other heteroethylenic nuclei in Chapter VII.

In Chapter V, it was explained that pyrrole (I) is aromatic,
and that this property arises from the formation of a sextet by
the lone pair of electrons on the hetero-atom and the four
π-electrons from the two double-bonds. Thus there are six
π-electrons as in benzene. Similarly furan (II) and thiophen
(III) are aromatic, and owe their aromaticity to the same
phenomenon.

The relative order of π-electron excess in pyrrole, furan and thiophen has been established as follows. In the Friedel-Crafts reaction, pyrrole reacts most energetically, then furan. Thiophen is the least reactive, but it is still much more reactive than benzene. This means that under the demand of the reagent (and possibly in the resting-state also) π-electron densities increase in this order: benzene < thiophen < furan < pyrrole (the densities under consideration are in the 2-positions of the heterocyclic substances, where substitution occurs). Hence it is not surprising that the nitration of 2-furyl-2-thienylketone occurs in the furan nucleus to give (IV).

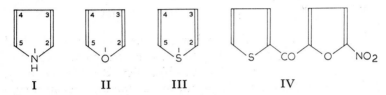

I   II   III   IV

The relative aromaticity of benzene, thiophen, furan and pyrrole does not follow directly from these data. It is not always clear what criteria of aromaticity various authors have in mind.

Nevertheless, of two π-excessive substances containing double-bonds, the more aromatic substance will have (a) the longer double-bonds (ethylene has the shortest possible double-bond), and the greater equalization of $C-C$ bond-length throughout the molecule (all $C-C$ bonds in benzene have the same length), (b) the greater tendency to substitute and the less tendency to add, (c) the greater stability to combustion and hydrogenation. The following discussion will deal with these points in order.

Electron-diffraction measurements of the 2:3-bonds in pyrrole, furan and thiophen show them all to be the same length (1.35 ± 0.02 Å) as the double-bonds in butadiene and cyclopentadiene, but shorter than in benzene (1.39 Å). The 3:4-bonds, on the other hand, are longer than in benzene: that of furan is the same length as, and those of pyrrole and thiophen are only slightly shorter than, the longer bonds in butadiene and cyclopentadiene (1.46 Å). On this evidence, these heterocycles are less aromatic than benzene, and furan most particularly so.

But the most precise information comes from electron-diffraction measurements of the carbon-heteroatom distances. From these, it has been calculated that these bonds have 12, 5, and 17% double-bond character in pyrrole, furan and thiophen respectively (Schomaker and Pauling, 1939). Hence the contribution of charged structures in these three substances is 24, 10, and 34% respectively.

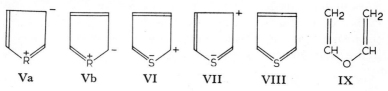

Va   Vb   VI   VII   VIII   IX

The tendency for the 1:2-bond to be somewhat 'double' was attributed to the participation in the resonance hybrid of charged forms such as (Va) and (Vb) (where R=NH, O, or S). It is understandable that oxygen, by far the most electronegative of these three radicals, is the most reluctant to carry a positive charge.[1] Of the charged forms shown above, (Va) is thought to make a smaller contribution than (Vb) because of the greater separation of charge, and it is true that all these substances substitute (electrophilically) in the 2-position, preferentially.

Thiophen can have yet other canonical forms in its resonance hybrid. Because sulphur is a second row element, the valency-electron octet can expand to a decet or duodecet. Thus two electrons from the sulphur atom can occupy two pd^2 orbitals, thus facilitating conjugation with the π-electrons contributed by the carbon atoms (Longuet-Higgins, 1949). It has been suggested that these other forms (VI–VIII) contribute 10% to the resonance hybrid of thiophen (Schomaker and Pauling, 1939). Thus if sharing double-bonded character among all bonds is a criterion of aromaticity, it is evident that thiophen has gained in aromaticity at the expense of ease of electrophilic substitution. For a discussion on the bond-angles and bond-lengths of doubly bound sulphur in aliphatic and aromatic situations, see Abrahams (1956).

[1] The $2p$ orbital is contracted relative to the $2p$ orbitals of the carbon atoms, and this constitutes a hindrance to conjugation (Walsh, 1948).

Continuing to apply the criteria for determining relative aromaticity, it has been shown that pyrrole has almost no tendency to addition reactions, but that these are more in evidence in thiophen, and still more in furan, although even furan readily undergoes substitution. Finally, resonance energies may be considered. Here the information is scanty. Furan has resonance energy, determined from the heat of hydrogenation, of 17 Kcal./mole compared to 3·4 for divinyl ether (IX), and 36 for benzene (Wheland, 1944), and thus has an intermediate degree of aromaticity. Unfortunately comparable figures for pyrrole and thiophen are not available. Heats of combustion are not usually very accurate for nitrogen- or sulphur-containing substances, and it is not surprising that this section of the literature is contradictory and little information on resonance energies can be deduced from it (Schomaker and Pauling, 1939; Sunner, 1955).

To sum up: furan is the least aromatic of the π-excessive N-heterocycles, and the other two nuclei are more aromatic and do not differ greatly from one another in this property.

1. THE PARENT SUBSTANCES

With the exception of benzofuran and thiophen, none of the parent substances dealt with in this chapter is commercially available in greater quantity than a few grams, but several derivatives are manufactured on a large scale, notably in the furan, thiazole and benzothiazole series.

The lack of hydrogen on the hetero-atom simplifies the treatment of furan and thiophen as compared to pyrrole. No question of tautomerism, comparable to the pyrrole-pyrrolenine tautomerism, arises and no acidic properties exist.

Furan (II) can be annelated with benzene giving benzofuran (X), which is sometimes called by the old, rather nonsensical, name coumarone. The isomeric *iso*benzofuran (XI) is known only as derivatives, notably phthalic anhydride. A double annelation of furan gives dibenzofuran (XII). Similarly, thiophen (III) can be annelated with benzene to such substances as benzothiophen, often known as thionaphthen (XIII), or with other thiophen nuclei to give e.g. thienothiophen (XIV).

From diacetonyl-acetone and phosphorus pentasulphide, a substance has been prepared which is believed to have the nucleus (XV). It readily undergoes electrophilic substitution and the sulphur atom resists oxidation: these are signs of aromatic character (Arndt, 1956). If its constitution can be upheld, and nuclear magnetic resonance spectra seem to do so (Bothner-By, 1957), this will be the first monocyclic aromatic substance with eight π-electrons, or (in fact) with other than six π-electrons.

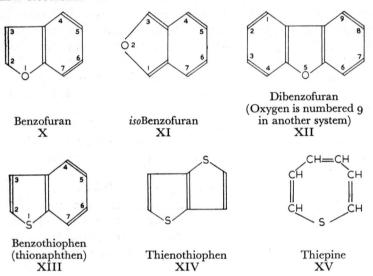

Benzofuran
X

*iso*Benzofuran
XI

Dibenzofuran
(Oxygen is numbered 9
in another system)
XII

Benzothiophen
(thionaphthen)
XIII

Thienothiophen
XIV

Thiepine
XV

All the substances discussed so far undergo electrophilic substitution readily in the heterocyclic nucleus.

Azalogues of these substances, in which one or more −CH= groups are replaced by −N=, are well known. Thus related to furan (II) are oxazole (XVI), isoxazole (XVII) and several oxadiazoles, e.g. 1:2:5-oxadiazole (furazan) (XVIII). Azalogues related to thiophen (III) include thiazole (XIX), the recently discovered *iso*thiazole (XX), and several thiadiazoles, e.g. 1:3:4-thiadiazole (XXI).

These azalogues can be further annelated with benzene to give benzoxazole (XXII), benzothiazole (XXIII) and two benzo*iso*thiazoles.

There are too few data to determine how much the excess of π-electrons in furan and thiophen is diminished by the insertion of doubly-bound nitrogen. 2-Aminothiazole readily diazotizes and couples with phenols, in contrast to 2-aminopyridine, and this may be an indication that thiazole is not π-deficient, or at least not so π-deficient as pyridine. On the other hand, thiazole requires heating to 200° for bromination, which is thus no easier than in pyridine, and it reacts with sodamide like pyridine, giving 2-aminothiazole, but in poor yield. 2-Methylthiazole resists nitration, but thiazole has been sulphonated in excellent yield (Erlenmeyer and Kiefer, 1945). The presence of an electron-releasing group ($-NH_2$, $-OH$) in the 2-position enables electrophilic substitution to occur in the 5-position: even Friedel-Crafts reactions can then be performed, which points to a higher electron-concentration than in the hydroxy-pyridines which do not react (Ochiai, 1938, 1939; Ochiai and Nagasawa, 1939).

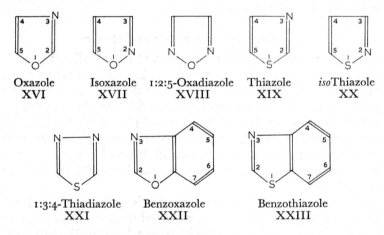

Oxazole   Isoxazole   1:2:5-Oxadiazole   Thiazole   isoThiazole
XVI   XVII   XVIII   XIX   XX

1:3:4-Thiadiazole   Benzoxazole   Benzothiazole
XXI   XXII   XXIII

Electron-density diagrams show thiazole with a large depot of electrons in the 5-position (Pullman and Metzger, 1948). Little relevant data is available for the oxazoles.

One is left with an impression that thiazole has areas of both π-deficiency and π-excess (the latter preponderating) in the same molecule. Oxazole, on the other hand, should be entirely π-excessive, because furan reacts so much more readily than thiophen with electrophilic reagents. However only one electrophilic substitution of an oxazole is in the literature. Very little is known also about isoxazole, but 3-methylisoxazole nitrates readily.

In numbering the more complex systems, oxygen, sulphur and nitrogen are dealt with in that order, i.e. oxygen has the lowest number, and so on.

2. CORRELATION OF STRUCTURE AND PROPERTIES

With some exceptions, the chemistry of O- and S-heterocycles has grown in a more haphazard way than that of the N-heterocycles. In general, the parent substances have come in for little investigation. Indeed several of them (e.g. oxazole, *iso*thiazole, 1:3:4-thiadiazole) have been discovered only since 1947.

To facilitate comparison between the divisions of this section and the corresponding ones in Chapters IV and V, the same index-letters will be used.

(a) Solubility, with a Note on Isosterism

Furan is immiscible with water, in fact its solubility at 20° is only about 1–100. This may seem surprising because the oxygen atom should have a free pair of electrons (i.e. other than the pair participating in the π-pool) with which to bind the hydrogen atoms of water. Ingold (1953, p. 181) has made the interesting suggestion that these unshared and unconjugated electrons of the oxygen atom are in a linear orbital, and hence not easily available for forming bonds. Furan is soluble in light petroleum and all organic solvents.

The solubility of thiophen in water is quite small (but not known exactly). This would be expected from the low solubility of furan, because sulphur is less hydrogen-bonding than oxygen. In addition, Ingold (loc. cit.) points out that the sulphur atom in thiophen forms σ ring-bonds with pure p orbitals (as is shown by the $C - S - C$ angle being a right-angle). Hence the unshared, unconjugated electrons of the sulphur atom are in a pure s orbital, and are unavailable for binding hydrogen.

The insertion of a hydroxy- or amino-group should increase the water-solubility of furan and thiophen for reasons set out in

Chapter V (p. 140). The few facts available are in agreement with this hypothesis: 2-hydroxythiophen is soluble 1–16 at 15°, and 2-hydroxy-5-methylfuran (α-angelica lactone) 1–20, both greatly in excess of their parent substances. However these figures must be read in conjunction with data on the tautomerism of such substances (see (e) below).

The insertion of a ring-nitrogen atom (necessarily a doubly-bound nitrogen) into the molecule of furan or thiophen should increase solubility because of the free pair of electrons on this nitrogen atom. Thus the solubility of isoxazole in water is 1–6 at 20°, and oxazole is completely miscible with water. Moreover, although the solubility of thiazole is unrecorded, it is known that 2- and 4-methylthiazole are miscible with cold water in all proportions. 1:2:3-Thiadiazole is soluble 1–3 in water at 20°.

Annelation with a benzene ring of the substances described in this chapter decreases their solubility (as would be expected) although no exact figures are available.

It is now appropriate to discuss certain difficulties which arise in attempting to separate benzene and thiophen, the latter being a common contaminant in the former.

As can be seen from Table 11, the boiling-points of thiophen and its derivatives usually lie very close to those of corresponding members of the benzene series, and separation by fractional distillation is seldom worthwhile. On the other hand, the melting-points lie far apart, but this is also of no avail because benzene and thiophene derivatives, whilst not isomorphous, form solid solutions. Benzene and its derivatives are freed from thiophens by making use of the greater chemical reactivity of the latter; aluminium chloride, chlorosulphonic acid and, more recently, Raney-nickel are used for this purpose. Finally, the boiling-points for 2- and 3-substituted thiophens are usually close together, and this has often proved troublesome.

The odours of thiophen, its chloro-, formyl- and acyl-derivatives closely resemble those of benzene and its corresponding derivatives.

These and other resemblances between thiophene and benzene and between thiazole and pyridine have been much discussed (e.g. Steinkopf and Ohse, 1933), and have led Erlenmeyer and Leo (1933) to put forward the idea that these substances are *isosteric*, on the grounds that the same number of peripheral electrons are present in each, and with the implication that the $-S-$ unit occupies the same space as the $-CH:CH-$ unit. The concept of isosterism was originated by Langmuir (1919), who observed that carbon dioxide and nitrous oxide had remarkably similar physical properties, and showed that the number and arrangement of electrons in these two molecules are the same.

TABLE 11. Constants of Thiophen and Benzene Derivatives
(Steinkopf, 1941)

Thiophen	b.p. °C.	m.p. °C.	Benzene	b.p. °C.	m.p. °C.
(unsubstituted)	84	-30	(unsubstituted)	80	6
2-Methyl-	113		Methyl-	110	
2-Chloro-	127	-70	Chloro-	132	-45
2-Bromo-	150		Bromo-	156	-31
2-Formyl-	198		Formyl-a	180	
2-Acetyl-	214	9	Acetyl-b	200	20
3-Methyl-	114				
3-Chloro-	136				
3-Bromo-	157	-63			
3-Formyl-	199				
3-Acetyl-	210	57			

a Benzaldehyde.   b Acetophenone.

So much has been written about the physical similarity of thiophen and benzene derivatives (no close *chemical* similarity is claimed) that it is worth noting here that the hydroxy-thiophens are physically very different from phenol (see (*e*) below).

(*b*) Acidic and Basic Strength

Furan reacts, sometimes violently, with aqueous acids and forms a dark brown polymer. Hydrochloric acid in methanol has, in addition, a hydrolytic action and gives some succindialdehyde tetramethylacetal (XXIV). The necessity for hydrogen ions to initiate these reactions suggests that furan has slight basic properties, although apparently less than those of pyrrole (see p. 141). Thiophen, on the other hand, is perfectly stable to acid and gives no evidence of even feeble basic properties. The polymerization of furan by acid parallels the similar behaviour of pyrrole and *cyclo*pentadiene (see p. 141), and the hydrolysis of furan by acid is analogous to the easy hydrolysis of divinyl ether (IX), and all other ethers containing the vinyl group.

No ionization constants are available for the hydroxy- and amino-derivatives of furan and thiophen. The furan and thiophen carboxylic acids are of the same strength as, or slightly weaker than, benzoic acid.

$$\text{(CH}_3\text{O)}_2\,\overset{\displaystyle \overset{\text{CH}_2\text{——CH}_2}{|\qquad\quad|}}{\text{CH}}\qquad \text{CH(OCH}_3)_2$$

XXIV

The azalogues of furan and thiophen should be basic, because doubly-bound nitrogen, as we have seen in the last two chapters, can bind a proton. Figures are available only for thiazole ($pK_a = 2\cdot53$) which is a very much weaker base than pyridine ($5\cdot23$). Likewise 2-aminothiazole ($pK_a = 5\cdot39$) is weaker than 2-aminopyridine ($6\cdot86$). Again, 2-aminobenzothiazole ($pK_a = 4\cdot51$) is weaker than 2-aminoquinoline ($7\cdot34$) (Albert, Goldacre and Phillips, 1948).

(c) Ultraviolet Spectra

The ultraviolet spectra of furan, thiophen and their benzologues, like those of pyrrole and its benzologues, can be related to the spectra of benzene, naphthalene and phenanthrene (Badger and Christie, 1956). However, the resemblance is less close for the furans than for the pyrroles and thiophens. Thus dibenzothiophen (see Figure 19 in Chapter VIII) has a spectrum very similar to that of dibenzopyrrole (carbazole), but shifted to slightly shorter wavelengths: in both cases the curves roughly coincide with those for phenanthrene, except that at the long-wave end of the spectrum, the heterocyclic compounds absorb much more intensely. In dibenzofuran, this region of long-wave absorption has disappeared, but the other two absorption regions resemble those of phenanthrene (Badger and Christie, 1956).

Turning to smaller ring-systems, benzothiophen (thianaphthen) (XIII) has a spectrum quite similar to that of naphthalene (although not so close as that of indole) whereas that of benzofuran is moved to shorter wavelengths (see Figure 22 **in**

Chapter VIII). As is usual with one-ring systems, comparison of the spectra of thiophen, furan and pyrrole is not very profitable because of maxima too short in wavelength for the usual techniques. Only thiophen has a well-developed spectrum (λ_{max} = 231; log ε_{max} 3·85) (see Figure 24 in Chapter VIII).

The insertion of a ring-nitrogen atom has as little effect on the spectra of these heterocycles as has been already found in the two previous chapters. Chapter VIII should be consulted for details. As in all aromatic systems, the insertion of alkyl- or halogen-groups into the molecules of π-excessive O- and S-heterocycles moves the spectrum slightly (e.g. 5–10 mμ) to longer wavelengths, whereas aldehyde and ketone groups, and particularly groups with carbon-carbon double-bonds capable of conjugating with the nucleus, shift the spectrum further. Thus an acetyl-group in the 2-position of thiophen moves the spectrum by 42 mμ (Hartough, 1952).

(d) Action of Acid and Alkali

The high sensitivity of furan to acid (polymerization and some hydrolysis) and the insensitivity of thiophen were mentioned under (b) (p. 208). Nevertheless thiophen is polymerized by concentrated sulphuric acid, but only after prolonged contact. Both furan and thiophen are stable to strong alkali, and even to sodium. Like pyrrole, furan is protected from polymerization by the presence of alkyl-groups in both the 2- and the 5-position (a steric effect); however this procedure allows hydrolysis to proceed without competition, and hence acetonylacetone is produced in excellent yield. Furans with electron-attracting substituents are not very sensitive to acids.

Benzofuran (X) is easily polymerized by concentrated sulphuric, but not by hydrochloric, acid; the product is much used as a soluble resin in the varnish industry. The 'solvent naphtha' of coal-tar is a mixture of benzofuran and the hydrocarbon indene: copolymerization of this mixture gives the commercially important 'cumar' and 'coumarone' resins. Benzothiophen is stable to acid and alkali.

The insertion of a ring-nitrogen into these molecules inclines them to hydrolysis (compare the cumulative hydrolysis-increasing effect of doubly-bound nitrogen atoms in the pyridine and quinoline series, p. 50). This hydrolysis takes place at the expense of polymerization, which is minimal when doubly-bound nitrogen is present (see Chapter V, p. 148).

The oxazoles (e.g. XVI) are highly resistant to alkali and, with certain exceptions, to acid. Although 2:5-dimethyl-oxazole is unchanged by several hours' heating at 100° with 5N-hydrochloric acid, 5-ethoxy- and 5-amino-oxazoles are hydrolysed by dilute acids. Benzoxazole (XXII) gives 2-form-amidophenol on attempted titration at 20° with dilute acid (Albert, Goldacre and Phillips, 1948). Isoxazole (XVII), on the other hand, is stable to acids but gives cyanacetic aldehyde (NC·CH$_2$CHO) with cold sodium ethoxide solution. An alkyl group in the 5-position has a stabilizing influence, and 3:5-disubstituted isoxazoles are highly resistant to alkalis. 4:5-Benzisoxazole is rearranged by alkali to salicyclic nitrile. The 1:2:5-oxadiazoles (e.g. XVIII), like isoxazoles, are labile to alkali, which rearranges them to oximes of α-oxoacetonitrile.

Both thiazole and benzothiazole have good stability to acid and alkali, but 1:2:3-, 1:2:4- and 1:3:4-thiadiazoles are easily decomposed by alkali; and 1:2:4-thiadiazole is also very sensitive to acid (Goerdeler, Ohm and Tegtmeyer, 1956).

(e) Nature of the Hydroxy- and Amino-derivatives

The hydroxy- and amino-derivatives of furan and thiophen are not readily accessible substances. Dunlop and Peters (1953) and Cava, Wilson and Williams (1956) agree that the substances synthesized by Hodgson and Davies (1939) are not 2- and 3-hydroxyfuran, as had been thought. This clears the ground for consideration of the other claimants. There is no doubt that 3-butenoic-γ-lactone (β:γ-butenolide; XXV) and its more stable tautomer, 2-butenoic-γ-lactone (XXVI) are themselves tauto-meric with 2-hydroxyfuran, but the difficult task remains of finding where the equilibrium lies in various states and solvents. If a Zerewitinoff determination gave no methane, it would be fair to conclude that equilibrium did not favour the enol. But this has not been tried, and no spectral comparisons have been made, although genuine enolic derivatives are available, e.g. 2-methoxyfuran (Petfield and Amstutz, 1954; Cava, Wilson and Williams, 1955) and 2-acetoxyfuran (Cava, Wilson and

P

Williams, 1956) are known. 2-Hydroxybenzofuran (*o*-hydroxy-phenylacetic lactone) requires similar investigation. Succinic anhydride (p. 16) may be in tautomeric equilibrium with 2:5-dihydroxyfuran, but this has not been looked at.

$$
\begin{array}{cc}
\text{HC}\!\!-\!\!-\!\!\text{CH}_2 & \text{HC}\!=\!=\!\text{CH} \\
\| \quad | & | \quad | \\
\text{HC} \diagdown \quad \diagup \text{CO} & \text{HC} \diagdown \quad \diagup \text{CO} \\
\quad \text{O} & \quad \text{O} \\
\text{XXV} & \text{XXVI}
\end{array}
$$

The simplest known 3-hydroxyfuran is 2-methyl-3-hydroxy-furan (Votoček and Malachta, 1932) about which little is known except that it yields only one-third of an equivalent of methane in a Zerewitinoff determination. 2:3-Dihydroxyfuran may be a mono-enol like cyclic diketones in general, which behave in this way to minimize electrostatic repulsion (Dewar, 1949).

The simplest known aminofuran is 3-amino-2-methylfuran (Stevenson and Johnson, 1937) which discolours and resinifies in the air. It diazotizes and couples with β-naphthol. 2-Acetamido-furan has been prepared but decomposition took place on attempted hydrolysis. Nothing is known of tautomeric equilibria in these substances.

The hydroxythiophens have been better investigated than the hydroxyfurans. The infrared spectrum of 2-hydroxythiophen in carbon tetrachloride showed strong carbonyl (and weak hydroxyl) absorption (Hurd and Kreuz, 1950). The O-methyl- and O-acetyl-derivatives resembled their benzene analogues in boiling-point and odour, whereas 2-hydroxythiophen was quite unlike phenol in these respects. 3-Hydroxythiophen, in liquid film, showed equally strong infrared absorption for a phenolic hydroxyl- and a carbonyl-group. In carbon tetrachloride solution, the hydroxyl- increases at the expense of the carbonyl-absorption on increasing dilution (Hurd and Kreuz, 1950). It has a strong phenolic odour, and gives an O-benzoate. Two interconvertible 2-hydroxybenzothiophens have been reported and should repay investigation (Marschalk, 1913).

2- and 3-Aminothiophen are, like the hydroxythiophens, highly unstable in air (Campaigne and Monroe, 1954; Stein-kopf, 1941). 2-Aminothiophen diazotizes and couples normally, but nothing is known of the tautomeric composition of these substances at equilibrium, in marked contrast to amino-derivatives of thiazole (see below), pyridine and quinoline.

Little is known about the equilibrium in rings containing both oxygen and nitrogen. 2-Hydroxy- (and 2-mercapto-) oxazoles are seen, from infrared spectra, to be mainly in the amide (and thioamide) form in the solid state and in carbon bisulphide (Gompper and Herlinger, 1956). 5-Hydroxy-3-phenylisoxazole gives an O-methyl-derivative with diazo-methane, and a N-methyl-derivative when the silver salt is warmed with methyl iodide. 5-Hydroxy-oxazoles and -isoxa-zoles can tautomerize to form a methylene-group in the 5-position, because they readily give styryl-derivatives with benzaldehyde. However such tautomerism may be only in response to the reagent and throws no light on the structure.

The ultraviolet spectrum of 6-methyl-2-hydroxybenzo-thiazole has been compared with those of its O- and N-methyl-derivatives and it is evident that the amide- (i.e. $-CO \cdot NH-$) form predominates at equilibrium (Hunter and Parken, 1935). That 2-mercaptothiazole is mainly in the $-CS \cdot NH-$ form was shown similarly (Morton and Stubbs, 1939). The spectra of 2-hydroxythiazole, its N- and O-methyl-derivatives have been compared in the ultraviolet and infrared (Klein and Prijs, 1954), and it is evident that equilibrium favours almost entirely the amide tautomer, at least in the solvents examined (alcohol and carbon bisulphide, respectively). 2-Hydroxythiazole gives (a) 2-methoxythiazole with diazomethane in ether, and (b) the N-methyl-isomer with methyl iodide in sodium methoxide.

In 2-aminothiazole, the ratio of amino- to imino-forms at equilibrium is 20,000:1 in water at 20°, as determined by the potentiometric method (see Chapter IV, p. 54) (Angyal and Angyal, 1952). 2-Aminothiazole acylates on the ring-nitrogen atom before transferring the acyl-group to the primary amino-group (Angyal, 1952).

(f) Substitution by Electrophilic Reagents

Because the five-membered O- and S-heterocycles are π-excessive, electrophilic substitution is their most characteristic type of reactivity.

Furan (II), in ease of electrophilic substitution, is intermediate between thiophen and pyrrole. It substitutes in the 2-position preferentially, and the electron-density diagram (XXVIII) is compatible with this. However, when both 2- and 5-positions are blocked, substitution occurs in the 3-position, for example in nitration and the Friedel-Crafts reaction.

The nett charges of the series pyrrole (XXVII), furan (XXVIII), and thiophen (XXIX) have been calculated by the valence-bond (resonance) method (Pullman, 1948). Because of the complex electronic situation which thiophen presents (see p. 202), comparisons between these three diagrams may not be very fruitful, but each has its own internal interest. A particular criticism is that comparison of (XXVIII) and (XXIX) would lead one to think that thiophen is more readily substituted (electrophilically) than furan, whereas the reverse is the case. Rather surprisingly, it has been suggested, from molecular orbital considerations, that all the carbon atoms of thiophen carry no charge at all, and that their differing reactivity is due to differing polarization in response to the approach of an electrophilic reagent (Longuet-Higgins, 1949; see also de Heer, 1954). Clearly, the electronic structure of thiophen presents special difficulties.

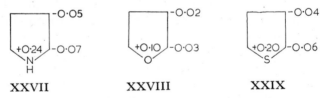

In substituting furan, strong acidic reagents must be avoided to prevent polymerization and hydrolytic splitting, but if electron-attracting groups are present there is much less risk. The Friedel-Crafts reaction is the only method known for direct alkylation. Because aluminium chloride (the only effective catalyst for alkylation) causes polymerization, electron-attracting groups must be present, which is an unfortunate limitation.

Furan readily undergoes acylation by the Friedel-Crafts reaction: zinc chloride, stannic chloride, or iodine are suitable catalysts. Furan also undergoes the Gattermann reaction with hydrogen cyanide, giving furfural (furan-2-aldehyde). Actually furan is manufactured from furfural, but this reaction is useful for substituted aldehydes.

The hydrogen atom in the 2-position of furan is replaceable by sodium on treatment with sodium phenyl (Gilman and Breuer, 1934), and the product gives furoic acid (furan-2-carboxylic acid) with carbon dioxide. 2-Methylfuran metallates in the 5-position, in contrast to toluene which metallates in the methyl-group. Mercuric chloride converts furan to furan-2-mercurichloride in 33% yield. This product is used in reactions reminiscent of those given by Grignard reagents, for example it gives 2-ketones with acyl halides, and 2-bromofuran with bromine.

Aminomethylation of furans with formaldehyde and methylamine gives 2-methylaminomethylfurans (Holdren and Hixon, 1946). Other aldehyde reactions include the green colour which most furans give with a pine splinter dipped in 10N-hydrochloric acid (a few furans give a red colour like pyrrole does). Some furans give the red colour reaction with p-dimethylaminobenzaldehyde usually considered characteristic of pyrroles (Ehrlich's reaction).

Direct halogenation of furan is almost explosive, and gives a difficultly separable mixture of mono- and poly-substituted products, but bromination of furan in dioxan at 0° gives a good yield of 2-bromofuran (Terentev, Belenkii and Yanovskaya, 1954). Mono-halogenfurans are also prepared by chlorinating (etc.) furoic acid, followed by a decarboxylation (Shepard, Winslow and Johnson, 1930). Chlorination of furfural takes place in the 5-position, and a special catalyst (sulphur + benzoyl peroxide) helps to regulate the reaction (Chute and Wright, 1945).

Sulphonation is best carried out with the non-acidic pyridine-sulphur trioxide complex (Terentev and Kazitsyna, 1946), and gives the 2-sulphonic acid. However sulphuric acid can be used if an electron-attracting substituent (e.g. −COOH) is present.

Nitration of furan, with a well-chilled mixture of acetic anhydride and anhydrous nitric acid, gives 2-nitro- and 2:5-dinitro-furan in 35 and 27% yields respectively. 2-Methylfuran-5-carboxylic acid nitrates in the 3-position, a convenient route to 3-nitrofuran (Rinkes, 1938).

Sometimes, in electrophilic substitution, a group (usually —COOH) other than hydrogen is replaced by the reagent.

Benzofuran (X) reacts with electrophilic reagents much more vigorously than thiophen (Bisagni, Buu-Hoï and Royer, 1955) and it substitutes preferentially in the 2-position. If this is blocked by an electron-releasing group (e.g. —CH$_3$), the 3-position is substituted, and if blocked by an electron-attracting group (e.g. —COOMe), the 5- and 7-positions are attacked instead. C-Formylation, with dimethylformamide and phosphorus oxychloride, is highly successful in this series.

Thiophen (III) is intermediate in electrophilic reactivity between benzene and furan. Relevant to this grading is the coupling of diazotized aniline with 2-acetamidothiophen, whereas acetanilide does not couple (Hurd and Priestley, 1947).

The Friedel-Crafts reaction gives only low yields with alkyl halides, apparently because this reaction needs forcing conditions, which induce polymerization. The Wurz-Fittig reaction (e.g. the reaction of 2-bromothiophen with ethyl bromide and sodium to give 2-ethylthiophen) also does not give good yields. The best method for direct alkylation appears to be an addition reaction with olefins (see (*h*) below). Alkyl-thiophens are usually made by direct synthesis, or by reduction of the aldehydes and ketones.

Grignard reagents are easily formed from 2-bromo- and 3-iodo-thiophen, and are as useful as in the benzene series for producing acids, aldehydes and alcohols. Also the reaction of these reagents with water has been much used to replace a bromine atom in the 2- or 5-position by hydrogen. Thiophen forms 2:5-dichloromercurithiophen (66% yield) with mercuric chloride (2-nitrothiophen does not react). Acid hydrolysis regenerates thiophen (Steinkopf and Killingstad, 1937). The chloromercuri-group is easily replaced by acyl-, bromine or iodine.

Thiophen is acylated in the 2-position by acetyl chloride and aluminium chloride (90% yield). Acetic anhydride can be used instead with phosphoric acid or a trace of iodine as catalyst. The Gattermann reaction is useless for introducing the formyl-group, but excellent yields of thiophen-2-aldehyde are obtained from N-methylformanilide and phosphorus oxychloride (King and Nord, 1949).

Thiophen does not react readily with aromatic aldehydes, and hence the Ehrlich and pine-splinter tests, given so readily by pyrrole, are negative. However formaldehyde and hydrogen chloride give 2-chloromethylthiophen (47% yield) (Blicke and Leonard, 1946), and thiophen, formaldehyde and ammonium chloride give N-(2-thenyl)formaldimine (XXX). With isatin (p. 185) in sulphuric acid, thiophen forms the intensely blue indophenine (XXXI) (Steinkopf and Hanske, 1939), long known as a test for thiophens. Two positions in the thiophen, either 2:5- or 2:3-, must be free.

CH$_2$N:CH$_2$

XXX   XXXI

Direct chlorination of thiophen gives a mixture of mono- and poly-chlorothiophens, but sulphuryl chloride specifically produces 2-chlorothiophen, and converts 2-methyl- to 5-chloro-2-methyl-thiophen. 2-Methylthiophen has no tendency towards side-chain chlorination even under conditions that are effective for toluene (Campaigne and Le Suer, 1948). Bromination of thiophen gives 2-bromo- and 2:5-dibromo-thiophen (Blicke and Burckhalter, 1942). 2-Bromothiophen is now commercially available. Thiophen is satisfactorily iodinated in the 2-position with iodine and mercuric oxide.

Sulphuric acid (95%) converts thiophen to the 2-sulphonic acid in 75% yield. Nitration with nitric acid in acetic anhydride gives 2-nitro- (70%) and 3-nitro- (5%) thiophen (Steinkopf and Höpner, 1933). 2-Nitrothiophen can be nitrated further to a mixture of 2:4- and 2:5-dinitrothiophen, but no trinitration takes place. Similarly, 2-carboxythiophen nitrates to a mixture of the

4- and 5-nitro-derivatives (Rinkes, 1932). Thus, groups which are *meta*-directing in the benzene series are not exclusively so in thiophen chemistry because of the strong directing influence of sulphur.

Electrophilic reagents sometimes replace atoms other than hydrogen, for example bromine has been known to replace chlorine, alkyl-, acyl-, carboxyl-, and nitro-groups. Conversely bromine has been replaced by chlorine, nitro-, acyl- and phenylazo-groups.

Benzothiophen (XIII, Thionaphthen) is electrophilically substituted in the 3-position preferentially. This difference from thiophen is parallel to the difference between indole and pyrrole whereas furan and benzofuran both substitute in the 2-position. Mercuration, Friedel-Crafts acylation, chloromethylation, halogenation, sulphonation and nitration all go well (Hartough and Meisel, 1954). An electron-releasing group in 3- directs further substitution to 2-, whereas 3-nitrobenzothiophen further nitrates at 4- and 5- (Fries *et al.*, 1937). When benzothiophen reacts in turn with sodium and carbon dioxide, benzothiophen-2-carboxylic acid is obtained, but the mechanism is unknown. 3-Hydroxybenzothiophen couples with diazotized amines in the 2-position.

The introduction of doubly-bound nitrogen reduces the ease of electrophilic substitution: it is not easy to say how much, because few of the relevant experiments have been done.

Isoxazole (XVII) has not been submitted to electrophilic attack, but 3-methylisoxazole nitrates in 40% yield and 3:5-dimethylisoxazole in 90% yield: in each case the nitro-group enters the 4-position (Quilico and Musante, 1941). Halogenation and sulphonation also take place in the 4-position.

Oxazole (XVI). The only electrophilic substitution recorded in the oxazole series is the bromination (in the 4-position) of 2-phenyl-5-ethoxyoxazole with N-bromoacetamide. Nitration of *benzoxazole* (XXII) gives a mixture of 5- and (mainly) 6-nitro-derivatives.

Thiazole (XIX) is not easily substituted electrophilically, but it sulphonates in 65% yield at about 200° (in the 5-position) (Erlenmeyer and Kiefer, 1945). 4-Methylthiazole gives the 5-nitro-derivative, but only at 160° (Prijs, Ostertag and

Erlenmeyer, 1947), and 2-methylthiazole is hardly attacked. The presence of electron-releasing groups (e.g. NH_2-, CH_3CONH-, OH-) in the 2-position permits nitration, halogenation and sulphonation to proceed in the 5-position under mild conditions. Even Friedel-Crafts acylations can then be carried out, but the Gattermann aldehyde synthesis gives only a small yield. Diazotized aniline couples (in the 5-position) with 2-acetamidothiazole.

Lithiumthiazole (from butyl lithium and 2-bromothiazole) reacts with solid carbon dioxide to give thiazole-2-carboxylic acid (60% yield) (Beyerman, Berben and Bontekoe, 1954). 5-Bromothiazole reacts similarly. A hydrogen-lithium exchange reaction on thiazole gives 2-lithiumthiazole (Metzger and Koether, 1953), but not in such good yield.

An electron-density diagram of thiazole shows a large negative charge on 5-, a positive charge of roughly one-third that amount on 2-, whereas the 4-position is neutral (Pullman and Metzger, 1948). For experiments comparing the reactions of thiazole and its derivatives with those of pyridine, see Ochiai (1938, 1939) and Ochiai and Nagasawa (1939). The bromination of thiazole to 2-bromothiazole at 250–400° (Wibaut, 1939) is likely to be a free-radical reaction (see (j) below).

Benzothiazole (XXIII) almost always substitutes in the benzene ring with electrophilic reagents, a property reminiscent of quinoline, but which derives from the fact that a benzene ring obscures the electron-rich 5-position of thiazole. Sulphonation, which requires fuming acid at 100°, gives the 4- (65%) and 6- (28%) sulphonic acids and nitration gives 6-nitrobenzothiazole. Bromination is usually of the free-radical type (see (j) below), and no Friedel-Crafts reaction has been recorded. The presence of chlorine, or an amino- or hydroxy-group, in the 2-position enables 6-bromo-compounds to be formed (Colonna, 1943). An electron-density diagram of benzothiazole shows that the greatest excesses of electrons in a substitutable position occur at 4- and 6-, and even these are only one-fourteenth of that in the 5-position of thiazole (Pullman and Metzger, 1948).

Miscellaneous. The electrophilic substitution of 4:5-benziso-thiazole, like that of most of the remaining substances, has not been described, but the 5-hydroxy-derivative brominates in the 4-position. Benzo-1:2:3-thiadiazole nitrates mainly in the 4-position.

(g) Substitution by Nucleophilic Reagents

No nucleophilic reactions involving thiophen or furan appear to be known, but the introduction of a ring-nitrogen atom naturally facilitates nucleophilic reactions.

Replacement of hydrogen. Both thiazole and benzothiazole are aminated in the 2-position by sodamide, but the yields are very poor (Ochiai and Nagasawa, 1939, 1940). However 2-amino-benzothiazole and -benzoxazole are prepared in good yield by the action of alkaline hydroxylamine on the parent substances (Skraup, 1919). The other nucleophilic reactions, as used for replacing hydrogen in pyridine and other π-deficient N-hetero-cycles (see p. 69), do not appear to succeed with the substances described in the present chapter. For example lithium butyl and thiazole give lithium thiazole, and not butylthiazole.

Replacement of halogen.[1] Only when a ring-nitrogen atom is present is a halogen labile enough for easy replacement in the π-excessive N-heterocycles, and such replacement is usually con-fined to the 2-position. Thus, the unreactivity of 4- and 5-halogenated thiazoles stands in contrast to their 2-halogenated isomers. The kinetics of the combination of the very unreactive 2-bromobenzothiophen with amines, especially piperidine, have been examined (Brower and Amstutz, 1954), and also those of the far more reactive 2-chlorothiazole and 2-chlorobenzothia-zole (Young and Amstutz, 1951; Brower, Way, Samuels and Amstutz, 1954). From these studies, it is seen that 2-chloro-thiazole reacts more slowly than 2-chlorobenzothiazole and 2-chloroquinoline, but faster than 2-bromopyridine (see p. 76). 2-Chlorobenzoxazole gives 2-anilinobenzoxazole readily with aniline.

The halogen in 2-chlorothiazoles is readily hydrolysed to the hydroxy-group by alkali, but not by acid unless an electron-attracting group is in the 5-position. 2-Chloro-benzoxazole and -benzothiazole also have labile halogen. In 2-chloro-1:3:4-thiadiazole and 5-chloro-1:2:4-thiadiazole, the halogen is easily

---

[1] See p. 73 for available reactions.

replaced by hydroxyl- (with acid), mercapto- (with thiourea), and methylamino-groups (Goerdeler, Ohm and Tegtmeyer, 1956). 2-Methoxythiazole is obtained from 2-chlorothiazole and sodium methoxide, the 5-chloro-group in oxazoles is similarly replaceable, and 2-chlorobenzoxazole gives the 2-ethoxy-analogue.

2-Chlorobenzoxazole gives 2-mercaptobenzoxazole with sodium hydrogen sulphide (Desai, Hunter and Khalidi, 1934), and 2-chlorothiazole reacts similarly. 2-Chlorobenzoxazole and sodium sulphite give benzoxazole-2-sulphonic acid (I. G. Farben, 1934), which is easily converted to 2-cyanobenzoxazole. The 2-methylsulphonyl-group ($-SO_2CH_3$) is also very reactive, and 2-methylsulphonyl-derivatives of benzothiazole, benzoxazole and 1:3:4-oxadiazole can be converted to 2-alkoxy-, 2-hydroxy- and 2-alkylamino-derivatives (Hoggarth, 1949). Ammonia, and secondary amines give less satisfactory yields.

Other replacements. The conversion of a mercapto- to a chloro-substituent is seldom called for in six-membered rings, because only in the pyrimidine series do mercapto-compounds arise early in a chain of syntheses. The ready availability of 2-mercaptobenz-oxazole and -thiazole makes the substitution of $-Cl$ for $-SH$ worthwhile: phosphorus pentachloride, or chlorine in acetic acid is suitable for this reaction (Findlay and Dougherty, 1946).

The exchange of hydroxyl-groups for chlorine, which is believed to proceed through a phosphoric ester stage, has been less developed in the π-excessive than in the π-deficient N-heterocycles (see p. 80). At least the 2-hydroxythiazoles give 2-chlorothiazoles with phosphorus pentachloride. Nuclear chlorination takes place to some extent also in the 5-position if this is not protected (Ganapathi and Venkataraman, 1945).

2-Amino-thiazole and -benzothiazole diazotize well when sodium nitrite is added to the amine dissolved in a mixture of phosphoric and nitric acids, and are then easily replaced by chlorine or bromine (Ganapathi and Venkataraman, 1945; Beyerman, Berben and Bontekoe, 1954; Erlenmeyer and Überwasser, 1940, 1942). Similar changes are undergone by 2-aminobenzoxazoles (Desai, Hunter and Khalidi, 1934) and 4-aminoisoxazoles (Quilico, Fusco and Rosnati, 1946). 4-

Aminoisoxazoles, when diazotized in sulphuric acid, give 4-hydroxyisoxazoles.

The 5-amino-group in thiazole, and the *Bz*-amino-groups in benzothiazole diazotize much more readily than 2-amino-groups and can be preferentially substituted when both are present.

(h) Addition Reactions

Of the parent substances discussed in this chapter, furan is most susceptible to addition reactions across double-bonds (it will be recalled that it is the least aromatic). Thus furan combines with maleic anhydride and dimethyl acetylenedicarboxylate to give bicyclic adducts, e.g. (XXXII), but unlike butadiene it does not add acrolein (Kloetzel, 1948). Furfural (2-formyl-furan) and other furans with electron-attracting groups do not even add maleic anhydride. For the polymerization of furan and benzofuran, see p. 210. Furan does not combine with sodium bisulphite (compare the π-deficient N-heterocycles, p. 83) but it does add bromine across the double-bonds. Benzofuran, too, adds bromine across the 2:3-double-bond, and the adduct gives 2-bromobenzofuran on heating.

Furfuryl alcohol gives 2:4:5-trimethoxy-2-methyltetrahydro-furan with acidified methanol at 60°, and severer treatment leads to methyl laevulate (Clauson-Kaas and Nielsen, 1955; Lewis, 1957).

Thiophen does not react with maleic anhydride or any other dienophile, but at 30° chlorine converts it to the 2:3:4:5-tetrachloride, which alkali changes to a mixture of halogenated thiophens (Coonradt and Hartough, 1948). In this type of reaction, thiophen and furan stand between butadiene and the aromatic hydrocarbons.

No similar addition reactions for thiazole and oxazole seem to be recorded.

The alkylation of thiophen with *iso*olefins (e.g. *iso*butene), using phosphoric acid as a catalyst, gives a mixture of equal parts of 2- and 3-alkylthiophens (Appleby *et al.*, 1948). The unusual orientation suggests that this reaction may occur through a preliminary addition.

4-Methylthiazole-N-oxide, obtained in 27% yield by the

action of hydrogen peroxide and acetic acid on 4-methylthiazole, represents a type of compound little investigated as yet (Ochiai and Hayashi, 1947).

Thiazole, treated with bromine in chloroform solution, gives an N-perbromide, just as pyridine does.

Thiophen is destroyed by hydrogen peroxide but 3:4-diphenylthiophen forms the sulphone by adding two atoms of oxygen to the sulphur atom, and benzothiophen does the same (Hückel and Nabih, 1956).

| | Thiamine |
| XXXII | XXXIII |

The N-methylation of oxazoles and thiazoles proceeds readily, and no O- or S-methylation takes place (S-methylation of thiophen is also unknown). The quaternary salts of thiazole are less readily oxidatively destroyed by bromine water, but more readily desulphurized by lead acetate, than simple salts of thiazole.

Thiazolium salts having a particular type of alkyl-group (viz. one consisting of an electron-attracting group linked by a methylene bridge to the ring-nitrogen atom) are readily split by sodium sulphite. Benzylthiazolium chloride is a simple example of this, and thiamine, i.e. vitamin B_1 (XXXIII), is a slightly more complex one (see Chapter XI).

When thiazolium salts have a methyl-group in the 2-position, this is much more reactive than in the non-quaternized analogues (cf. pyridinium salts, p. 97); but a methyl-group in the 4-position is not activated by quaternization.

Upon addition of alkali, thiazolium salts undergo hydroxylation in the 2-position, giving e.g. (XXXIV) (cf. pyridinium salts, p. 70); usually (XXXIV) splits open to give (XXXV), creating an extra acidic group, recognizable in potentiometric titration (Williams and Ruehle, 1935). Mild oxidation of (XXXV) (exposure to air often suffices) gives the disulphide. The presence of a methyl-group in the 2-position prevents the hydroxylation reaction. Thiamine (XXXIII) is stable to acid, but in alkaline solution it is converted, by the stages outlined above, to the disulphide.

$$\text{XXXIV} \longrightarrow \text{XXXV}$$

XXXIV   XXXV

In thiazolium salts, the equilibrium lies much more in favour of the 'carbinol-base' or 'pseudo-base' (e.g. XXXIV) than in pyridinium salts. Thus, too, benzothiazolium salts give carbinol-bases more readily than quinolinium salts, and these in turn more than pyridinium salts (Sprague and Land, 1957). This readiness is a sign of diminished aromatic character.

(i) Oxidations and Reductions

Furans are easily destroyed by oxidation. Even furfural, in spite of its electron-attracting substituent, is attacked by oxygen directly on the nucleus, and gives formylacrylic acid ($OHC \cdot CH:CH \cdot CO_2H$) upon long standing in air (Dunlop, Stout and Swadesh, 1946). The addition of a ring-nitrogen atom decreases this tendency. Nevertheless, bromine water, fuming nitric acid or cold, dilute potassium permanganate destroy oxazoles and (particularly) isoxazoles. Benzoxazole resists all but the most vigorous oxidation, because the most vulnerable (4:5-) bond is protected: however it gives 2:2′-dibenzoxazolyl with copper acetate.

Thiophen resists potassium permanganate, but is readily oxidized by hypobromites, and fuming nitric acid. Hydrogen peroxide also attacks it giving sulphuric acid. When passed through a red-hot tube, thiophen is oxidized to 2:2′- and 3:3′-dithienyl.

Thiazoles are resistant to mild oxidation, but they break up under very vigorous conditions.

The formation of S- and N-oxides is discussed above (p. 223). The oxidative removal of a mercapto-group with nitric acid or hydrogen peroxide is easily accomplished in the thiazole series (Buchman, Reims and Sargent, 1941).

Hydrogenation. Furans hydrogenate to tetrahydrofurans in good yield, and under much milder conditions than benzene needs: nickel or palladium catalysts at 100° are frequently used. Furfural is converted in industry to tetrahydrofurfuryl alcohol over a copper chromite and nickel catalyst. Tetrahydrofuran is manufactured from furfural by catalytic removal of the side-chain (Wilson, 1945). Benzofuran is readily reduced to 2:3-dihydrobenzofuran.

Thiophen is much less readily hydrogenated to tetrahydro-thiophen. Thiophen is completely destroyed by sodium in liquid ammonia, whereas benzothiophen is quantitatively converted to o-ethylthiophenol, and dibenzothiophen to 1:4-dihydrodi-benzothiophen.

Oxazoles and thiazoles, and their benzologues, strongly resist hydrogenation. However, benzothiazolium iodide is reduced by zinc and acid to 2:3-dihydrobenzothiazole. The isoxazole ring is split open when hydrogenation is attempted. 1:2:4-Thiadiazole also is readily ring-opened by reducing agents, even hydrogen sulphide (Goerdeler, Ohm and Tegt-meyer, 1956).

Removal of halogen, nitrogen and sulphur. 2:5-Dibromothiazole-4-sulphonic acid is converted by hydrogen over Raney-nickel to thiazole-4-sulphonic acid (Erlenmeyer and Kiefer, 1945), a treatment which desulphurizes thiophen. The removal of a chlorine atom from the 2-position of thiazole has special preparative significance, as it is not always easy to obtain a thiazole with a free 2-position by direct synthesis. This dechlor-ination can be accomplished with zinc and acid (Jensen and Friediger, 1943), or hydrogen iodide and phosphorus. In the benzothiazole series, Raney-nickel and sodium hydroxide, or hydrogen iodide and phosphorus can be used (Erlenmeyer and Überwasser, 1940, 1942). Catalytic dechlorination has also been used in the oxazole series.

The 2-amino-group in thiazole is readily removed by di-azotization in the presence of hypophosphorous acid (Ganapathi and Venkataraman, 1945; Beyerman, Berben and Bontekoe, 1954).

The removal of a 2-mercapto-group from a thiazole is easily accomplished by oxidation (Buchman, Reims and Sargent, 1941), or, in favourable cases, heating with Raney-nickel, a reaction which is often ring-opening as well (Cook, Heilbron and Levy, 1947; Hurd and Rudner, 1951).

Decarboxylation. As in Chapters IV and V, this is treated as a reduction. It need only be said here that the carboxylic acids of furan, thiophen and oxazole readily decarboxylate. Isoxazole-carboxylic acids decompose profoundly on heating. Thiazole-2-carboxylic acid readily decarboxylates, but the 4-isomer is stable. The quinoline and copper technique has proved the most popular for decarboxylating these O- and S-heterocycles.

(j) *Homolytic or Free-radical Reactions*

Very few homolytic reactions have been recorded for the substances discussed in this chapter. As with pyridine, it is supposed that the bromination of thiazole and benzothiazole takes place with free bromine atoms because these are plentiful at the high temperature required (250–450°). In each case, the 2-position is attacked (Wibaut, 1939; Jansen and Wibaut, 1937). The chlorination of benzothiazole in the (electron-deficient) 2-position, by heating with phosphorus pentachloride to 160°, may be a similar reaction, or else a nucleophilic reaction with PCl_6^-.

p-Chlorobenzene diazonium acetate and furan gave 29% of 2-*p*-chlorophenylfuran and 0·7% of the 3-isomer (Johnson, 1946). A methyl-group has been introduced into the 5-position of 4-carbomethoxy-2-phenyloxazole with lead tetracetate (Cornforth and Cookson, 1952).

(k) *Side-chain Reactions*

For the substances discussed in this chapter, most side-chain reactions proceed as in aromatic chemistry generally.

The methyl-group in the 2-position is specially activated in the oxazoles and thiazoles, and condenses readily with aldehydes to give 2-styrylthiazole, etc. A 2-benzyl-group reacts with these reagents and also with nitrosobenzene, diazotized aniline, and amyl nitrite. 2-Methylthiazolium chloride reacts with *p*-nitroso-dimethylaniline, but 2-methylthiazole does not. The 4- and 5-methyl-groups in thiazoles do not react with aldehydes, even after quaternization. 4-Nitro-5-methylisoxazole (but not the 4-nitro-3-methyl-isomer) reacts with aldehydes.

The condensation of two molecules of the 2-methyl-hetero-cycles mentioned in this chapter has led to cyanines, valuable as sensitizers of photographic film (see p. 98). This condensation can be effected with ethyl orthoformate, which gives a con-jugated three-carbon bridge; whereas a one-carbon bridge is neatly effected by the Kendall reaction in which the 2-methyl-group in one molecule is condensed with a 2-methylthio-group in another, methylmercaptan being liberated (Kendall, 1935). The cyanines derived from benzothiazoles have proved particularly useful as sensitizers (Hamer, 1950).

The reduction of ketones and aldehydes of the thiophen series, by means of the Clemmensen and Wolff-Kishner reactions, is much used for the synthesis of alkylthiophens. Conversely acylthiophens can be oxidized to carboxylic acids with sodium hypochlorite (Hartough and Conley, 1947). The oxidation of the 2-methyl- to the 2-formyl-group in benzothia-zoles is possible with selenium dioxide (Erne, 1949).

The carboxylic acids of the substances described in this chapter undergo the usual reactions of aromatic acids. They readily form esters, acid chlorides, and amides; they give aldehydes by the Rosenmund technique, and their amides can be dehydrated to nitriles.

3. MONOGRAPHS

The following short summaries of occurrence, uses, physical properties, and syntheses are to supplement the information on properties in Section 2 of this chapter.

A. SYSTEMS WITHOUT A RING-NITROGEN ATOM

Furan (II) is a colourless liquid, b.p. 31°, with a strong ether-like odour, miscible with light petroleum and all other organic solvents. It is prepared commercially by the catalytic decarbonylation of furfural (furan-2-aldehyde) by passing it with steam over a zinc chromite and iron catalyst at about 400°. On a smaller scale, nickel or cobalt catalysts have been successful (Wilson, 1945). The usual

Q

laboratory preparation of furan is by decarboxylating furan-2-carboxylic acid at about 200° (Wagner and Simons, 1936). The radical of furan is called 'furyl'; whereas 'furfuryl' is the radical of 2-methylfuran, the analogue of 'benzyl' in the benzene series.

Furan and 2-methylfuran (sylvan) have been found in oils obtained by destructively distilling pine, beech and other woods, and among the volatile carbonization products of cellulose, sugars, peat and coffee.[1] Some furans occur as such in plants, e.g. elsholtzione (3-methyl-2-furyl *iso*butyl ketone), carlina oxide (benzyl-furylacetylene) and perillene (3-hexenylfuran). The most important furan industrially is furfural, obtained by the acid hydrolysis of industrial carbohydrate waste, principally maize cobs (the carbohydrate which yields the furfural is xylan, a pentosan $(C_5H_8O_4)_x$).

The story of the industrial development of furfural is one of the most romantic in the whole of heterocyclic chemistry. In the 1920's, the Quaker Oats Company in Iowa were accumulating 200 tons of oat husks per day, in the course of preparing breakfast cereals. As this presented a serious problem in disposal, the company established a research fellowship to find a use for the husks. Under this sponsorship, Miner and Brownlee discovered that acid digestion of the hulls produced a satisfactory cattle food. Furfural was recognized as a volatile by-product, but the market at that time was so small that one day's supply of oat husks would give the world's requirements of furfural for the next 200 years. Accordingly, the Quaker Oats Company set up a subsidiary, The Miner Laboratories, for research into the uses of furfural, and for promoting its sale (Dunlop, 1956).

This was in 1922, and at first the principal outlet was in plastics, to produce a modified bakelite (phenol-furfural-formaldehyde plastic). In 1927 furfural was adopted as a solvent to remove the colour from crude pine rosin, and by 1931 furfural was established in the petroleum industry as a selective solvent for refining lubricating oil. Furfural is also used for the azeotropic separation of butadiene from other C_4 hydrocarbons in the preparation of artificial rubber, and for the separation of saturated and unsaturated glycerides in the refinement of vegetable oils. From these processes it can be recovered by steam-distillation and re-used.

The continuous hydrogenation of furfural over copper and nickel, giving respectively furfuryl alcohol and tetrahydrofurfuryl alcohol (see p. 11), is carried out commercially, although these substances have so far found only minor outlets in technology. The hydrolysis

---

[1] Furfuryl mercaptan, one of the constituents of coffee aroma, is manufactured for flavouring artificial coffees (Reichstein and Staudinger, 1950).

of cellulose gives 5-hydroxymethylfurfural, which can be further hydrolysed to a mixture of formic and laevulinic acid, a reaction with possibilities for the commercial production of aliphatic substances, apart from those already produced from furan (Jones and Taylor, 1950), and tetrahydrofurfuryl alcohol (see Chapter II, p. 11). The attractive aspect of these syntheses is that the raw material is of agricultural origin, and hence annually renewable, in contrast to the usual source: petroleum.

As a result of these uses, as a highly selective solvent and as an intermediate, about 50,000 tons of furfural were produced in 1956 at 11 cents a pound. A yield of about 10% is obtained, based on the dry weight of the carbohydrate waste.

Several nitrofurans have been used as antibacterials and antiprotozoal agents having a favourably low toxicity to mammals and poultry. An example, Furacin, is 5-nitrofurfural semicarbazone.

Two general methods are available for the synthesis of furans. 1:4-Dialdehydes and -diketones can be dehydrated by acid, e.g. succindialdehyde gives furan, and acetonylacetone gives 2:5-dimethylfuran. In the Feist-Benary synthesis, an α-haloketone (or aldehyde) is condensed with a β-keto-ester in the presence of a weak base (Archer and Pratt, 1944). For example, chloroacetone and ethyl acetoacetate (XXXVI) give 3-carboethoxy-2:4-dimethylfuran (XXXVII). Some particular preparations from carbohydrates are also used, such as 5-methylfurfural from sucrose (Rinkes, 1943), and furan-2:5-dicarboxylic acid from mucic acid.

| XXXVI | XXXVII | XXXVIII |

For further reading, see Dunlop and Peters (1953) and Elderfield and Dodd (1950).

Benzofuran (X) is a colourless liquid, b.p. 177°, obtained by fractionating coal-tar (in which homologues also occur), or by heating its 2-carboxylic acid, or by the ring closure of various *o*-substituted phenols, or phenolic ethers. Thus *o*-formyl-phenoxyacetic acid gives benzofuran in an internal Perkin reaction followed by decarboxylation; *o*-hydroxy-β-chlorostyrene gives benzofuran on heating with alkali, and *o*-hydroxy-bromoacetophenone similarly gives 3-hydroxy-coumarin. Catalytic dehydrogenation of 2-ethylphenol gives benzofuran in 10% yield (Hansch, Scott and Keller, 1950).

The conversion of coumarin (Chapter VII) to benzofuran-2-carboxylic acid (coumarilic acid) by successive treatment with bromine and sodium hydroxide is the historical source of the curious synonym 'coumarone', sometimes used for benzofuran. This reaction has *o*-hydroxy-α-bromocinnamic acid as an intermediate and hence its final stage resembles a synthesis of benzofuran mentioned above. Benzofuran is used entirely for the production of resinous plastics and varnishes (see p. 210).

For further reading, see Elderfield and Meyer (1951).

IsoBenzofuran (XI) is known only as derivatives such as 1:3-dimethyldihydro*iso*benzofuran, obtained by condensing butadiene with diacetylethylene (Schenck, 1947), and 1:3-diphenyl*iso*benzofuran, obtained by treating phenyl-phthalide with the phenyl Grignard reagent. 1:3-Diphenyl*iso*benzofuran can be readily oxidized, in good yield, to *o*-dibenzoylbenzene, a reaction which has preparative value.

Phthalide, or 1-hydroxy*iso*benzofuran, m.p. 73°, is usually written as the lactone of *o*-methylolbenzoic acid (XXXVIII) with which it doubtless forms a tautomeric equilibrium. It is obtained by reducing phthalic anhydride (Gardner and Naylor, 1943).

Methoxyphthalides have been obtained in the degradation of opium alkaloids. Phenolphthalein is 3:3-*bis*-*p*-hydroxyphenol-phthalide. It is much used as a laxative, and is the parent of a large family of pH indicators. When the two phenyl-groups in the 3-position of a diaryl-phthalide are united by an *o:o'*-ether linkage, a fluoran (XXXIX) is formed, a nucleus which has both a five- and a six-membered oxygen-containing ring. The fluoresceins (including eosin) are hydroxy-derivatives of fluoran and are much used as fluorescing indicators and in microscopical stains; the rhodamines are amino-derivatives of fluoran and are used as brightly fluorescing red dyes. Fluorans may also be regarded as lactones of 9-*o*-carboxy-phenylxanthydrols (see p. 276 for xanthydrol).

Phthalic anhydride, 1:3-dioxodihydro*iso*benzofuran, m.p. 131°, is entirely aromatic in character. It is electrophilically substituted by nitric acid and chlorine to give respectively the 3- and 3:6-derivatives: because of its electron-attracting carbonyl-groups, moderately severe conditions are required. Phthalic anhydride is manufactured by the carefully controlled vapour-phase oxidation of naphthalene. Enormous quantities are produced every year. The industrial uses of phthalic anhydride are: (*a*) to make esters of phthalic acid, which are used as plasticizers and insect repellants, (*b*) condensation with benzene by the Friedel-Crafts reaction to *o*-benzoylbenzoic acid which is the key intermediate for the anthraquinone dyes so highly valued by the dyestuff industry, (*c*) condensation with glycerides to give the alkyd (or glyptal) resins, the basis of many modern paints, (*d*) condensation with phenols to make the various fluorans discussed immediately above.

For further reading on *iso*benzofuran, including phthalide, see Elderfield (1951); for fluoran, fluoresceins and rhodamines, see Wawzonek (1951), and for phthalic anhydride see Barrett (1949).

Dibenzofuran (XII), also known as diphenylene oxide, is formed by pyrolysis of phenol, or of diphenyl ether, also by diazotizing either *o:o'*-diaminodiphenyl or *o*-aminodiphenyl ether. Dibenzofuran and several homologues are present in, but not usually isolated from, coaltar. The dibenzofuran nucleus forms part of the molecule of morphine, one of the more complex alkaloids.

For further reading on dibenzofurans, see Parham (1951).

Fluoran
XXXIX

Thiophen (III) is found in coal-tar and has been, in the past, a troublesome contaminant in commercial benzene (see p. 207). Coaltar also contains 2- and 3-methylthiophen. It is more convenient to synthesize thiophen than to extract it from tar, and most of the classical work of Victor Meyer, and all of that of Steinkopf, was performed on thiophen made by heating sodium succinate with phosphorus tri- and penta-sulphide. In 1940, during the preparation of butadiene for the synthesis of artificial rubber, American industrial chemists discovered that thiophen could be economically produced by heating butane with sulphur. In a pressure apparatus with inbuilt fractionation and recycling, the Socony-Vacuum Oil Company began small-scale production by this process in 1944 (Rasmussen, Hansford and Sachanen, 1946), and distributed samples in order to stimulate new uses.

'Thienyl' is the name given to the radical of thiophen. 2:5-Dithienylthiophen has been isolated from the flowers of the common marigold (Zechmeister and Sease, 1947). A fungus growing on juniper trees produces 5(α-propinyl)-2-formylthiophen (Birkinshaw and Chaplen, 1955). 'Thenyl' is the radical thienylmethyl.

So far, the only commercial outlet for thiophens is in the production of antihistamine drugs, such as Diatrin (N-phenyl-N-2-thenyl-N':N'-dimethylethylenediamine) and Histadyl, which is also known as Thenylene and Thenylpyramine and differs from Diatrin in that the phenyl is replaced by α-pyridyl.

Thiophens can be prepared synthetically by heating 1:4-dicarbonyl compounds with phosphorus sulphides, thus acetonylacetone gives 2:5-dimethylthiophen. In a different type of synthesis, two molecules of ethyl acetylenedicarboxylate react with one of sulphur at 150° to give tetracarbomethoxythiophen.

For further reading, see Hartough (1952), Steinkopf (1941), and Blicke (1950). The synthesis of substituted thiophens is further discussed by Wolf and Folkers (1951).

Benzothiophen (thionaphthene, thianaphthene, XIII) is a colourless solid, m.p. 32°, with an odour resembling naphthalene. It is found in coal-tar, but it can be prepared by heating 2-mercapto-β-chlorostyrene. The commercial material is believed to arise by the action of hydrogen sulphide on styrene at 600°. The formerly used method, viz. reduction of 3-hydroxy-benzothiophen (thioindoxyl) with zinc, gives a product containing dihydrobenzothiophen (Hansch, 1947). Thioindoxyl is a colourless solid, m.p. 71°, with an odour like α-naphthol. It is formed by the alkaline or acid cyclization of o-carboxyphenylthioglycollic acid (XL) to thioindoxyl-2-carboxylic acid which is then decarboxylated. Alternatively the acid chloride of phenylthioglycollic acid (XLI) is heated with aluminium chloride.

Thioindoxyl readily undergoes electrophilic substitution in the 2-position, and also gives the reactions characteristic of a ketone (in the 3-position) and of a reactive methylene-group (in the 2-position). The most important reaction is its oxidation to thioindigo (XLII) with alkaline ferricyanides (for indigo, see p. 186). Thioindigo is a red substance, soluble in alkali only after reduction (e.g. with sodium hydrosulphite), and used like indigo as a vat dye for cotton goods.

*Iso*Benzothiophen, the 3:4-benzologue of thiophen, is known only as derivatives such as 1:3-dihydro*iso*benzothiophen (m.p. 26°,

from *o*-xylylene dibromide and sodium sulphide), also 1-phenyl*iso*-
benzothiophen, m.p. 237°, from *o*-benzoylbenzoic acid and phosphorus pentasulphide. So far these substances have a very small
literature.

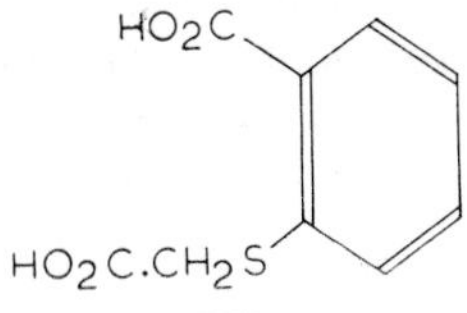

XL

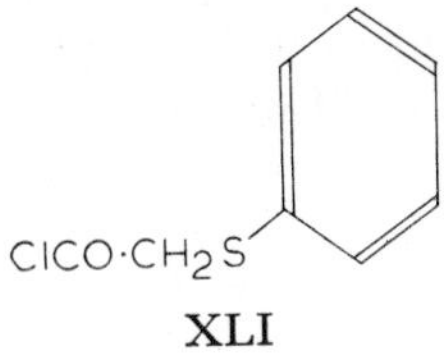

XLI

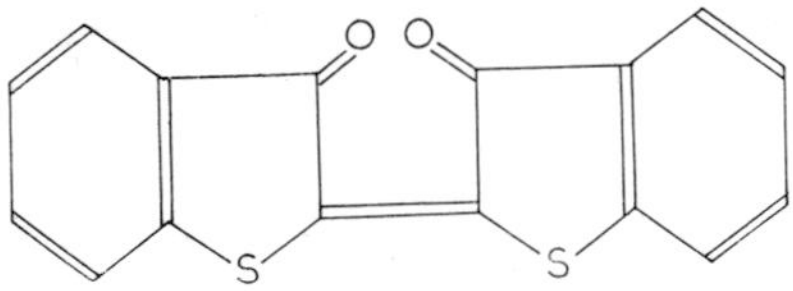

XLII

Dibenzothiophen (diphenylene sulphide), m.p. 81°, is a colourless solid found in coal-tar. It is synthesized by the action of sulphur
on diphenyl in the presence of aluminium chloride.

For further reading on benzothiophens, thioindigos, dibenzothio-
phens and *iso*benzothiophens, see Fukushima (1951) and Hartough
and Meisel (1954).

B. Systems with One or more Ring-Nitrogen Atoms

Oxazole (XVI), a colourless liquid, b.p. 70°, with a pyridine-like
odour, was first prepared in 1947 by the decarboxylation of oxazole-
4-carboxylic acid (Cornforth and Cornforth, 1947), prepared as
follows. Ethyl *iso*propoxymethyleneaminoacetate (XLIII), from
formimido*iso*propyl ether and glycine ethyl ester, was condensed with
ethyl formate and potassium to give potassium ethyl α-*iso*propoxy-
methyleneamino-β-hydroxyacrylate (XLIV). Acidification of this
salt gave oxazole-4-carboxylic acid. 2-Methyloxazole was obtained
similarly. To date this seems to be the only method for producing
simple oxazoles. No oxazoles have been found in nature (see, however, oxazolidines, p. 29).

Di- and tri-substituted oxazoles are also formed by the condensation
of α-halogeno-ketones with amides. Thus formamide and methyl
α-bromoethyl ketone give 4:5-dimethyloxazole at 100° (Theilig,
1953; Bredereck and Gompper, 1954). A similar but more useful

reaction is the dehydration of α-acylamidocarbonyl compounds obtained by reducing *iso*nitroso ketones in acetic anhydride (Wiley, 1947). Acylated aliphatic acyloins give 2:4:5-trisubstituted oxazoles with ammonium acetate, and acetol acetate gives 2:4-dimethyl-oxazole. Finally α-hydroxy-acid amides and aldehydes give oxazoles when condensed with phosphorus oxychloride (Theilig, 1953; Cornforth and Cornforth, 1949).

$$Pr \cdot O \cdot CH{:}N \cdot CH_2 CO_2 \, Et$$

XLIII

(a)   XLV   (b)

XLIV

Oxazoles can often be converted to iminazoles by ammonia under pressure (Cornforth and Cornforth, 1947), or by boiling with formamide (Theilig, 1953).

Of the hydroxyoxazoles, the 5-isomers (XLV) are the best known, and are often referred to as azlactones and 5-oxazolones. They are the cyclic anhydrides of acylated amino-acids. The ratio of tautomers (a) and (b) at equilibrium is unknown, but the common azlactones are so substituted in the 4-position that (a) is the only possible state. These substances, e.g. (XLVI), are formed in the Erlenmeyer synthesis of the aromatic amino-acids such as phenylalanine, tryptophan and histidine. Thus acetic anhydride and acetylglycine give 2-methyl-5-hydroxyoxazole, which in the presence of benzaldehyde gives the 4-benzylidene derivative (XLVI). Hydrolysis of this gives phenyl-α-acetamidoacrylic acid, which is reduced by sodium to phenylalanine. Conversely, reduction can precede hydrolysis, or the two may be accomplished together with hydriodic acid and phosphorus.

Whereas 5-hydroxyoxazoles are decomposed by cold water, the 4-benzylidene derivatives are stable. These substances have been known to cause dermatitis. 2-Hydroxyoxazoles have been made from methane and propionoin or other α-hydroxyketone (Gompper, 1956).

2:5-Dihydroxyoxazole, m.p. 100°, is more often written as 2:5-dioxo-oxazolidine (XLVII), and most commonly called 'N-carboxyglycine anhydride'. It is obtained almost quantitatively by heating N-carbobenzyloxyglycine with thionyl chloride. It has been much used in polypeptide synthesis to introduce a glycine residue. The 4-alkyl derivatives similarly introduce residues corresponding to other natural amino-acids.

XLVI   XLVII

For further reading on oxazoles, see Cornforth (1957); for oxazol-5-ones and azlactones, see Baltazzi (1955), and Carter (1946).

Benzoxazole (XXII), a colourless solid, m.p. 31°, is obtained by heating *o*-aminophenol with formic acid, and other benzoxazoles are obtained similarly. Many are hydrolysed back to the starting materials with hot water or cold, dilute mineral acid. 2-Hydroxy-(and 2-mercapto-)benzoxazole are made from *o*-aminophenol and ethyl chloroformate (and carbon bisulphide). 2-Aminobenzoxazole is obtained from benzoxazole and hydroxylamine (Skraup, 1919).

2-Hydroxybenzoxazole (benzoxazolone) is the substance in rye seedlings which combats fungus infection in winter (Virtanen and Hietala, 1955), and 2-hydroxy-6-methoxybenzoxazole is a similar antifungal substance found in wheat and maize (Hietala and Wahlroos, 1956). The cyanines of benzoxazole are among the most effective sensitizers of photographic film (see p. 98).

For further reading, see Cornforth (1957).

Isoxazole (XVII) is a liquid, b.p. 95°, with a pyridine-like odour. Just as pyrazoles are prepared from the 1:2-dicarbonyl-compounds and hydrazines, the isoxazoles are made from 1:2-dicarbonyl-compounds and hydroxylamine. Thus malondialdehyde and hydroxylamine give isoxazole, and propargylic aldehyde ($HC\equiv C \cdot CHO$) can, as usual, be used in place of malondialdehyde. The best preparation (75% yield) is from hydroxylamine and β-chloroacrolein (Guadiano, Quilico and Ricca, 1956). Isoxazoles are converted to pyrazoles on heating with ammonia. Isoxazole chemistry has played a part in determining the configuration of *syn*- and *anti*-oximes.

For further reading, see Barnes (1957).

Benzisoxazoles. There are both 4:5- and 3:4-benzologues of isoxazole. 4:5-Benzisoxazole (indoxazene), m.p. 84°, is prepared by warming α-triazo-*o*-cresol (XLVIII), or by condensing salicylaldehyde with N-hydroxyurea. 3:4-Benzisoxazole or anthranil (XLIX) is obtained, not by dehydrating anthranilic acid of which it is an anhydride, but by the gentle reduction of 2-nitrobenzaldehyde. It is a colourless, pleasant-smelling liquid, b.p. 210° with decomposition, which is easily volatile in steam and resinifies under the combined influence of air and light. Warming with dilute sodium hydroxide converts it to anthranilic acid; reduction with ferrous hydroxide gives *o*-aminobenzaldehyde. The structure of 3:4-benzisoxazole has been much debated because of some reluctance to accept a non-kekulé structure for the benzene portion, as in (XLIX). Today this is not considered a drawback, for many other substances with such a structure are known, e.g. the *iso*indoles (p.187), *iso*benzofurans (p. 230), *iso*benzothiophens (p. 232), and the very stable indolizines (p. 188). A study of the dipole moments suggests that anthranil is a resonance hybrid of (XLIX) and a smaller proportion of a form which has a separation of charge across the 1:3-positions, the nitrogen being negatively charged (Jensen and Friediger, 1943). No review of the benzisoxazoles is available.

XLVIII   XLIX

L   LI

Oxadiazoles can exist in four isomeric forms. The best known of these are the 1:2:5-oxadiazoles, e.g. (XVIII), also known as furazans. The simplest known members are the 3:4-dimethyl-derivative (obtained by heating dimethylglyoxime with alkali) and the 3-carboxylic acid, obtained by oxidizing the anhydride of 4:5-dioximinovaleric acid. Furoxans are the N-oxides of 1:2:5-oxadiazoles, obtained by the oxidation of (two molecules of) oximes with nitrogen dioxide. The 1:2:4-oxadiazoles are obtained by condensing aliphatic acids with the oximes of acid amides. The 1:3:4-oxadiazoles are formed by dehydrating s-diacylhydrazines with acetic anhydride. No 1:2:3-oxadiazoles appear to be known except for the sydnones. No survey of the oxadiazoles is available.

Sydnones are curious substances, with an apparently divalent nitrogen atom, and are related to the oxadiazoles. They were isolated in Sydney in 1935 from the reaction of N-aryl-glycines with nitrous acid to give N-nitroso-derivatives which were then dehydrated to sydnones with acetic anhydride (Earl and Mackney, 1935). They have large dipole moments of the order of 5–7D, and hence must have a large separation of charge. Earl (1956) thinks that the formula (L) most satisfactorily represents the behaviour of sydnones (it shows 3-phenylsydnone, the best-known member of the series). In previous discussions of electron densities (see pp. 33 and 214), it was shown that even large changes in properties are usually accompanied by only a small electronic transfer (equal often to only one-tenth of an electron). However it is reasonable to believe that the presence of suitable substituents can cause a much larger fraction to be transferred, short of producing a complete betaine or zwitterion. Such seems to be the case with the sydnones, as the nett charge diagram (LI) suggests (Orgel *et al.*, 1951).[1] The high solubility in organic solvents and low solubility in water seem to rule out the possibility of their being zwitterionic, also the dipole moments are too low for this extreme state. The term 'mesoionic' has been applied to the sydnones, and other substances of high dipole moment having an apparent anomaly of valency (Baker and Ollis, 1957). However it is not certain that a new term is needed because the condition seems to be only a slightly more or less pronounced example of a frequently encountered state (Katritzky, 1955). Pyocyanine (see p. 125), with its dipole moment of 7·0D, is a case in point.

The sydnones are truly aromatic and π-excessive: they are readily chlorinated in the 4-position, a fact which would not have been predicted solely from the diagram (LI). The reduction of phenyl-sydnone gives N-phenylglycine; acid hydrolysis gives phenylhydrazine, and alkaline hydrolysis gives aniline (Earl, 1956).

Thiazole (XIX) is a liquid, of b.p. 120° and *d.* 1·2, with a pyridine-like odour. It is best obtained by reducing 2-chlorothiazole (from 2-aminothiazole) (Ganapathi and Venkataraman, 1945) with

---

[1] The parameters used by these authors differ somewhat from the Coulson and Longuet-Higgins parameters principally used in this book.

zinc and acetic acid (Jensen and Friediger, 1943). The thiazole ring occurs in thiamine (vitamin B_1, p. 223) which forms part of an enzyme (cocarboxylase) which plays an important part in carbohydrate metabolism. Sulphathiazole (2:p-aminobenzenesulphonamidothiazole) which was so much used as a chemotherapeutic agent during the period 1940–50 has now largely been displaced by the sulphonamidopyrimidines (p. 115). Micrococcin, an antibiotic, seems to contain a polythiazole structure (Brookes, Fuller and Walker, 1957).

In the most valuable synthesis (LII) of *substituted* thiazoles (LIII), α-halocarbonyl substances are condensed with thioamides. Thus thioformamide and ω-bromoacetophenone give 4-phenylthiazole; thioacetamide and α-chloropropionaldehyde give 2:5-dimethylthiazole; thiourea and chloroacetaldehyde give 2-aminothiazole. Thiourethane is similarly used for 2-alkoxythiazoles, and ammonium dithiocarbamate for 2-mercaptothiazoles. Instead of the thioamide, it is often more convenient to use a mixture of the amide and phosphorus pentasulphide (Schwartz, 1945). This improvisation is particularly useful for the rather unstable thioformamide (required for the synthesis of thiazoles with a free 2-position and hence in the synthesis of thiamine). In another useful synthesis, 2-hydroxythiazoles are obtained by heating α-thiocyanoketones with acid.

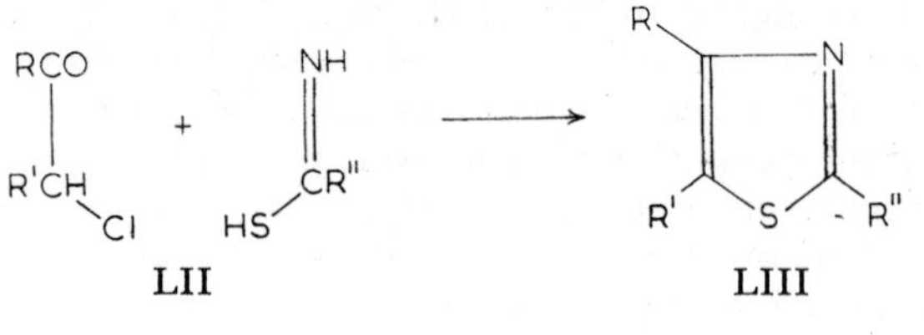

LII   LIII

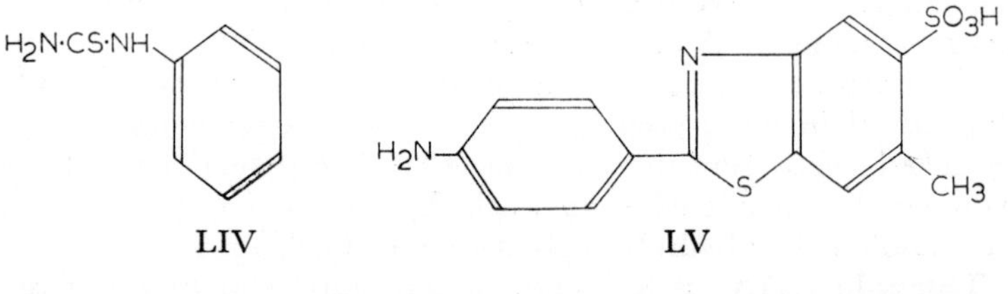

LIV   LV

A new series of syntheses of 5-aminothiazoles was discovered in 1947. Sodium dithioformate and ethyl aminocyanoacetate, in cold neutral aqueous solution, give 5-amino-4-carboethoxythiazole (Cook, Heilbron and Levy, 1947). Aminoacetonitrile and carbon disulphide in ethyl acetate gave 5-amino-2-mercaptothiazole, converted to 5-hydroxy-2-mercaptothiazole by 2N-hydrochloric acid at 20°, and to 2:4-dithiohydantoin (see p. 191) by methanolic alkali (Cook, Heilbron and Levy, 1948). *For further reading*, see Sprague and Land (1957), Prijs (1952). Preparative methods are reviewed by Wiley, England and Behr (1951).

Benzothiazole (XXIII) is a liquid of b.p. 233° and *d.* 1·23, with an odour resembling quinoline. It is prepared by heating *o*-aminothiophenol with a mixture of formic acid and acetic anhydride. When the formic acid is omitted, 2-methylbenzothiazole is obtained, but a higher temperature is required. *o*-Aminothiophenol, when condensed with aldehydes, gives dihydrothiazoles which are very easily oxidized to thiazoles (Lankelma and Sharnoff, 1931). The oxidation of phenylthiourea (LIV) with bromine or sulphuryl chloride gives 2-aminobenzothiazole (Kirk, Johnson and Blomquist, 1943).

2-Mercaptobenzothiazole ('Captax') is manufactured in large quantities as an accelerator of the vulcanization of rubber. It is prepared by heating carbon bisulphide with *o*-aminophenol or (at a higher temperature) with aniline. Cyanines derived from benzothiazole are much used as sensitizers of photographic film (see p. 98). Durazol Yellow G, Chlorazol Fast Yellow B, Sirius Supra Yellow RR and Columbia Yellow are synonyms for a direct dye for cotton, obtained by heating *p*-toluidine with sulphur, followed by sulphonation to 'dehydrothiotoluidinesulphonic acid' (LV), which is then oxidized to the azo-dye with hypochlorous acid. Thioflavine (Acronol Yellow) is a basic dye of similar origin. Primuline and many of the earlier benzothiazole dyes have now lost their importance. *For further reading* on benzothiazoles, see Sprague and Land (1951).

*Iso*Thiazole (XX), a colourless liquid, b.p. 113°, with a pyridine-like odour, was first made in 1956. 5-Amino-4:5-benzo*iso*thiazole was oxidized by potassium permanganate to *iso*thiazole-4:5-dicarboxylic acid. This, when heated, gave a monocarboxylic acid which was converted by a Curtius degradation to an amino*iso*thiazole, which gave *iso*thiazole upon diazotization (Adams and Slack, 1956).

Benzo*iso*thiazoles. The 3:4-isomer, a yellow oil, b.p. 242°, is obtained by the reduction of *o*-nitrobenzyl mercaptan. It is degraded by hydrazine to the hydrazone of *o*-aminobenzaldehyde.

4:5-Benzo*iso*thiazole (LVII), a colourless solid, with an odour resembling benzaldehyde, m.p. 37°, is obtained by oxidizing 2:3-

dioxo-dihydrobenzothiophen (LVI) in the presence of ammonia to
4:5-benzo*iso*thiazole-2-carboxamide, which is hydrolysed and decarboxylated. It is soluble in concentrated acids with a yellow colour.

LVI   LVII   Saccharin
                              LVIII

LIX

Saccharin (LVIII) is 3-hydroxy-4:5-benzo*iso*thiazole sulphone
(3-oxo-2:3-dihydro-4:5-benzo*iso*sulphonazole). It is obtained by
oxidizing *o*-tolylsulphonamide with potassium permanganate.
Saccharin is the most universally used of the artificial sweeteners, but
is useless for baked goods because of its ready hydrolysis to *o*-carboxy-
benzenesulphonic acid (LIX). Methylation of saccharin gives either
O- or N-methyl-derivatives according to the conditions.

Naphthosultam, the anhydride of 8-aminonaphthalene-1-sul-
phonic acid, is also an *iso*thiazole sulphone.

For further reading on benzo*iso*thiazoles, see Bambas (1952).

Thiadiazoles (e.g. XXI) can exist in four isomeric forms. The
only parent substance in the literature before 1953 was 1:2:3-thiadi-
azole, b.p. 157°, prepared as follows. Ethyl acetoacetate gave an
α-nitroso-derivative with nitrous acid, reduced to ethyl acetoamino-
acetate. With more nitrous acid, this gave a stable diazoanhydride
(at one time thought to be one of the as yet unknown 1:2:3-oxadia-
zoles). With ammonium hydrogen sulphide this anhydride gave
4-carboethoxy-5-methyl-1:2:3-thiadiazole, oxidized by permanganate to 1:2:3-thiadiazole-4:5-dicarboxylic acid, which was eventually decarboxylated. 1:2:3-Thiadiazole and its homologues are
weak bases, the hydrochlorides being almost entirely hydrolysed by
cold water.

1:2:5-Thiadiazoles are unknown, but 3:4-benzo-1:2:5-thiadiazole, m.p. 44°, is obtained by the action of sulphur dioxide (or thionyl chloride) on o-phenylenediamine.

1:2:4-Thiadiazole was first obtained in 1956 by the diazo-conversion of 5-amino-1:2:4-thiadiazole to the 5-bromo-analogue, which was hydrogenated. It is a colourless liquid, with b.p. 121° similar to that of pyrimidine (b.p. 124°), of which it is an isostere (see p. 206). It is very soluble in water and all organic solvents (Goerdeler, Ohm and Tegtmeyer, 1956).

1:3:4-Thiadiazole (XXI) has b.p. 203° corresponding to that of pyridazine (207°) and m.p. 43°. It was first obtained by Goerdeler and Ohm in 1953 from formylthiosemicarbazide which was condensed with acetyl chloride to 2-amino-1:3:4-thiadiazole, and this was converted to the parent substance as outlined above. 1:3:4-Thiadiazole neither nitrates nor combines nucleophilically with lithium alkyls. It is soluble in water and in most organic solvents, but not in light petroleum (Goerdeler, Ohm and Tegtmeyer, 1956).

Acetazolamide ('Diamox') is 2-acetamido-1:3:4-thiadiazole-5-sulphonamide (Roblin and Clapp, 1950). It is a powerful diuretic that is effective when taken orally, and works by inhibiting carbonic anhydrase.

For further reading on thiadiazoles, see Bambas (1952).

CHAPTER VII

Heteroethylenics

[i.e. non-aromatic, unsaturated heterocyclic substances]

Introduction

THE PREVIOUS CHAPTERS have dealt with heteroparaffinic and heteroaromatic substances. There still remains an intermediate type, the heteroethylenic, which is unsaturated without being aromatic. Bromine is often used to differentiate between aromatic and ethylenic substances: similarly heteroaromatics are substituted by bromine whereas heteroethylenics are not, and usually add it to a double-bond.

The dihydro-derivatives of five-membered heteroaromatic rings are obvious heteroethylenics, as are the di- and tetra-

hydro-derivatives of six-membered rings. But other heteroethylenics are unrelated to substances encountered in earlier
chapters. For example, pyran (I) and other six-membered
rings containing oxygen or sulphur are heteroethylenic;
quinolizine (II) provides another example. Both pyran and
quinolizine readily form some aromatic derivatives: it has been
decided to treat these derivatives in this chapter, although a
case could be made out for placing them in a heteroaromatic
chapter.

A number of difficult decisions have had to be made concerning aromatic character. The guiding principle is that
aromatic status is accorded substances which can tautomerize
to an aromatic form. The energy gain on becoming aromatic is
usually such that it can be assumed that substances adopt an
aromatic form when possible. Thus 4-hydroxypyridine (p. 58)
is considered aromatic although there is a proportion of (III) in
the resonance hybrid. On less certain grounds, possibly, 2-
hydroxy-pyrrole, -furan, and -thiophen have been included in
aromatic chapters (pp. 149 and 211), but they may eventually
be shown to exist largely as (IV). Succinimide (V) is an example
of how difficult it is to draw the line: it could be called 2:5-
dihydroxypyrrole or 2-hydroxy-5-oxopyrroline. However, succinimide (see p. 27) shows no indubitably aromatic or ethylenic
properties.

Infrared studies (e.g. O'Sullivan and Sadler, 1957) indicate
that, in general, no justification exists for writing ethylenic
formulae for those paraffinic substances which could conceivably
tautomerize to ethylenic forms. Thus 2-ketopyrrolidine (VI)
and 2-ketopiperidine are treated as heteroparaffinic, and will be
found in Chapter II.

Fortunately, the majority of heteroethylenic substances do
not present classificational difficulties of this kind.

The diagnosis of $\alpha:\beta$-unsaturation, as distinct from more distant ethylenic bonds, in N-heterocycles is possible by ultraviolet
(Leonard and Locke, 1955) and infrared (Leonard and Gash,
1954) spectra. The rearrangement of hydro-derivatives by
prototropy should be kept in mind. Examples will be found
below under pyridine, tetrazine and pyrrole, and it may be
more common than is realized. Many hydrocarbons show a

R

similar lability, viz. 1:4-dihydronaphthalene becomes the
1:2-isomer on heating with sodium ethoxide (Strauss and Lemmel, 1921). In addition, many instances of disproportionation
have been recorded: e.g. 1:2-dihydroquinoline in cold dilute
acid gives quinoline plus tetrahydroquinoline.

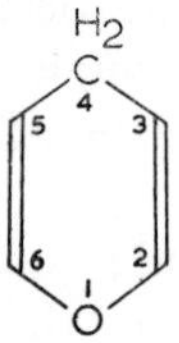

Pyran
I

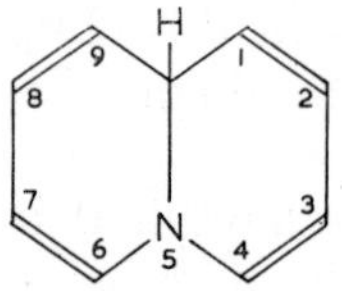

Quinolizine
II

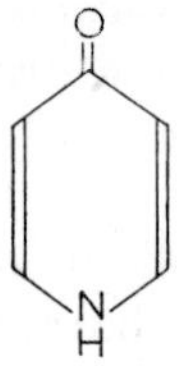

III

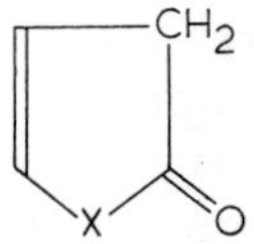

IV

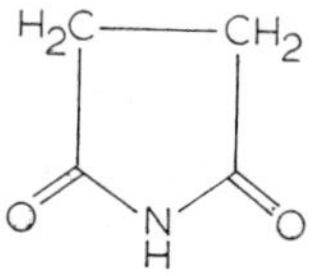

V

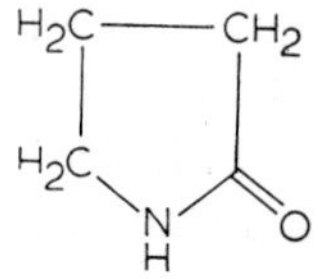

VI

A. HYDROGENATED DERIVATIVES OF SYSTEMS PREVIOUSLY DEALT WITH

(a) Dihydro- and Tetrahydro-derivatives of π-deficient N-heteroaromatics

The production of these substances by reducing their heteroaromatic counterparts has already been dealt with (p. 90).
Hence, direct syntheses remain to be discussed below. In
general, heteroethylenics are easily oxidized and attempts to
form their picrates often convert them to the aromatic analogues
(cf. Knowles and Watt, 1943). Usually dihydro-derivatives are
more stable to dehydrogenation than their tetrahydro-analogues.
Heteroethylenics often fluoresce more strongly than the
corresponding heteroaromatics.

Some further classes of substance on the borderline between
heteroethylenic and heteroaromatic will now be mentioned.
Firstly there are substances, obtainable by reducing heteroaromatics, which have their unsaturation shared with an aromatic ring. Such substances, naturally, do not give the bromine

test for unsaturation as mentioned above, but have been included in this chapter because of their reductive origin. Examples are the tetrahydro-quinolines (X) and *iso*quinolines (XI), also 5:10-dihydroacridine (XII). Secondly there are the methides, such as 1-methyl-2-methylene-1:2-dihydropyridine (VII), also called 'N-methyl-α-pyridonemethide'. These substances were discovered by Decker in 1905, and further studied by Tschichibabin (1936) and by Mumm and Petzold (1938). The example given is the anhydrobase of 2-methylpyridine methochloride, and similar substances have been found in all heteroaromatic series containing doubly-bound nitrogen ($=N-$). The methides have already been discussed as possible intermediates in the formation of derivatives (e.g. styryl-compounds) from active methyl-groups (see p. 97). Finally all quaternary salts of heteroaromatics give pseudo-bases of the type 1-methyl-2-hydroxy-1:2-dihydropyridine which is the pseudobase of pyridine methochloride (see p. 70). The anhydrobases and pseudobases will not be further dealt with in this chapter.

Pyridines. The dihydropyridines are readily oxidized by air unless equipped with electron-attracting substituents. Some 1:2-dihydropyridines have been found in nature: the 2:4-dimethyl-derivative in rancid cod-liver oil, and the 3:4-dimethoxy-N-methyl-derivative which is the alkaloid arecolidine. Few 1:2-dihydropyridines have been made by direct synthesis (Panouse, 1953). Reduction of pyridines with lithium aluminium hydride seems the best method of preparation. Pyridine was reduced thus by Bohlmann (1952) and pyridine methiodide by Panouse (1953), but the products were impure. Cold, highly alkaline sodium borohydride solution proved a better reagent, and several N-alkyl- 1:2-dihydropyridines have thus been prepared (Panouse, 1951).

1:2-Dihydropyridines are usually volatile liquids which oxidize rapidly in air to black resins, but they are stable to heat and to alkali. They are dimerized by dilute acids. Hydrogenation over platinum leads to tetrahydropyridines.

The best known 1:4-dihydropyridine is diphosphopyridine nucleotide (DPN). For many years this was believed to be a 1:2-dihydropyridine, but its true structure was revealed by deuteration (Pullman, San Pietro and Colowick, 1954). It is now realized that enzymic (and some hydrosulphite) reductions give 1:4-dihydropyridines, and that many substances thus prepared are wrongly described in the literature. Other 1:4-dihydropyridines are intermediates in the Hantzsch synthesis (see p. 102); most of those which have been isolated have a blue fluorescence and readily disproportionate, three molecules giving two of the pyridine and one of the piperidine (hexahydropyridine). 1:4-Dihydropyridine itself is not known.

No dihydropyridines have been satisfactorily prepared by the action of Grignard reagents on quaternary salts of pyridine, nor by the dehydrogenation of tetra- or hexa-hydropyridines.

Δ^3-Tetrahydropyridines (sometimes called Δ^3-piperideins) occur in nature as alkaloids of areca nut, and as minor alkaloids in tobacco and lobelia. Δ^3-Tetrahydropyridine arises in the commercial (electrolytic) reduction of pyridine to piperidine, and is a relatively stable substance. Δ^3-Tetrahydropyridine can be obtained by abstraction of water from 4-hydroxypiperidine (from reduction of 4-hydroxypyridine), and by the action of alkali on 4-bromopiperidine (Renshaw and Conn, 1938). The action of hot, neutral sodium borohydride solution on quaternary pyridine salts affords an easy synthesis of Δ^3-tetrahydropyridines (Panouse, 1951). 1-Methyl-Δ^3-tetrahydropyridine-3-aldehyde is obtained by the cold combination of formaldehyde, acetaldehyde and methylamine (Mannich, 1942): in this reaction a 4-hydroxypiperidine is first formed. In Wohl's synthesis, amino-acetals such as (VIII), upon treatment with acids, cyclize easily to Δ^3-tetrahydropyridine-3-aldehyde. The acetal (VIII) is obtained by the action of ammonia on 3-chloropropional acetal.

The Δ^3-tetrahydropyridines are strongly basic liquids, soluble in water, resistant to heat. They oxidize slowly in the air to brown resins, but are stable to sulphuric acid and to alkali. They very readily add bromine and hydrogen chloride to the double-bond. Selenium dehydrogenation gives the corresponding pyridine. They instantly decolorize potassium permanganate solution.

Δ^1-Tetrahydropyridine, the cyclic anhydride or anil of δ-aminovaleraldehyde, has a transitory existence but rapidly forms the dimer (IX) known as tetrahydroanabasine (m.p. 72°), as well as two trimers which have four fused six-membered rings (Schöpf, Komzak, Braun and Jacobi, 1948). Δ^1-Tetrahydropyridine is formed by chlorinating piperidine to N-chloropiperidine and treating this with alcoholic potassium hydroxide.

VII   VIII   IX

Ammonia acts on δ-bromobutyl methyl ketone to give 2-methyl-Δ^2-tetrahydropyridine, which hydrolyses to δ-aminobutyl methyl ketone in aqueous solution but is reconstituted on isolation (an example of ring-chain tautomerism). In 1:2-dimethyl-Δ^2-tetrahydropyridine there is evidence of quaternization by bond-migration to Δ^1, but this has not yet been demonstrated when the nitrogen is not alkylated (Adams and Mahan, 1942; Leonard and Gash, 1954). The synthesis and properties of Δ^2-tetrahydropyridines have been reviewed (Leonard and Hauck, 1957).

For further reading on di- and tetra-hydropyridines, see Panouse (1953).

Quinolines. 1:2-Dihydroquinoline, a colourless solid, m.p. 41°, is formed by the action of lithium aluminium hydride on quinoline (Bohlmann, 1952). It quickly resinifies in air, reduces cold silver nitrate solution, and is disproportionated by cold dilute acids to a mixture of quinoline and 1:2:3:4-tetrahydroquinoline. Similar properties are shown by the N-methyl-derivative, an oil which has a blue fluorescence in daylight. It is similarly formed from quinoline methiodide, and also by the action of lithium aluminium hydride on the N-methyl-derivative of 2-hydroxyquinoline (Sutter-Kostic and Karrer, 1956). The 1:2-dihydroquinolines are most stable as hydrochlorides, or as N-acyl-derivatives (Rosenmund, Zymalkowski and Schwarte, 1954). They readily add bromine to the 3:4-double-bond.

1:2-Dihydroquinolines are intermediates in the Doebner-Miller and Skraup syntheses of quinolines (see pp. 105 and 104). Methylquinolinium iodide gives 1:2-dimethyl-1:2-dihydro-quinoline with methyl magnesium iodide. 1-Acyl-2-cyano-1:2-dihydro-quinolines are obtained by shaking together e.g. quinoline, benzoyl chloride and aqueous potassium cyanide (Reissert's reaction). The product gives benzaldehyde and quinoline-2-carboxylic acid on hydrolysis, and the reaction is useful for converting an acid chloride to an aldehyde. 1:2-Dicyano-1:2-dihydroquinoline is produced by the action of cyanogen bromide and hydrogen cyanide on quinoline. On standing it is slowly converted to 1:2-dicyano-1:4-dihydro-quinoline (Seeley, Yates and Noller, 1951). The reduction of quinoline with sodium in ammonia is believed to give 1:4-dihydroquinoline (Knowles and Watt, 1943), but this class of substance has so far been little investigated. 2-Hydroxy-3:4-dihydroquinoline (2-oxo-tetrahydroquinoline; dihydrocarbo-styril) is an example of an almost unexplored class: the *unsaturated lactams*. It is obtained by reduction of 2-hydroxy-quinoline, and also by reduction of *o*-nitrodihydrocinnamic acid. It is quite resistant to oxidation.

1:2:3:4-Tetrahydroquinoline (X) is formed by reduction of quinoline (see p. 90) and by heating *o*-(3-chloropropyl)-aniline. It is a colourless liquid, b.p. 248°, and stable in air. It is a weak base ($pK_a = 5$), because it is essentially a 2-alkylaniline in cyclic form; but 1:2:3:4-tetrahydro*iso*quinoline (XI) is a much stronger base ($pK_a = 9$) because it is essentially a cyclic 2-alkylbenzylamine. 1:2:3:4-Tetrahydroquinoline is oxidized to quinoline by mercuric acetate.

4-Oxo-1:2:3:4-tetrahydroquinoline has been shown spectro-scopically to have very little amide character (Braunholtz and Mann, 1957).

5:6:7:8-Tetrahydroquinoline is synthesized from ethyl tetra-hydroanthranilate in 70% yield by the successive action of ethyl malonate, acid, phosphorus oxychloride and hydrogen (Prelog and Geyer, 1945). It is a stable substance, but can be dehydrogenated to quinoline by palladized charcoal at 300°, or by selenium.

Octahydroquinoline has only one double-bond, and this has been allocated to the 1:9-position because of the azomethine band at 6·0 µ in the infrared (Witkop, 1956).

cis-Decahydroquinoline, m.p. about −40°, is prepared from 2-(3-ethoxypropyl)*cyclo*hexanone by the successive action of ammonium formate and hydrogen bromide. The *trans*-isomer, m.p. 48°, is obtained from 2-carboethoxy*cyclo*hexanone and ethyl 3-bromopropyl ether followed, in turn, by alkali, hydroxylamine, sodium, benzoyl chloride and hydrogen bromide (King, Henshall and Whitehead, 1948). A mixture of both isomers, separable through the different solubility of their hydrochlorides, arises in the reduction of either tetrahydroquinoline. Both isomers are dehydrogenated to quinoline by selenium or platinum.

For further reading on hydroquinolines, see Elderfield (1952).

X   XI   XII

Iso*quinoline*. 1:2-Dihydro*iso*quinoline was obtained, for the first time, in 1955, by reducing *iso*quinoline with lithium aluminium hydride. It is a colourless solid, m.p. 138°, and is oxidized to *iso*quinoline by tetrachloro-*o*-quinone. Catalytic hydrogenation gives 1:2:3:4-tetrahydro*iso*quinoline (XI) (Jackman and Packham, 1955).

N-alkyl-1:2-dihydro*iso*quinolines, similarly obtained by reduction of quaternary salts (Schmid and Karrer, 1949), are oils which have a blue fluorescence in ultraviolet light. They reduce cold ammoniacal silver nitrate solution. N-alkyl-1:2-dihydro-*iso*quinolines can also be obtained by the disproportionation of quaternary salts of *iso*quinoline, the by-product being N-alkyl-1-oxo*iso*quinoline. Grignard reagents add on to quaternary *iso*quinoline salts, giving 1:2-dialkyl-1:2-dihydro*iso*quinoline. *Iso*-quinoline gives a Reissert compound similar to that formed by quinoline (see above). 1:2-Dihydro*iso*quinolines alkylate on the 4-carbon atom as well as on the nitrogen (Freund and Fleischer, 1915) (for other examples of C-alkylation, see Robinson, 1916 and Albert, Brown and Wood, 1956). 1:2-Dihydro*iso*quinolines are easily oxidized to *iso*quinolines by iodine or mercuric acetate. 3:4-Dihydro*iso*quinolines are produced in the Bischler-Napieralski reaction (p. 108). They are stable to heat, acid, alkali and aerial oxidation; thus dehydrogenation is more difficult than that of the 1:2-isomers and requires selenium, sulphur or palladium. Hydrastinine and cotarnine are two simple derivatives of 3:4-dihydro*iso*quinoline, of alkaloidal origin. They are in tautomeric equilibrium, by ring-chain isomerism, with an *o*-(2-aminoethyl)benzaldehyde.

1:2:3:4-Tetrahydro*iso*quinoline (XI), prepared by reduction of *iso*quinoline, is a colourless liquid, b.p. 234°. The basic strength of this substance is discussed above (under 1:2:3:4-tetrahydroquinoline). It is oxidized to *iso*quinoline by iodine, mercuric acetate or by catalytic dehydrogenation. 5:6:7:8-Tetrahydro*iso*quinoline is obtained by dehydrogenating deca-hydro*iso*quinoline. The latter occurs in *cis*- and *trans*-forms, separable by fractional crystallization of the picrates or by taking advantage of the more rapid dehydrogenation of the *cis*-isomer.

For further reading on hydro*iso*quinolines see Gensler (1952).

Acridine. 5:10-Dihydroacridine, or acridan (XII), is an odourless white solid, m.p. 172°, which occurs in coal-tar and is best made by vigorously reducing 5-hydroxyacridine ('acridone') or by gently hydrogenating acridine. It has only feeble basic properties. Acridan is stable to aerial oxidation, but the amino-acridans rapidly oxidize to aminoacridines in air. Acridan is best converted to acridine by dilute chromic acid, the amino- and hydroxy-acridans are better oxidized with ferric chloride. Acridan is readily acetylated. 5:10-Dimethylacridan is obtained by the action of methyl magnesium iodide on N-methylacridinium iodide.

1:2:3:4-Tetrahydroacridine, a white solid, m.p. 55°, occurs in coal-tar. It has been obtained, not by the hydrogenation of acridine, but by heating isatin with *cyclo*hexanone and decarboxylating the tetrahydroacridine-5-carboxylic acid. It may be regarded as a cyclized 2:3-diethylquinoline, and has much the same odour and basic strength as quinoline. Tetrahydroacridine and its derivatives resist dehydrogenation. The methylene group in the 1-position is activated by the neighbouring nitrogen atom and hence gives a styryl-compound with benzaldehyde. 5-Hydroxytetrahydroacridine (m.p. 358°) is obtained by heating anthranilic acid and *cyclo*hexanone. Treatment with phosphorus oxychloride gives the 5-chloro-analogue, and this is readily aminated to 5-aminotetrahydroacridine (m.p. 180°), which has a powerful analeptic (awakening) action.

No hexahydroacridine is known, but there are three octahydroacridines. Symmetrical octahydroacridine, m.p. 84°, has three double-bonds in the central ring. The asymmetrical octahydroacridines retain a lateral benzene ring: they differ from one another as geometrical isomers do, and both can be resolved into *d*- and *l*-modifications. All are stable to oxidation. No decahydroacridine is known, but dodeca- and tetradeca-hydroacridine have been briefly described.

For further reading on hydroacridines, see Albert (1951).

Phenanthridine. 9:10-Dihydrophenanthridine, m.p. 123°, is readily obtained by reducing phenanthridine. It is basic, and oxidizes in the air to phenanthridine, but the N-acetyl-derivative is stable. The dihydrophenanthridines fluoresce brilliantly, in contrast to the phenanthridines. 5:6:7:8-Tetrahydrophenanthridine (m.p. 63°) is prepared by heating *cyclo*hexanone, dimethylamine, formaldehyde and aniline. 1:2:3:4:5:6:7:8-Octahydrophenanthridine (m.p. 38°) is obtained from *cyclo*hexanone (2 mols.), ammonia and formaldehyde. These derivatives are stable to oxidation.

For further reading, see Walls (1952).

The azines are heteroaromatics with two ring-nitrogen atoms. The stability of the *para*-dihydro-derivatives of aromatic hydrocarbons increases as the number of linearly annelated rings increases. This seems also to be the case with the 1:4-azines (Badger, 1954). Thus it has not been possible to prepare the 1:4-dihydride of pyrazine or quinoxaline but that of phenazine is moderately stable in air, oxidizing only as far as a molecular complex of phenazine and dihydrophenazine. Finally the di-hydride of 2:3-(linear)benzophenazine is quite stable in air, and

2:3:6:7-(linear)dibenzophenazine is so stable that it resists all common oxidizing agents.

Pyrazines. Unsubstituted hydropyrazines have scarcely been investigated. 2:5-Dihydropyrazines are intermediates in the synthesis of pyrazines from α-amino-aldehydes (see p. 118), into which they are reconverted by acid. They readily oxidize in the air to pyrazines. 2:3-Dihydropyrazines are formed from 1:2-diketones and ethylenediamine, and some 1:4-dihydropyrazines (in which the 1- and 4-positions are blocked) have been made from α-bromoketones and primary amines. 1:4:6-Triphenyl-1:2:3:4-tetrahydropyrazine has been made from N:N^1-diphenyl-ethylene diamine and α-bromoacetophenone. Pyrazines on reduction give 2:5-dihydropyrazines and hexahydropyrazines (piperazines).

Quinoxalines. Unsubstituted dihydroquinoxalines are unknown. 2:3-Diphenyl-1:2-dihydroquinoxaline is made by condensing *o*-phenylenediamine with benzoin, or by reducing 2:3-diphenylquinoxaline with stannous chloride. 3-Hydroxy-1:2-dihydroquinoxaline is made from *o*-nitrophenylglycine by reduction, from *o*-phenylenediamine, bromoacetic acid and aqueous ammonia, or by reducing 2:3-dihydroxyquinoxaline with zinc and hydrochloric acid. It is amphoteric and very readily oxidized to 3-hydroxyquinoxaline, e.g. by distillation in air, or by boiling in solution with charcoal. Alkylation of $N_{(1)}$ stabilizes this substance. The existence of 1:4-dihydroquinoxalines is not firmly established. The reduction of quinoxaline yields 1:2:3:4-tetrahydroquinoxaline, m.p. 99°, a base that readily undergoes acylation, or alkylation (Cavagnol and Wiselogle, 1947). It is also obtainable by condensing catechol with *o*-phenylenediamine, or 1:2-dibromoethane with dibenzene-sulphonyl-*o*-phenylenediamine followed by hydrolysis. It is stable to acid, alkali and aerial oxidation, but alkaline potassium ferricyanide converts it to quinoxaline.

For further reading on hydroquinoxalines, see Simpson (1953).

Phenazines. 5:10-Dihydrophenazine, m.p. 212°, is a colourless solid obtained by reducing phenazine with sodium hydrosulphite or ammonium sulphide. When exposed to the air it gives a blue, quinhydrone-like complex of phenazine and dihydrophenazine (1:1), m.p. 255°, and on further exposure a violet 2:1 complex, m.p. 216° (Dufraisse, Étienne and Toro-manoff, 1951). Oxidation with ammoniacal silver nitrate gives phenazine. Tetrahydrophenazine, made by condensing *o*-phenylenediamine with 1:2-*cyclo*hexanedione, may be dehydro-genated to phenazine with iodine, but not by sulphur or selenium (Clemo and McIlwain, 1934). Octahydrophenazines, similarly prepared, are quantitatively dehydrogenated with palladium at 200° (Clemo and McIlwain, 1936).

Pyridazine and the other 1:2-diazines have had relatively little investigation of their hydro-derivatives. Dihydropyrida-zines are intermediates in the synthesis of pyridazines from 1:4-diketones and hydrazine (see p. 113). They readily oxidize in the air to pyridazines.

Cinnoline. Dihydrocinnoline, m.p. 87°, is obtained by reducing 4-chloro-cinnoline with iron and acid, and may be oxidized to cinnoline with mercuric oxide. 4-Phenyl-1:2-dihydrocinnoline disproportionates to 4-phenylcinnoline and 4-phenyl-1:2:3:4-tetrahydrocinnoline when heated with acid. A few other hydro-cinnolines, not all of established constitution, have been reviewed (Simpson, 1953).

Phthalazine. Alkaline decomposition of quaternary salts of phthalazine gives the pseudobase, 1-hydroxy-2-methyl-1:2-dihydrophthalazine, which disproportionates during steam distillation (in hydrogen) to (*a*) $N_{(2)}$-methyl-1:2-dihydro-phthalazine and (*b*) the N-methyl-derivative of 1-hydroxy-phthalazine. Only (*a*) is volatile, and on exposure to the air it quickly becomes (*b*). 1:2:3:4-Tetrahydrophthalazine arises from sodium reduction of phthalazines. It is strongly basic and darkens rapidly in air. For a review of hydrophthalazines, see Simpson (1953).

The hydro-derivatives of the 1:3-diazines are somewhat better known.

Pyrimidine is hydrogenated in acid solution only, and 1:4:5:6-tetrahydropyrimidine hydrochloride, m.p. 122°, is obtained. This is stable to dilute acid and alkali, but is decomposed by strong alkali. Many analogues are obtained similarly (Smith and Christensen, 1955), or by the condensation of 1:3-diamines with organic acids or derivatives of these acids, or by heating trimethylene dibromide with an acid amide. Hydrogenation of the three mono-aminopyrimidines (in acid solution) gave dihydro-derivatives of unknown constitution.

The 'dihydrouracils' may be regarded as 2:4-dioxo-hexahydropyrimidines, and hence are heteroparaffinics (see p. 22). '5:6-Dihydrouracil', m.p. 275°, is formed by reducing uracil or by condensing urea with acrylic acid or β-aminopropionic acid. It is unstable to alkali and resists oxidation with concentrated nitric acid or acidified permanganates. Similarly methyl β-methylaminopropionate and sodium cyanate give 5:6-dihydro-1-methyluracil (Brown, Hoerger and Mason, 1955, a). 5:6-Dihydrouracil-6-carboxylic acid (dihydro-orotic acid) is a precursor in the biosynthesis of uracil. 5:6-Dihydrouracils are best dehydrogenated by bromine-substitution in the activated methylene-group, followed by elimination of hydrogen bromide, e.g. by heating at 160°.

Quinazoline. 3:4-Dihydroquinazoline, m.p. 127°, is obtained by reducing quinazoline, or 2- or 4-chloro-quinazoline (Elderfield *et al.*, 1947). Thus quinazoline adds hydrogen across the same double-bond which apparently adds water (see p. 121). 3:4-Dihydroquinazoline is also obtained by heating 2-aminobenzylamine with formic acid. These dihydroquinazolines are oxidized to quinazolines with alkaline potassium ferricyanide. Tetrahydroquinazoline (m.p. 79°) is formed by condensing *o*-aminobenzylamine with formaldehyde, or by the reduction of 3:4-hydroquinazoline with sodium amalgam. It gives formaldehyde on heating with dilute acid, a reaction typical of an $N-CH_2-N$ group (see Chapter II, p. 22). 2-Hydroxytetrahydroquinazoline is obtained from 2-aminobenzylamine and phosgene, or by heating 2-ureidobenzylamine.

Tetrazine. 1:2-Dihydro-1:2:4:5-tetrazine, yellow, m.p. 125°, is formed by reducing tetrazine with hydrogen sulphide, and gives tetrazine again when a solution is shaken with air. Movement of hydrogen atoms from the 1:6- to the 1:2-positions has been observed in dihydro-1:2:4:5-tetrazine-3:6-carboxylic acids, under the influence of alkali.

Pteridine. Most of the hydropteridines are hydrogenated in the pyrazine, not the pyrimidine, ring. Pteridine, reduced with lithium aluminium hydride, gives 5:6:7:8-tetrahydropteridine (XIII), m.p. 147°, which is also obtained by the catalytic

hydrogenation of 2:4:6:7-tetrachloropteridine (Taylor, 1954).
It is stable to boiling N-hydrochloric acid and sodium hydroxide. It is also formed by the action of sodium in ammonia, on
8-benzyl-2-chloro-5:6:7:8-tetrahydropteridine which is formed
from 2:4-dichloro-5-nitropyrimidine and N-2-chloroethylbenzyl-
amine. Tetrahydropteridine formylates in the 5-position (Brook
and Ramage, 1955; 1957).

Substituted 7:8-dihydropteridines are obtained by the condensation of 2:4-dichloro-5-nitropyrimidine with aminoacetone,
giving 4-acetonylamino-2-chloro-5-nitropyrimidine which is
catalytically reduced to 2-chloro-6-methyl-7:8-dihydropteridine
(Boon and Jones, 1951). The use of glycine in place of aminoacetone gives the 6-hydroxy-analogues (Boon, Jones and
Ramage).

6-Hydroxy-7:8-dihydropteridine is obtained by reducing
6-hydroxypteridine, and 7-hydroxy-5:6-dihydropteridine by
reducing 7-hydroxypteridine (Albert, Brown and Cheeseman,
1952): it should be noted in both examples that, as expected, no
−CO·NH− group is reduced. Both of these substances are
easily ring-opened by alkali, for example 6-hydroxy-7:8-di-
hydropteridine gives 5-amino-4-carboxymethylaminopyrimi-
dine (XIV); the dihydropteridines are regenerated by acid
(Albert, 1955). Both hydroxydihydropteridines are oxidized to
hydroxypteridines by potassium permanganate (Albert, Brown
and Cheeseman, 1952).

7:8-Dihydropteridines not containing a 6- or 7-hydroxyl-
group have been hydrogenated to 5:6:7:8-tetrahydropteridines
(platinum in acetic acid, or Raney-nickel under pressure).
These tetrahydropteridines are stable in 0·1 N-acid for several
weeks, whereas the 7:8-dihydropteridines become oxidized to
pteridines under these conditions (Lister and Ramage, 1953).
This change is quantitative under alkaline conditions (Lister,
Ramage and Coates, 1954), and those tetrahydropteridines
which bear electron-releasing groups (e.g. −OH) are also
autoxidized in alkaline solution. The reason for the non-
oxidation of tetrahydropteridines lacking such a group, e.g.
tetrahydropteridine itself (Taylor, 1954), is that pteridine is not a
true aromatic substance because of the high N:C-ratio (see
p. 50); however it becomes aromatic when an electron-

releasing substituent is inserted. Tetrahydropteridines, all derivatives of pteroylglutamic acid (see p. 130), occur in nature (May *et al.*, 1951; Pohland *et al.*, 1951; Cosulich *et al.*, 1952): various examples are unformylated, others are formylated in the 5- or (more important) the 10-position, and others are combined loosely with formaldehyde.

XIII   XIV   XV

(b) *Dihydro-derivatives of π-excessive N-heteroaromatics*

As the aromatic progenitors of this series have only two double-bonds, their heteroethylenic analogues are all *di*hydro-derivatives: the tetrahydro-derivatives will be found in Chapter II (heteroparaffinics) together with their oxo-derivatives, such as pyrrolidone, sometimes written as hydroxydihydro-derivatives. It is worth noting that N-alkyl-derivatives of indole, carbazole, etc., reduce (to dihydro-derivatives) much more easily than their non-alkyl analogues.

The literature regarding the action of bromine on these substances is scanty. The strong basic character of pyrrolines (p. 257) shows that there is no base-weakening conjugation (of the lone pair of electrons on the nitrogen atom) with the double-bond, as there is in pyrrole.

Pyrrole, on reduction with zinc and acid, gives Δ^3-pyrroline (XV), a liquid, b.p. 91°. The Δ^3-pyrrolines are strong bases ($pK_a = 10$) with an ammoniacal odour and are stable to polymerization. They can be reduced, but only under vigorous conditions, to pyrrolidines (tetrahydropyrroles). Nitrous acid gives an N-nitroso-derivative, and methyl iodide gives a N:N-dimethylpyrrolinium iodide. 1-Methyl-Δ^3-pyrroline occurs in traces among the alkaloids of tobacco.

The Δ^2-pyrrolines are obtained from 2-oxopyrrolidines (2-oxotetrahydropyrroles) and a Grignard reagent (Craig,

1933) or from the cyclization of γ-aminoketones (Allen and Wilson, 1947). They do not react with phenylhydrazine and hence, unlike Δ²-dihydropyridines, do not exhibit ring-chain tautomerism. The Δ²-pyrrolines resinify in air, are readily reduced to tetrahydropyrroles, and dehydrogenated to the corresponding pyrroles. The N-alkyl-Δ²-pyrrolines are distinguished by being stronger bases (pK_a about 12) than the corresponding N-alkyltetrahydropyrroles (pK_a about 10). This exaltation (a depression would be expected) has been attributed to a shift of double-bond, from (XVI, a) to (XVI, b), thus forming a quaternary ammonium ion. The *secondary* Δ²-pyrrolines do not exhibit this exaltation (Adams and Mahan, 1942). Myosmine, a minor alkaloid of tobacco, long believed to be 5-pyridyl-Δ²-pyrroline, is now classified as the Δ¹-isomer on the infrared evidence (Witkop, 1956). It will be interesting to see if other, or all, Δ²-pyrrolines will be thus reclassified (see Leonard and Gash, 1954).

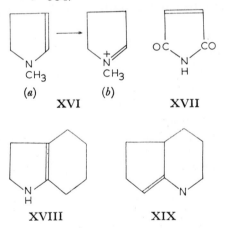

(a)　　　(b)
XVI　　　　　XVII

XVIII　　　　　XIX

Maleimide (XVII), or 2:5-dioxo-Δ³-pyrroline, is remarkably inaccessible for so simple a substance. It is best prepared by condensing furan and maleic anhydride, and treating the adduct in turn with bromine, ammonia and zinc, followed by a pyrolysis (Berson and Swidler, 1954).

Indole is easily reduced to 2:3-dihydroindole (indoline), b.p. 221°, which is most readily prepared by heating 1-methylindole with hydriodic acid and phosphorus. The dihydroindoles resemble alkyl-anilines rather than indoles in reactions, but can be oxidized to indoles with silver sulphate. Hexahydroindole, originally thought to be (XVIII), is now written as (XIX) because it gives a prominent azomethine peak in the infrared at $6 \cdot 1$ μ, whereas no $N - H$ stretching band is present (Witkop, 1956).

Carbazole. Tetrahydrocarbazoles are formed by Borsche's synthesis from *cyclo*hexanone phenylhydrazone (p. 189), and can be dehydrogenated with palladium. Carbazole can be hydrogenated to tetra-, hexa- (i.e. the whole of one benzene ring), deca- and dodeca-hydrocarbazoles (Adkins and Coonradt, 1941). Very severe conditions are needed for complete hydrogenation. 2:3-Dihydrocarbazole is obtained by dehydrating 11-hydroxy-2:3:4:11-tetrahydrocarbazole with acetic anhydride (Plant and Tomlinson, 1931). '1:4-Dihydrocarbazole' has been shown to be a mixture. Hexahydrocarbazole (carbazoline) has a *cis*-form, m.p. 99°, and a *trans*-form, m.p. 127°. In octahydrocarbazole the central ring has two double-bonds, as in pyrrole.

Pyrazole. Δ^2-Pyrazolines (4:5-dihydropyrazoles) are formed by condensing α:β-unsaturated aldehydes with hydrazines. Thus acrolein and hydrazine give pyrazoline, a weak, acid-stable base, b.p. 144°, oxidized to pyrazole by bromine, and to a red unstable dye by other oxidizing agents. Pyrazoline is also obtained by the action of diazomethane on ethylene, and by reducing pyrazole with sodium in alcohol. In pyrazolines, the hydrogen on the nitrogen atom is not mobile because its migration to the other nitrogen would involve the migration of a hydrogen from a carbon atom, always a more energy-consuming change. Hence 5-methyl- and 3-methyl-pyrazoline are isomers, but not rapidly interconvertible tautomers. Some unstable Δ^1-pyrazolines have been isolated: these rearrange to Δ^2-pyrazolines on melting. Pyrazolines resist further reduction.

Indazole. 2:3-Dihydroindazoles are formed by the reduction of indazoles with sodium and alcohol, but have been little studied. Indazoles can be catalytically hydrogenated, but only with the greatest difficulty (Fries, Fabel and Eckhardt, 1941). Tetrahydroindazole, m.p. 84°, is obtained from *cyclo*hexanone-2-aldehyde and hydrazine.

Iminazoles cannot be reduced, either chemically or by catalytic hydrogenation. Δ^1-Iminazolines (2-imidazolines; 4:5-dihydro-iminazoles) are formed by submitting a solution of ethylene diamine and an aliphatic acid, dissolved in benzene, to azeotropic distillation. The simplest known member is 2-methyl-Δ^1-iminazoline (lysidine), m.p. 105°. Boiling water hydrolyses it in ten minutes to acetylethylenediamine. It is a strong base, and the salts are more resistant to hydrolysis than the free molecule. Iminazolines require dehydrogenation with nickel at 350° for conversion to iminazoles, and resist hydrogenation. Quaternary salts are formed by heating with alkyl halides.

Δ^1-Iminazolines containing $C_{12} - C_{18}$ side-chains in the 2-position have been used as emulsifiers, de-emulsifiers, mineral flotation aids, textile auxiliaries, and asphalt additives. They (like most surface-active strong bases) have disinfectant properties. 2-Heptadecyl-Δ^1-iminazoline and its derivatives are used as fungicides on fruit trees. 2-Benzyl-Δ^1-iminazoline ('Priscol') strongly dilates peripheral blood-vessels and is used as a stimulating application in human medicine. 2-(1-Naphthyl)methyl-Δ^1-iminazoline (tolazoline; 'Privine') is, on the contrary, a potent constrictor of blood-vessels and is used both locally (e.g. as a nasal decongestant) and orally for its antagonism of some functions of the body's adrenaline. The much-used antihistaminic drug ('Antistine') is 2-(N-phenyl-N-benzyl-aminomethyl)-Δ^1-iminazoline.

For further reading on iminazolines, see Hofmann (1953); Ferm and Riebsomer (1954).

Benziminazole. The primary products from the interaction of *o*-phenylenediamine and aldehydes are almost certainly di-hydrobenziminazoles, but only benziminazoles are isolated. The most drastic reduction of benziminazoles yields 4:5:6:7-tetrahydrobenziminazoles, and no simple dihydrobenzimin-azoles have yet been prepared.

Purine. Hydropurines have been little investigated. The catalytic hydrogenation of purine leads, apparently, to 1:6-dihydropurine (Bendich, 1957). The electrolytic reduction of xanthine (2:6-dihydroxypurine) gives 'deoxyanthine', i.e. 2-oxo-1:2:3:6-tetrahydropurine (otherwise known as 2-hydroxy-1:6-dihydropurine). Acid hydrolysis leads to 4-hydroxy-5-

S

aminomethyliminazole. Several analogues were similarly obtained.

(c) Dihydro-derivatives of π-excessive O- and S-heteroaromatics

As with the N-analogues dealt with under *(b)*, only *di*hydro-derivatives are ethylenic.

Furan. Δ^2-Dihydrofurans (2:3-dihydrofurans) are anhydrides of aldehydo-(or keto-)alcohols, from which they are formed on heating (cf. dihydropyran, below), e.g. 2-methyl-Δ^2-dihydrofuran from 4-keto-*n*-amyl alcohol. Unsubstituted Δ^2-dihydrofuran was first made by passing tetrafurfuryl alcohol over metals at 200° (Wilson, 1945), but is better prepared by the action of sodium on 3-chloro-2-alkoxytetrahydrofurans (made from tetrahydrofuran) (Normant, 1949).

Δ^3-Dihydrofuran, b.p. 67°, is obtained by reducing erythritol with formic acid, by removing the elements of hydrogen bromide from 3-bromotetrahydrofuran (Amstutz, 1944), or in the commercial production of tetrahydrofuran from acetylene (p. 11) by reducing the butyndiol only as far as *cis*butenediol (Jones and Taylor, 1950).

The five-membered *unsaturated lactones* will now be discussed. They are anhydrides of enolic forms of γ-aldehydo-(or keto-) carboxylic acids. Crotonolactone (XX), m.p. 4°, the anhydride of γ-aldehydopropionic acid, has been little studied. It is tautomeric with 2-hydroxyfuran (p. 211). β-Angelica lactone, the 5-methyl-derivative of (XX), is formed (together with α-angelica lactone) by the dry distillation of laevulinic acid (acetylpropionic acid). It is 2-oxo-5-methyl-Δ^3-dihydrofuran, and is an oil, b.p. 209°, miscible with water. Hydrolysis to laevulinic acid is incomplete after five days' boiling with water, but alkaline catalysis completes it in twelve hours at 20°. The cardiac glycosides have an α:β-unsaturated lactone ring, usually crotonolactone, attached in the β-position at $C_{(17)}$ of the steroidal nucleus.

'α-Angelica lactone' (XXI), formed as described above, is a solid, m.p. 18° and b.p. 167°. It is 2-oxo-5-methyl-Δ^4-dihydrofuran, also known as γ-methyl-$\Delta^{\beta,\gamma}$-butenolide. It is soluble in 20 parts of water (at 18°), which slowly hydrolyses it: at 100° it is completely hydrolysed in five hours. Hydrolysis is accelerated by hydrogen and hydroxyl ions, although hydrogen ions usually catalyse the *formation* of lactones. Organic bases (triethylamine is often used) catalyse its isomerism to 'β-angelica lactone'.

The antibiotic protoaenemonin, found in some buttercups and pulsatilla, is 5-methylene-crotonolactone. Penicillic acid (unrelated to penicillin), clavacin and crepin are other antibiotics with an unsaturated lactone structure. It has been suggested that they injure cells by combining with biologically essential thiols, adding the elements of −SH across the double-bond (Cavallito and Haskell, 1945).

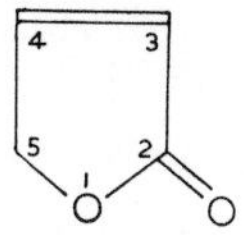

XX 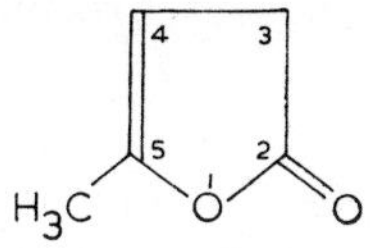 XXI 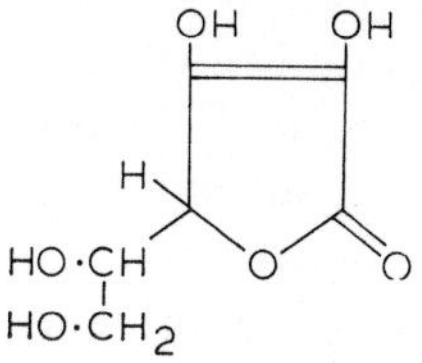 Ascorbic acid
XXII

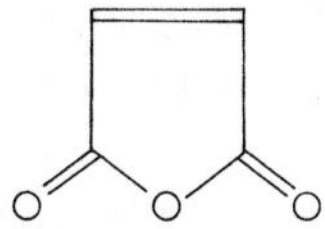

XXIII

Ascorbic acid (XXII), also known as vitamin C, is the lactone of 2-keto-L-gulonic acid. It is another naturally-occurring derivative of crotonolactone. The acidic properties are located in the 'enediol' structure: this is a powerful reducing group, easily oxidized by iodine to the corresponding diketone which has no double-bonds *in* the ring. This diketone, dehydroascorbic acid, may be reduced to ascorbic acid with hydrogen sulphide or hydriodic acid. For further information, see Rosenberg (1942).

Maleic anhydride (XXIII), m.p. 53°, is prepared commercially by the vapour-phase oxidation of benzene. It has a faint, unpleasant odour. Maleic anhydride is noted for the ease with which it combines, even at 20°, with substances having conjugated double-bonds, particularly dienes (the Diels-Alder reaction). It is used to detect this kind of unsaturation, and is an important intermediate in the formation of new carbocyclic rings.

Benzofuran. 2:3-Dihydrobenzofuran, b.p. 189°, is formed by reduction of benzofuran with sodium, or by the action of alkali on o-(2-bromoethyl)phenol. It is a typical alkyl aryl ether, hydrolysed by hydriodic acid, and undergoing the Friedel-Crafts reaction in the 5-position.

Thiophen. Δ^3-Dihydrothiophen (2:5-dihydrothiophen) is not formed by the action of sodium sulphide on 1:4-dibromo-2-butene as has been reported, but together with the Δ^2-isomer by the reduction of thiophen with sodium in liquid ammonia (Birch and McAllen, 1950). The dihydrothiophens or 'thiolenes' have been little investigated.

Benzothiophen (thianaphthene), on reduction with sodium, gives 2:3-dihydrobenzothiophen, which is also obtained by cyclizing β-(o-mercaptophenyl)ethanol (Bennett and Hafez, 1941). It can be dehydrogenated by sulphur to benzothiophen and gives all reactions typical of a sulphide, such as ready oxidation to a sulphone, and formation of a methiodide and a mercurichloride. 1:3-Dihydro*iso*benzothiophen (o-xylylene sulphide), obtained from o-xylylene bromide and sodium sulphide, is unstable in air.

Oxazole. Δ^2-Dihydro-oxazole (oxazoline), b.p. 98°, is formed by heating the β-chloroethylamide of formic acid with alkali (Wenker, 1938). It is readily hydrolysed to hydroxyethyl-formamide by boiling water, but its homologues are more stable. Pyrolysis of N-acetylethanolamine gives 2-methyloxazoline (Wenker, 1935). The ethyl esters of serine and threonine give 2-phenyl-5-carboethoxy-Δ^2-oxazolines with benziminoethyl ether, a reaction used to separate serine and threonine from protein hydrolysates (Elliott, 1949). There is no change in configuration in this reaction, such as occurs in some oxazoline reactions, of which several others are known. Oxazolines have essentially the properties of imino-ethers, being stable to alkali, but hydrolysed by acid. 2-Amino-Δ^2-oxazoline is prepared by heating 2-bromoethylamine with potassium cyanate, or ethylene oxide with sodium cyanamide. It is a colourless, highly basic solid, and may be predominantly 2-imino-oxazolidine (a similar doubt applies to the amino-derivatives of all other heteroethylenics). The oxazolines often arise as labile intermediates in the syntheses of aliphatic substances. They have never been obtained by reduction of oxazoles, nor have they been oxidized to oxazoles.

For further reading, see Cornforth (1957), Wiley and Bennett (1949).

Benzoxazoles do not appear to give hydrogenated products on attempted reduction, and the preparation of benzoxazolines by direct synthesis has not yet been very successful (Cornforth, 1957).

Isoxazole. No hydrogenated products arise on attempted reduction. Δ^2-isoxazolines are prepared by mixing $\alpha:\beta$-unsaturated aromatic ketones with hydroxylamine. Vinyl acetate and sodium fulminate (NaONC) similarly give 5-acetoxy-isoxazoline (XXIV) which splits off acetic acid to give isoxazole when heated with sulphuric acid (D'Alcontres and Mollica, 1951). Almost all known isoxazolines have aromatic substituents. For further reading, see Barnes (1957). Very little is known about hydrogenated benzisoxazoles.

Thiazole. Δ^2-Dihydrothiazole (2-thiazoline) is an oil, b.p. 139°, resembling pyridine in odour. It is made from 2-bromo-ethylamine and thioformamide, and is decomposed by acid to 2-mercaptoethylamine. Thiazolines are also formed from acylated 2-bromo-(or hydroxy-)ethylamine and phosphorus pentasulphide. 2-Bromoethylthiourea readily cyclizes to 2-aminothiazoline (or 2-iminothiazolidine), and ethanolamine reacts with carbon bisulphide to give 2-mercaptothiazoline (or 2-thio-thiazolidine).

A thiazoline structure has been suggested to explain the masked thiol groups in proteins. An antibiotic, bacitricin A, contains a thiazoline nucleus attached to a polypeptide chain (Newton and Abraham, 1953). 2-Mercaptothiazoline is used commercially as an accelerator of the vulcanization of rubber: it is hydrolysed by acid to 2-mercaptoethylamine. No reduction of a thiazole to a thiazoline has yet succeeded.

For further reading on thiazoles, see Land (1957).

Benzothiazole. Aldehydes react with an *o*-aminothiophenol to give good yields of 2:3-dihydrobenzothiazoles, the 5-chloro-derivative being the simplest recorded (Lankelma and Sharnoff,

1931). These readily become oxidized to benzothiazoles by air, or ferric chloride. The reduction of 3-methylbenzothiazolium iodide with zinc and acid gives 3-methyl-2:3-dihydrobenzothiazole.

For further reading, see Land (1957), p. 677.

| XXIV | XXV | XXVI | XXVII |

B. QUINOLIZINES

Quinolizine (II) is known only as derivatives, the simplest of which is the yellow 4-oxoquinolizine (m.p. 72°), a substance with amide-like properties. It is made by condensing ethyl 2-pyridylacetate with diethyl ethoxymethylenemalonate, followed by hydrolysis and decarboxylation of the resulting 1:3-dicarboethoxy-4-oxoquinolizine. The thio-analogue is also known.

Although quinolizine is not aromatic, it is related to the aromatic dehydroquinolizinium cation (XXV), whose iodide was prepared by heating 2-lithiomethylpyridine with 2-ethoxypropionaldehyde, and dehydrating and dehydrogenating the 2-hydroxy-1:2:3:4-tetrahydroquinolizinium salt thus formed (Boekelheide and Gall, 1954; Diels *et al.*, 1933). A more quantitative synthesis is the transformation of 2-cyanopyridine to 2-pyridyl 3-ethoxypropyl ketone, which is cyclized by hydrogen bromide to 1-keto-1:2:3:4-tetrahydroquinolizine, which is dehydrated by acetic anhydride to dehydroquinolizinium acetate (Glover and Jones, 1956). Little is known of the properties of the dehydroquinolizinium ion, but it should be a π-deficient aromatic substance, open to nucleophilic substitution in the 2- and 4-positions. The alkaloid berberine has a 3:4-dihydroquinolizinium nucleus, flanked on each side by a benzene ring. Somewhat analogously to cotarnine and hydrastinine (p. 250), berberine takes part in ring-chain tautomerism.

C. SIX-MEMBERED RINGS CONTAINING OXYGEN OR SULPHUR

(a) Six-membered Rings containing Oxygen (Pyrans, their Derivatives and Benzologues)

This section deals with six-membered rings containing oxygen. The parent substances, e.g. γ-pyran (XXVI), have only two double-bonds and, for reasons of valency, no contribution of electrons from the oxygen can make these molecules aromatic. In any case, oxygen is a poor contributor of electrons to a conjugated system, as we have seen in studying furan (p. 201).

However, pyran does form two series of aromatic derivatives, the pyrylium salts and the pyrones. These have attracted much attention because of their widespread occurrence in nature, and an enormous literature has arisen accordingly.

Few connexions between structure and properties have yet been established for the pyrans and their derivatives which, from the viewpoint of this book, represent a territory in need of development. The pyrans were so named on account of the high thermal stability of their derivatives.

(i) *Pyrans, pyrylium salts and dihydropyrans.* α-Pyran (XXVII) and γ-pyran (XXVI) (also known as 1:4-pyran) have not yet been made. However, 1:4-dioxin, a six-membered ring containing two oxygen atoms, is well known (see (v) below), and hence 1:4-pyran should be stable enough to be synthesized, although numerous attempts to do so have failed. No alkyl-pyrans are known, but γ-pyrans containing phenyl- or carboxyl-substituents have been prepared.

γ-Pyran-2:6-dicarboxylic acid can be made by heating diketopimelic acid (XXVIII) with sulphuric acid. Attempts to decarboxylate it have led to profound decomposition. Attempts to cyclize δ-diketones to 2:6-dialkylpyrans have produced only alkyl*cyclo*hexanones, but 2:4:4:6-tetraphenyl-γ-pyran is readily prepared from (XXIX) (Carvalho, 1935).

Little is recorded of the properties of γ-pyrans, but those with a free hydrogen-atom in the 4-position are easily oxidized (e.g. by ferric chloride) to pyrylium salts, e.g. (XXX), which are aromatic, and contain tricovalent oxygen.

These pyrylium (or 'pyroxonium') salts can be synthesized in other ways. 2:4:6-Trimethylpyrylium perchlorate, perhaps the simplest of all known pyrylium salts, is made by the action of acetic anhydride and perchloric acid on mesityl oxide (2-methylpentenone, $CH_3CO \cdot CH:CMe_2$). It gives a highly acid solution, and hence must be a very weak base, as are all pyrylium salts. On titration with alkali, it forms the 'pseudo-base' (XXXI) by covalently binding a hydroxyl-group in the 2-position. This pseudobase is the anhydride of 4-methyl-Δ^3-heptene-2:6-dione, and slowly opens to this ketone in alkaline solution (Schwarzenbach and Lutz, 1940). Again, acetophenone and benzylideneacetophenone have been condensed, in the presence of ferric chloride, to 2:4:6-triphenylpyrylium chloride (XXX). The same cation is obtained by heating acetophenone and boron trifluoride, a methyl group being lost (Dovey and Robinson, 1935).

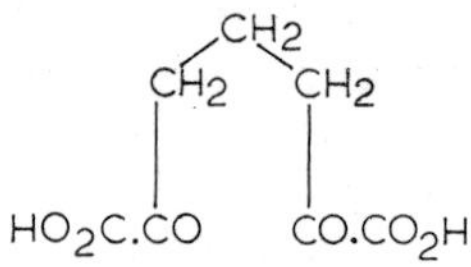

XXVIII

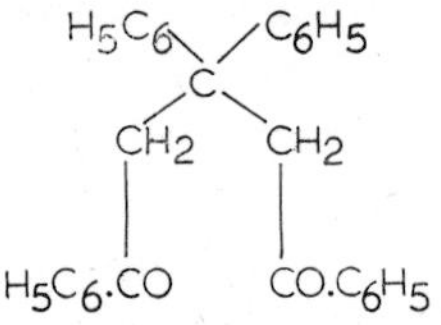

XXIX

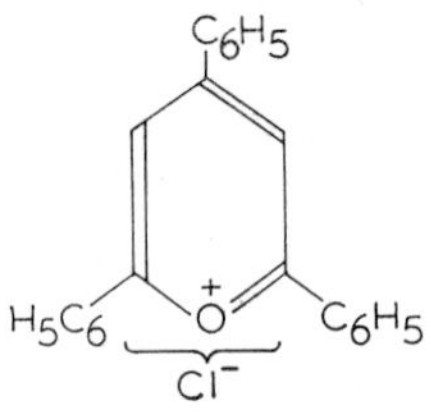

XXX

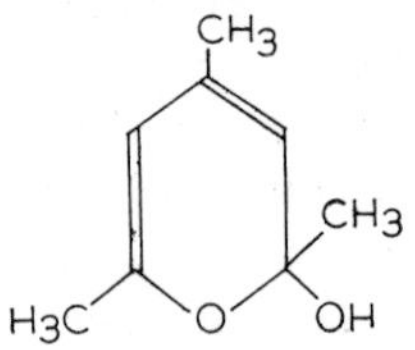

XXXI

The pyrylium salts are stable to acid. The transformation by alkali to ether-soluble, colourless 'pseudobases', e.g. (XXXI), recalls the parallel case of quinoline methochloride (p. 70). Triphenylpyrylium chloride (XXX) and aqueous ammonia readily give 2:4:6-triphenylpyridine. 2:4-Diphenyl-6-(p-hydroxy)phenylpyrylium chloride is red, and gives a blue 'anhydrobase' after loss of the elements of hydrogen chloride upon making alkaline. This blue colour disappears as the anhy-drobase becomes hydrated to the colourless pseudobase. These observations have thrown much light on the colour changes undergone by anthocyanins (see below) (Schneider, 1941).

Apart from the above, little is recorded about the properties of pyrylium salts. It would be interesting to know if they could be substituted by electro- and nucleo-philic reagents. Their stability led Dilthey to postulate that their positive charge is shared between oxygen and all five carbon atoms of the ring. Modern concepts of resonance support this view, but the extent to which the charge has left the oxygen atom, to give structures such as (XXXII), is unknown.

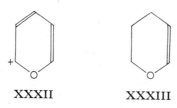

XXXII   XXXIII

Δ^3-Dihydropyran, b.p. 94°, is made by the action of potassium hydroxide on 4-bromotetrahydropyran. Being an allyl (and not a vinyl) ether, it is stable to acid hydrolysis below 150° (Paul and Tchelitcheff, 1947).

Δ^2-Dihydropyran (XXXIII) is made commercially by passing tetrahydrofurfuryl alcohol over alumina at 350° (see p. 11). It is a colourless liquid, b.p. 87° (Paul, 1933), readily hydrated by acid to 2-hydroxytetrahydropyran, which exists in ring-chain tautomerism with 5-hydroxypentanal (Schniepp and Geller, 1946). It readily adds chlorine or hydrogen chloride across the double-bond (Paul, 1944). Some α:β-unsaturated ketones dimerize to Δ^2-dihydropyans, e.g. methyl vinyl ketone gives 2-methyl-6-acetyl-Δ^2-dihydropyran. Crotonaldehyde reacts similarly, but, if acid-catalysed, it gives 2:6-dimethyl-3-formyl-Δ^3-dihydropyran (Delépine and Horeau, 1938).

Δ^2-Dihydropyrans are used as intermediates for the synthesis of 1:5-disubstituted pentanes, as protective agents for aromatic or aliphatic hydroxy-groups (Henbest, Jones and Walls, 1950), and for preparing (by addition across the double-bond) tetrahydropyrans that are simple models of sugars.

For further reading, see Fried (1950); Jones and Taylor (1950).

(ii) *The Pyrones.* α-Pyrone (XXXIV), or coumalin, is prepared by heating its 6-carboxylic acid (Fried and Elderfield,
1941). It is a colourless liquid, f.p. 5°, with the odour of new-
mown hay. Being the lactone of an enol, it is readily hydrolysed
by alkali. It is stable to acid, but lacks the basic properties of
the γ-isomer. Catalytic hydrogenation gives a mixture of
δ-valerolactone and valeric acid. It is a true diene, and adds
maleic anhydride to give a tricyclic product (Diels, Alder and
Müller, 1931). α-Pyrone rapidly polymerizes at room temperature, but phenyl or carboxylic substituents prevent this.

Coumalic acid (α-pyrone-5-carboxylic acid) is easily prepared by the action of sulphuric acid on malic acid; this
amounts to the self-condensation of two molecules of formyl-
acetic acid. With hot alkali, coumalic acid gives glutaconic
acid (propene-1:3-dicarboxylic acid) and formic acid; with
ammonia it gives 2-hydroxypyridine-5-carboxylic acid (both of
these reactions have proved useful in synthesis). Methyl
coumalate is methylated in the 6-position (i.e. a C-methylation)
by diazomethane (Fried and Elderfield, 1941) although 5-
methyl-α-pyrone is not attacked by diazomethane.

XXXIV   XXXV   XXXVI   XXXVII

'Glutaconic anhydride', formed by dehydrating glutaconic
acid with acetic anhydride, is 6-hydroxy-α-pyrone. It is a strong
acid, and is not decomposed by boiling water.

Substances with an active methylene group react with
α:β-acetylenic esters or ketones to give α-pyrones. For example,
diethyl malonate and methyl ethinyl ketone give 4-methyl-3-
carboethoxy-α-pyrone. The α-pyrone-3-carboxylic acids are
stable to hot alkali.

Parasorbic acid (XXXV), 6-methyl-dihydro-α-pyrone, is
also δ-hexenolactone, i.e. the lactone of 5-hydroxy-2-hexenoic
acid (Kuhn and Jerchel, 1943). It is found in the mountain ash.

It inhibits the germination of embryos, both plant and animal, an action that is antagonized by cysteine. It is formed by benzoylating aldol, and condensing the product with malonic acid (Medawar, Robinson and Robinson, 1943).

α-Pyrones brominate in the 3-position, which may be considered evidence of aromatic structure (see further the γ-pyrones, below). 6-Hydroxy-α-pyrones undergo a C-acylation reaction with acetyl chloride, the acetyl-group entering the 5-, and later also the 3-, positions (Gogte, 1938).

The cardioactive steroids in squill, and in toad-venom, have α-pyrone as a substituent in the 17-position of the steroid nucleus. It will be recalled that the majority of cardioactive steroids have the five-membered crotonolactone in this position instead (see p. 260).

γ-Pyrone (XXXVI) is a colourless solid, m.p. 33°, soluble in water and most organic solvents. It is faintly basic (see below) and forms a hydrochloride, m.p. 139°. γ-Pyrone is best made (Cornubert and Robinet, 1933) by decarboxylating its 2:6-dicarboxylic acid, the ester of which is formed by the condensation of acetone and ethyl oxalate. γ-Pyrone can also be formed by the ring-closure of acetone dialdehyde; acetone dicarboxylic acid similarly gives 2:6-dihydroxypyrone. β-Keto-esters, when refluxed with sodium bicarbonate, self-condense to pyrones, e.g. ethyl acetoacetate gives 2-methyl-5-acetyl-6-hydroxy-γ-pyrone (Arndt, 1940). This substance, known as 'dehydracetic acid', is much used as a fungicide, and is prepared commercially by the self-condensation of ketene. When boiled with concentrated hydrochloric acid, dehydracetic acid undergoes ring-opening to aceto-acetylacetone-3-carboxylic acid: this decarboxylates to acetoacetylacetone which cyclizes to 2:6-dimethyl-γ-pyrone.

In general, pyrones are stable to acid, whereas alkali readily opens the ring. For example, γ-pyrone and sodium hydroxide give acetone dialdehyde, i.e. diformylacetone (XXXVII), which reforms the pyrone upon acidification. The conversion of pyrones to the correspondingly substituted 4-pyridones by gentle warming with ammonia (see p. 104), also proceeds through (XXXVII). γ-Pyrone is not reduced by zinc and acetic acid, but catalytic hydrogenation gives a mixture of tetrahydropyrone and tetrahydropyranol. Unlike the α-isomer, γ-pyrone does not react with maleic anhydride. Oxidation of γ-pyrone with hydrogen peroxide and ferrous sulphate gives 3-hydroxypyrone, in small yield.

The γ-pyrones brominate in the 3-, and eventually the 3:5-positions, the halogen being firmly bound and quite unaltered by sodamide, or boiling barium hydroxide solution. The 3-hydroxypyrones submit even more readily to electrophilic substitution in the 2-position, e.g. by chlorine, nitric acid, or formaldehyde (Files and Challenger, 1940; Meunier, Mentzer and Vinet, 1946).

Although containing a $>$C:O group, pyrone is not a ketone, but the vinylogue of a lactone (i.e. an internal ester). Thus it is understandable that it gives no ketonic derivatives. But to explain the lack of addition reactions, and the behaviour on halogenation, it has been necessary to invoke the concept of aromatic stabilization by resonance, involving forms with a separation of charge,[1] e.g. (XXXVIII) and (XXXIX). The unexpectedly high dipole moment (4D) supports this hypothesis, but it is still far too small to permit, in the resonance hybrid, a preponderance of (XXXIX) for which a moment of 22D is calculated (Hunter and Partington, 1933; Le Fèvre and Le Fèvre, 1937; Pauling, 1939).

XXXVIII   XXXIX   XL   XLI   XLII

The basic properties of γ-pyrones have, perhaps, been exaggerated in the past. For example, the pK_a of 2:6-dimethylpyrone is only 0·3, i.e. in the same region as o- and p-nitroaniline or urea, but not as low as acetophenone ($-6·0$) (the supposed basic properties of ethers remain to be put on a quantitative footing). Had the hydrochloride not been easy to prepare and isolate under anhydrous conditions, the feeble basic properties

[1] The participation of separated charges was first suggested by F. Arndt and co-workers in 1924.

of the γ-pyrones would probably not have been recognized, for the cation has almost the same spectrum as the neutral molecule.[1] It is usually assumed that these are not simple oxonium salts, but are resonance hybrids derived from the canonical forms (XL) and (XLI), and even a proportion of the forms in which the positive charge is assumed by carbon, as in (XLII).

Upon treatment with methyl iodide, or methyl sulphate, 2:6-dimethyl-γ-pyrone does not methylate on the ring-oxygen as was once thought, but gives the 4-methoxypyronium cation, derived from (XL), and this again has a spectrum like that of γ-pyrone (Gibbs, Johnson and Hughes, 1930). The structure of this methoxy-derivative follows from its conversion by ammonium carbonate to 2:6-dimethyl-4-methoxypyridine.

γ-Pyrones are somewhat π-deficient, in spite of their ease of bromination in the 3-position. Methyl-groups in the 2- and 6-positions are activated, and condense with aromatic aldehydes; also they give bromomethylpyrones with N-bromosuccinimide (Buu-Hoï and Lecocq, 1946).

4-Thiopyrones are readily prepared by the action of phosphorus pentasulphide on the corresponding pyrones (Arndt and Pusch, 1925). They behave more like thioketones than pyrones behave like ketones, particularly if electron-attracting groups are in the 2- and 4-positions.

γ-Pyrone-2:6-dicarboxylic acid (chelidonic acid) and its 3-hydroxy-derivative (meconic acid) are present in the poppy and related plants. Kojic acid, produced by a number of moulds (mainly *Aspergilli*), is 3-hydroxy-6-hydroxymethyl-γ-pyrone. It has a reactive 2-position where it couples with diazonium salts, forms Mannich bases, and condenses with aldehydes. Maltol, 2-methyl-3-hydroxy-γ-pyrone, has been obtained by destructively distilling various carbohydrates, and is present in the bark and needles of conifers. It is also formed by the action of alkali on the antibiotic, streptomycin.

For further reading on pyrones, see Fried (1950); Cavalieri (1947).

---

[1] This happens also with 'γ-pyridone' (see Chapter VIII). Fortunately the Raman spectra of γ-pyrone and its hydrochloride are quite different, the $>$C:O absorption of the neutral molecule giving way to that of a more aromatic structure with a phenolic group (Kahovec and Kohlrausch, 1942).

(iii) *Benzopyrans, benzopyrylium salts and anthocyanins.* None of the four possible benzopyrans (also referred to as 'chromenes') appears to be known, although several derivatives are found in nature. The simplest natural chromene is evodionol (2:2-dimethyl-5-methoxy-6-acetyl-7-hydroxy-α-chromene). Many chromenes have a phenyl-group in the 2-positions, and are then termed flavenes (XLIII). They may be formed by the controlled hydrogenation of flavylium salts, such as (XLVIII) (Fonseka, 1947).

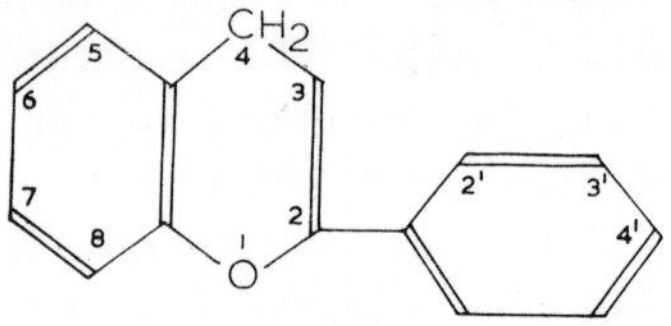

XLIII 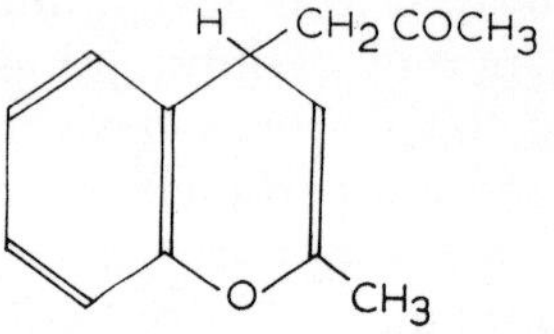   XLIV

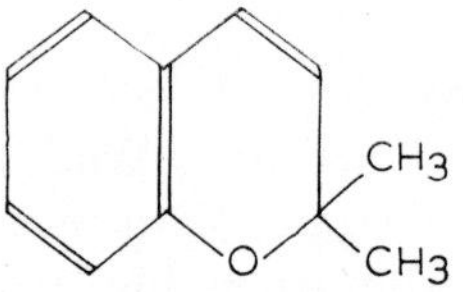

XLV 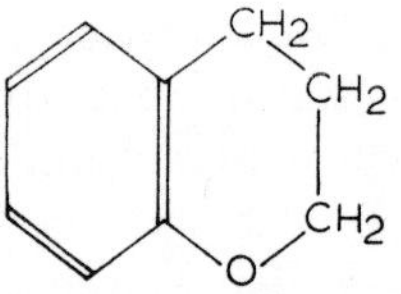   XLVI

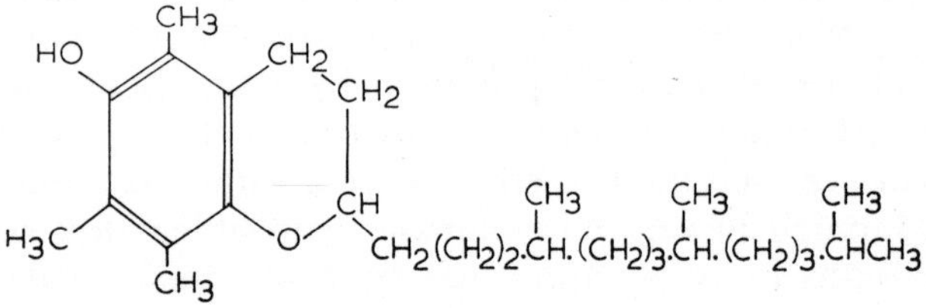

XLVII

A few simpler chromenes are known. 3:4:6-Trimethyl-α-chromene arises from the dehydration of 3:4:6-trimethyl-4-chromanol with phosphorus pentoxide. It is an oil, b.p. 136° (13 mm.), which resinifies on standing. The condensation of *o*-hydroxybenzalacetone and ethyl acetoacetate gives 2-methyl-4-acetonyl-γ-chromene (XLIV), colourless crystals, m.p. 135°. Coumarin (see (iv) below), treated with excess of methylmagnesium bromide, gives 2:2-dimethyl-α-chromene (XLV), a colourless liquid, b.p. 97° (15 mm.) (Smith and Ruoff, 1940). These α-chromenes are easily reduced to their dihydro-derivatives (known as *chromans*), which are also obtained by the action of Grignard reagents on dihydrocoumarin (Smith and Ruoff, 1940). Both α- and γ-chromenes must reduce to the same chroman.

Chroman (XLVI) (2:3-benzo-5:6-dihydro-γ-pyran) is a liquid, b.p. 214°, insoluble in water and soluble in organic liquids. It undergoes the Friedel-Crafts ketone reaction in the 6-position, and in general behaves as an ether of phenol. Chroman can be prepared by the action of trimethylene chlorhydrin on phenol, or by the reaction of phenol with allyl bromide and zinc chloride (Karrer *et al.*, 1938). Isoprene, and other conjugated dienes, similarly react with phenols to give chromans together with the related benzofurans. α-Tocopherol (XLVII), similarly made, is a valuable constituent of wheat-germ oil. It is one form of vitamin E; other natural forms, known as β- and γ-tocopherol, lack one or other methyl-group in the benzene ring, and are less biologically active. The tocopherols are rapidly oxidized by air and light, and hence are used in medicine only as the acetate. 6-Hydroxychromans, including the tocopherols, are oxidized to γ-hydroxyalkylquinones, a reaction used in their analysis. These one-ring quinones can be reduced and recyclized to the original 6-hydroxychromans.

Benzopyrylium salts are obtainable by oxidizing chromenes (benzopyrans) in the presence of acid (cf. the preparation of pyrylium salts, p. 265). The action of Grignard reagents on coumarins (see p. 278) can be modified to give 2-hydroxy-2-methylchromenes. These 'chromenols' are the pseudobases of benzopyrylium salts (cf. the pseudobases of pyrylium salts, p. 266), and revert to these salts on acidification. This type of synthesis was much used by Willstätter for the anthocyanidins (see below), whereas Robinson employed the condensation of *o*-hydroxybenzaldehydes with hydroxylated acetophenones. A simpler example of the latter reaction is the acid-catalysed condensation of salicylaldehyde and formaldehyde to give benzopyrylium chloride (Le Fèvre, 1934); likewise salicylaldehyde and acetone give 2-methylbenzopyrylium chloride. Resorcinol and acetylacetone condense to give 2:4-dimethyl-7-hydroxy-benzopyrylium chloride.

The benzopyrylium salts have high dipole moments (e.g. 8D), as would be expected for true salts (Le Fèvre and Le Fèvre, 1936). Oxidizing agents break them down to various benzene derivatives. They are reduced easily by catalytic hydrogenation to chromenes (Fonseka, 1947), and on further dehydrogenation to chromans. On nitration, benzopyrylium chloride gives 4:6-dinitrosalicylic acid. However 2-phenyl-benzopyrylium salts nitrate in the 3'-position, which reveals the π-deficient character of the flavylium skeleton (those benzopyrylium salts having a phenyl-group in the 2-position, e.g. (XLVIII), are known as flavylium salts).

The *anthocyanidins* are naturally-occurring flavylium salts with hydroxyl-groups in the 3-, 5-, 7- and 4'-positions, and sometimes in 3'- and 5'- as well. The 3'- and 5'-hydroxyl-groups are, in some examples, methylated. These anthocyanidins occur as glucosides known as anthocyanins in plants, and constitute the purple, violet and blue colouring-matters of flowers, fruits, leaves and stems, and provide some of the red colours as well. The sugar groups are attached to the 3-, or the 3- and 5-, positions.

Upon alkaline hydrolysis, the anthocyanidins give a mixture of a phenol and a phenol carboxylic acid, a reaction which has been used to determine their constitution. Milder alkaline treatment, which produces colourless pseudobases in other benzopyrylium salts, gives violet anhydrobases, e.g. (XLIX) in the anthocyanidins.

The acid salts of the anthocyanins are usually red, and the substance is then apparently an oxonium salt, i.e. as (XLVIII). Some authors write these salts with a positive charge on a carbon atom, and possibly such forms do contribute to the resonance hybrid. Anthocyanins have pK's of about 4, and hence are stronger than the pyronium salts (see p. 270). In neutral solution, they are violet, and this species is called the 'colour-base', i.e. as (XLIX). In alkaline solution, they are blue because of the formation of an anion, i.e. as (L), although the 7-hydroxy-group may not be the source of the negative charge in all cases. The absence of sugar-residues affects these colour changes very little. Extensive surveys of the occurrence of anthocyanins have revealed more than twenty types, derived from the combination of various sugars with only six anthocyanidins (Robinson and Robinson, 1938). In some cases the pigment formed 20–30 % of the dry weight of the petals.

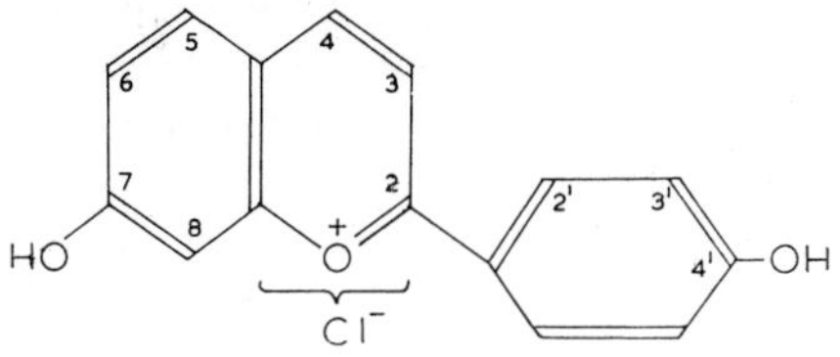

XLVIII

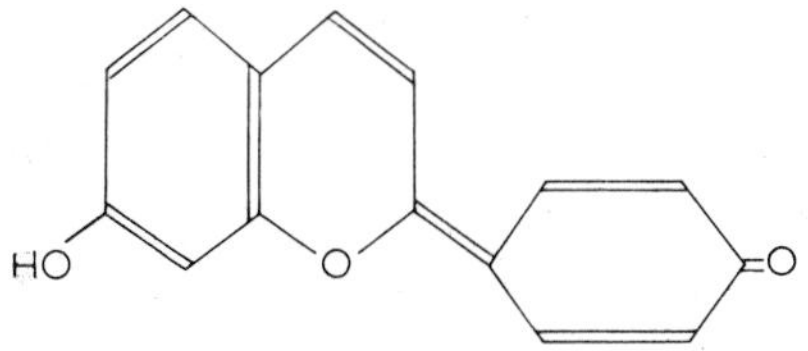

XLIX

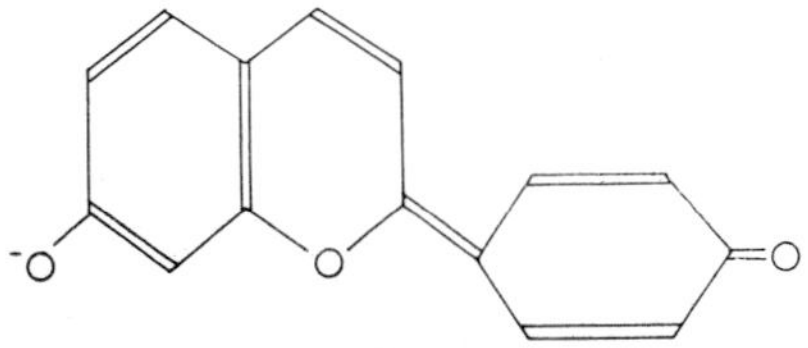

L

In degree of oxidation, the anthocyanidins are intermediate between two other classes of plant products, the flavonols (see (iv) below) and the catechins (2-phenylchromans). The flavonols can be converted by reduction with lithium aluminium hydride followed by acidification to anthocyanidins (Mirza and Robinson, 1950), and these, in turn, can be reduced with the same reagent to catechins (Karrer and Seyhan, 1950). The flavones and flavonols of plants are not regarded as precursors of anthocyanins, but are produced apparently from the same intermediates by competitive processes. The lack of correspondence between the substitution in the anthocyanin and the

T

flavone of any given flower may be cited in evidence (Geissman and Mehlquist, 1947).

Xanthene (LI), not to be confused with the purine xanthine, is dibenzo-γ-pyrone. It is a colourless solid, m.p. 99°, prepared by the reduction of xanthone (see (iv) below). Xanthene is stable to acid and alkali up to 200°. Strong oxidizing agents convert it to xanthone, but 9-substituted xanthenes give 9-hydroxyxanthenes (xanthydrols). 2-Hydroxy-9-methylxanthene is oxidized to 9-methyl*iso*xanthone (LIII), even by air in the presence of alkali: this reaction first forms the xanthydrol, which dehydrates spontaneously. With butyllithium, xanthene gives 9-xanthyl-lithium, and this gives xanthene-9-carboxylic acid with carbon dioxide. When halogenated, xanthenes react first at the 9-position. Under Friedel-Crafts conditions, xanthene gives 2-benzoylxanthene.

LI   LII

LIII

3:6-Dimethylxanthene occurs in coal-tar. 9:9'-Dixanthyl is obtained by heating xanthydrol (LII) with vanadium chloride, or acetophenone, or exposing it to sunlight. It and its analogues readily dissociate into highly-coloured free xanthyl radicals.

Xanthydrol (LII), m.p. about 124°, is prepared quanti-tatively by the reduction of xanthone (see (iv) below) with sodium amalgam. Like benzhydrol (diphenylcarbinol), to which it is closely related, it readily self-etherifies (to dixanthydryl ether, m.p. 200°). Xanthydrol is a common analytical reagent for the micro-determination of urea, with which it forms an insoluble precipitate (crystal lattice effect).

The hydroxyl-group in 9-phenylxanthydrol is mobile, as in triphenylcarbinol and 'pseudobases' generally. It is easily replaced by halogens when treated with cold dilute hydrochloric or hydrobromic acid; ammonia replaces it by $-NH_2$, and methanol by OMe. 9-Chloro-9-phenylxanthene is colourless, but gives a red hydrochloride, but 9-bromo-9-phenylxanthene is described as red. This paradoxical behaviour is apparently due to the easier ionization of the C-Br bond, which leads to the production of enough acid to ionize (in part) the ring-oxygen, giving xanthylium salts. Triphenylmethyl bromide can also give red salts with acids, but only under strictly anhydrous conditions (carbonium salts). Xanthydrol is thus seen to bear a similarr elationship to the xanthylium salts as the 'pseudobase', 2-hydroxy-α-pyran, bears to the pyrylium salts (p. 265), and 2-chromenol to the benzopyrylium salts (p. 273). These, in turn, are related to their nitrogen analogues, the pseudobases of the acridinium, quinolinium and pyridinium salts.

9-Phenylxanthylium salts are π-deficient for they do not nitrate; also bromine, introduced into the 3-position, is active. The reaction between xanthydrol and hydrogen chloride seems to stop at the 9-chloroxanthene stage, and the product is disproportionated by water into a mixture of xanthene and xanthone.

Fluorans are lactones of 9-*o*-carboxyphenyl-derivatives of xanthydrol. Fluoresceins are their 2:7-dihydroxy-, and rhodamines their 2:7-diamino-, derivatives. These contain also the *iso*benzofuran nucleus, and have already been described under that heading (p. 230).

The pyronine dyes, such as Pyronine G (LIV), are related to *iso*xanthone (LIII). They are made by condensing *m*-dialkyl-aminophenols with formaldehyde and dehydrating the resulting p:p′-tetraalkyldiamino-*o-o*′-dihydroxydiphenylmethane to the xanthene corresponding to (LIV), which is then oxidized with ferric chloride. Pyronine R is the corresponding tetraethyl-derivative, and 'Acridine Red' is not an acridine but the symmetrical dimethylanalogue of pyronine G. These pyronine dyes are red, with a strong yellow fluorescence. They are no longer used for textiles, but are important microscopical stains, much used for differentiating the nucleic acids. These dyes are resonance hybrids in which the positive charge is shared between the two nitrogen atoms: the oxygen atom may also participate, but to a much smaller extent as it is so much more electronegative.

For further reading on benzopyrans (also chromenes, flavenes), benzopyrylium salts (flavylium salts, anthocyanidins), and dihydrobenzopyrans (chromans, catechins), see Wawzonek (1951). For anthocyanins, see Link (1943), Robinson (1935), Hill (1936). For xanthenes, see Wawzonek (1951), and for pyronine dyes Coffey (1950).

LIV   LV

(iv) *The Benzopyrones: Coumarins, Chromones, Flavones and Xanthones.* Benzo-α-pyrone, or coumarin (LV), is present in the tonka bean and in many other plants. It has been much used in flavouring (especially of chocolate), but is passing into disuse as it is thought to be toxic. Coumarin is a colourless solid, m.p. 70°, readily soluble in boiling water and organic solvents. It is easily prepared, by the Perkin reaction, from salicylaldehyde and acetic anhydride: 2-hydroxycinnamic acid is an intermediate, but is cyclized during the reaction to coumarin which is its lactone.

The most used method for preparing substituted coumarins is the condensation of phenols with ethyl acetoacetate, e.g. phenol itself gives 4-methylcoumarin. Electron-attracting groups in the phenol inhibit this reaction (Chakravati, 1935).

On warming with alkali, coumarin is converted into *o*-hydroxycinnamic acid, which re-forms coumarin when heated with acetic anhydride. Coumarin nitrates and sulphonates in the 6-position, and disulphonates in the 3- and 6-positions, evidence that the pyrone ring of coumarin is aromatic and π-excessive.

Many 6- or 7-hydroxy- and methoxy-derivatives of coumarin occur in plants, usually as glucosides. The coumarins are among the most brightly fluorescing of all colourless substances.

Dicumarol, or 3:3'-methylene*bis*-4-hydroxycoumarin (LVI), causes haemorrhage in cattle fed on sweet clover which contains it. It is used medicinally to prevent blood-clotting. Many modifications of the molecule have been tested for this property, and it has been found that the 4-hydroxy-group is essential, but that only one coumarin ring is necessary. Thus 3-allyl-4-hydroxycoumarin is as active as coumarin. It is now known that these coumarins exert their anti-clotting action by antagonizing the vitamins K, of which (LVII) is the simplest member. The resemblance between the molecules may not look particularly close, but 3-methyl-4-hydroxycoumarin has vitamin K-like activity. The tautomerism existing between 4-hydroxy-coumarins and 2-hydroxychromones (Arndt, Loewe, Ün and Ayça, 1951) gives some support to the form in which (LVI) has been written. A spectroscopic examination is still required. Coumarins with anti-blood-clotting properties make good rodenticides, and 3-acetonylbenzyl-4-hydroxycoumarin ('Warfarin') is used for this purpose.

For further reading on coumarins, see Sethna and Shah (1945); Wawzonek (1951).

Benzo-γ-pyrone, or chromone (LVIII), is produced by the action of sulphuric acid on phenoxyfumaric acid (made from phenol and ethyl chlorofumarate) followed by decarboxylation of the chromone-2-carboxylic acid. It is a colourless solid, m.p. 59°, and the yellow solution in sulphuric acid has a blue fluorescence.

2-Substituted chromones are prepared by the Claisen condensation of *o*-hydroacetophenone with simple esters, e.g. ethyl acetate gives 2-methylchromone (Mozingo, 1941).

Unlike γ-pyrones, chromones react somewhat as α:β-unsaturated ketones, and a typical Raman spectrum is given (Mookerjee and Gupta, 1939). They readily give oximes with hydroxylamine, but do not react with phenylhydrazine. A methyl-group in the 2-position is activated and condenses with aldehydes. With cold alkali, chromones form o-hydroxy-β-diketones. Nitration of chromones occurs in the 6-position, and not very readily. Chromones are not substituted by bromine, nor do they add it across a double-bond. Catalytic reduction produces the corresponding 2:3-dihydro-derivative 'chromanone', and then chroman (p. 273).

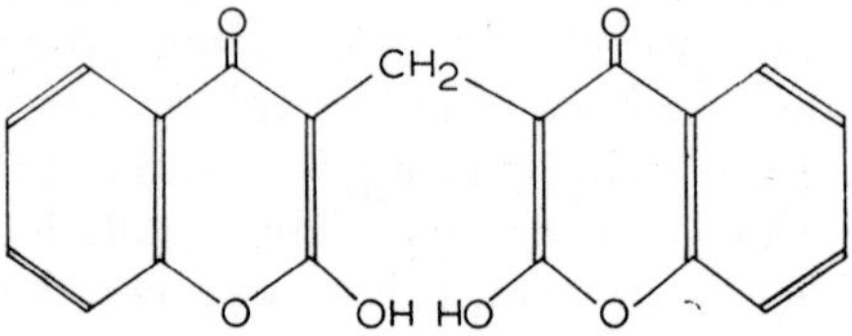

'Dicumarol'
LVI

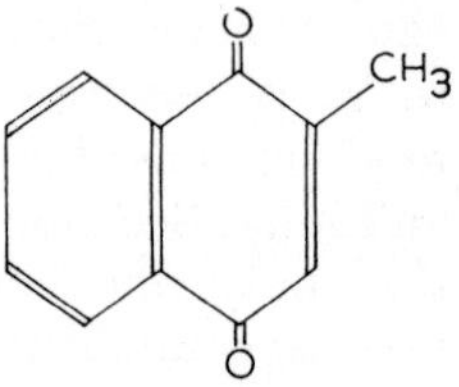

Menaphthone
(a vitamin K)
LVII

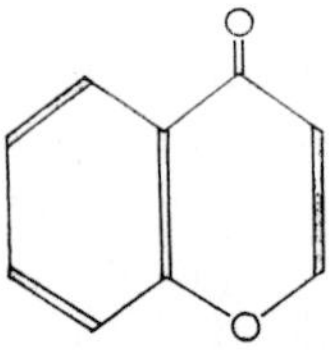

LVIII

Flavones are chromones with a 2-phenyl substituent. They are exceedingly widespread yellow pigments in plants, and at one time were much used as dyestuffs. They occur both free and as glycosides. Flavone itself, which can be seen as a dust on the flowers and leaves of primulas, is a yellow solid, m.p. 97°. It has been synthesized by cyclizing 1-salicoylbenzophenone, or by heating o-hydroxyacetophenone with benzoic anhydride (the Kostanecki-Robinson reaction which has been used to synthesize many flavones and is best carried out in glycerol at 250°, Dunne *et al.*, 1950).

On boiling with alkali, flavone is degraded to o-hydroxy-dibenzoylmethane, and this breaks down further in two ways, (*a*) to salicylic acid and acetophenone, and (*b*) to o-hydroxy-acetophenone and benzoic acid. This reaction has proved useful in determining the constitution of the natural flavones, which are often substituted by hydroxyl or methoxyl-groups in exactly the same positions as the anthocyanidins (p. 274): both classes of substance are believed to be biosynthesized from similar intermediates.

The increased solubility of the flavones in strongly acidic solution is due to basic properties similar in origin to those of pyrone (p. 270). But they are extraordinarily weak bases, with pK's lying between $-2\cdot5$ and $-0\cdot8$ (Davis and Geissman, 1954; flavone itself is $-1\cdot2$).

The *iso*flavones are 3-phenylchromones, the flavonols are 2-phenyl-3-hydroxyflavones, the flavenones (e.g. hesperidin, one of the main glucosides in orange-peel) are dihydroflavones. All occur in nature, but not to so great an extent as flavones.

Flavonols chelate with metals, by binding them between the 3-hydroxy- and 4-oxo-group. Chelation in flavones can take place when a 5-hydroxy-group is present (Clark and Geissman, 1948). The role of flavone and related substances in the fertilization of flowers has been reviewed by Moewus (1950).

For further reading on flavone and its derivatives, see Link (1943); Wawzonek (1951).

LIX

Xanthone (LIX), or dibenzo-γ-pyrone, is a yellow solid, m.p. 174°, obtained by distilling phenyl salicylate (Holleman, 1941) or by the action of nitrous acid on 2:2′-diaminobenzophenone. Upon careful fusion with alkali, it gives dihydroxybenzophenone, and on alkaline reduction xanthydrol is obtained. Xanthone forms a hydrazone directly, also an oxime. However the oxime is more easily formed from thioxanthone (from xanthone-9-anil and hydrogen sulphide). The dipole moment of xanthone (3·1D) indicates a much smaller contribution from ionized structures than in γ-pyrone.

As with chromone, the oxygen of xanthone can be replaced by two chlorine atoms, using thionyl chloride which gives

9:9-dichloroxanthene. This typically ketonic reaction should be contrasted with the introduction of only one chlorine atom into 'pyridones' and their benzologues upon chlorination, a reaction typical of acid amides (see Chapter IV, p. 80).

The four monohydroxyxanthones have been obtained by condensing salicylic acid with dihydroxybenzenes. 1:7-Dihydroxyxanthone, euxanthone or 'Indian Yellow', is a yellow solid, m.p. 237°, found in India in the urine of cows fed on mangoes, and is used there as a dye. o-Aryloxylbenzoic acids, made by condensing 2-chlorobenzoic acid (or diazotized anthranilic acid) with a phenol, are used to prepare other unsymmetrical xanthones. Finally o:o'-dihydroxybenzophenones, unsymmetrically substituted, can be prepared by the Hoesch reaction from o-cyanophenyl acetate and a phenol, and cyclized to xanthones with sulphuric acid.

There is spectroscopic evidence that xanthone has a tendency to form salts (Anderson, 1933), but no estimate of its ionization constant has been made. Nitration of xanthone gives a mixture of three dinitro derivatives. Chlorination and bromination give mainly the 2:7-derivatives. Intensive chlorination gives octachloroxanthone.

For further reading on xanthones, see Wawzonek (1951).

(v) *Six-membered rings with two oxygen atoms.* Although 1:4-pyran (p. 265) is unknown, the corresponding molecule containing two oxygen atoms, dioxin, or dioxadiene (LX), has been known for some years. It is obtained in good yield by the action of magnesium and magnesium iodide on 2:3:5:6-tetrachlorodioxan (from the chlorination of dioxan) and is a colourless liquid, b.p. 75° (Summerbell and Umhoefer, 1939). Its sparing solubility in water (contrast with dioxan, p. 12) suggests that some of the lone pairs of electrons on the oxygen atoms are conjugating with double-bonds. It is more stable to acids than divinyl ether; it adds two molecules of chlorine across the double-bonds. Dioxin polymerizes, two or three weeks after distillation, to an insoluble solid. No 1:2-isomer of dioxin has been described: it would be the peroxide of butadiene and quite unstable.

Benzodioxan (LXI) is made by heating ethylene bromide, catechol, potassium carbonate and a trace of copper. It is a liquid, b.p. 216°, insoluble in water. Benzodioxan brominates and nitrates easily in the 6-position. Benzodioxans have been reviewed by Elderfield (1957).

(b) Six-membered rings containing sulphur, or sulphur and oxygen

(i) *Substances with one sulphur atom.* The only candidate for membership of the thiapyran family is '3-methyl-1:4-thiapyran' (LXII), b.p. 134°, which was obtained in 1886 from α-methyl-glutaric acid and phosphorus pentasulphide (just as thiophen is obtained from succinic acid, see p. 231). It gives the same colour reactions as thiophen, and its constitution needs confirming.

| LX | LXI | LXII | LXIII |

1:4-Thiapyrone is a substance of well-established constitution, prepared by the dehydrogenating action of phosphorus pentachloride on tetrahydrothiapyrone (from diethyl thio-dihydracrylate). It is a colourless, odourless solid, m.p. 110°, easily soluble in water (Arndt and Bekir, 1930). Like 1:4-pyrone, 1:4-thiapyrone has (feeble) basic properties, unreactive double-bonds and an unreactive carbonyl-group. In accordance with these aromatic properties, the sulphur atom cannot be oxidized to a sulphone-group: the necessary electrons apparently participate in the aromatic sextet. Upon reduction to tetra-hydrothiapyran, these electrons are liberated, and a sulphone is readily formed by hydrogen peroxide (Arndt and Bekir, 1930).

For further reading on thiapyrans, see Fried (1950).

Some 1:2-thiachromenes have been formed by splitting out water from thiachromanols (LXIII, R = OH), but they have not been described in detail. Thiachroman (dihydrothiachro-mene) is a yellow liquid, b.p. 130° (15 mm.), prepared by the Clemmensen reduction of 4-thiachromanone (from β-phenyl-mercapto-propionic acid, on treatment with cold sulphuric acid). It gives a sulphone with potassium permanganate.

Thiachromone, a colourless solid, m.p. 78°, is obtained by splitting out hydrogen bromide from 3-bromochromanone, or by the action of phosphorus pentachloride on thiachromanone. Another method is available for thiaflavone (m.p. 130°), viz. the ring-closure of β-phenylmercaptocinnamic acids (from phenylpropiolic acid and phenylmercaptan). These substances form salts with acids, but only under anhydrous conditions, and add bromine across a double-bond.

Thiacoumarin is obtained by cyclizing 2-mercaptocinnamic acid with mineral acid. 3:4-Dihydrothiacoumarin is made by similar treatment of 2-mercaptophenylpropionic acid. Thiacoumarin, m.p. 80°, has the pleasant odour of coumarin. With phosphorus pentasulphide, it gives thiathiocoumarin, an unpleasant-smelling red solid, m.p. 104°.

LXIV   LXV

Thiaxanthene or dibenzothiapyran, m.p. 128°, is usually obtained by reducing thiaxanthone with hydriodic acid and phosphorus; thiaxanthydrol (colourless; m.p. 97°) is made by reducing thiaxanthone with zinc and alkali. 9-Phenylthiaxanthydrol, formed by a Grignard reaction on thiaxanthone, gives 9-phenylthiaxanthylium chloride with dilute acids, the xanthydrol being regenerated by alkali.

Thiaxanthone (LXIV), m.p. 207°, is obtained in 90% yield from thiosalicylic acid and benzene with concentrated sulphuric acid. Its dipole moment (5·4D) is greater by 4D than that calculated by vector addition of the moments of diphenyl sulphide and benzophenone, and hence it is likely that the resonance hybrid has a contribution from a form in which sulphur is positively, and oxygen negatively, charged (Weizmann, 1940). Thiaxanthone does not react with carbonyl reagents.

For further reading on thiachromenes, thiaflavones and thiaxanthenes see Tarbell (1951).

(ii) *Substances with two sulphur atoms, or one sulphur and one oxygen atom.* Dithiin (LXV), or 1:4-dithiadiene, is a sweet-smelling liquid, b.p. 181°, made by acidifying mercaptoacetal, and splitting out two molecules of ethanol from the 2:5-diethoxy-dithiane. It is oxidized by hydrogen peroxide to the disulphone (Parham, Wynberg and Ramp, 1953) and polymerizes readily with aluminium chloride. X-ray diffraction shows that the ring is not planar, but has a 'boat' configuration. Thus dithiin is essentially a non-aromatic substance. The CSC angle is 101°, similar to that of aliphatic sulphides (105°), and very different from that of thiophen (91°) (Parham, 1954; Abrahams, 1956).

Benzo-1:4-dithiadiene is obtained by condensing 1:2-di-mercaptobenzene with bromoacetal, and splitting out ethanol from the 2-ethoxybenzo-1:4-dithiene so produced (Parham, Roder and Hasek, 1953). It is a green oil, b.p. 220°, which gives a disulphone with hydrogen peroxide. Electrophilic reagents, such as nitric acid, N-methylformanilide, or acetic anhydride, attack the $C_{(2)}$ atom of the hetero-ring (Parham *et al.*, 1954).

Thianthrene (LXVI) is one of the principal products of the action of sulphur chloride (or of sulphur) on benzene in the presence of aluminium chloride (Dougherty and Hammond, 1935). It is a colourless solid, m.p. 159°, with a pleasant odour. As it has a dipole moment, and X-ray diffraction shows that the two rings are at an angle of 140°, it is clear that the molecule is not coplanar, and hence the hetero-ring is not aromatic. On bromination, thianthrene is substituted in the benzene rings; on oxidation with nitric acid it gives at first a mono-sulphoxide, and eventually a disulphone (Gilman and Swayampati, 1957). The homologue, prepared from toluene, has been used in the treatment of scabies under the name 'Mitigal'.

No analogue of dithiin (LXV) containing one oxygen and one sulphur atom is known, and the first benzologue is known only as derivatives of the dihydro-compound. However the diben-zologue (LXVII) is well known, and is called phenoxathiin (of which less desirable variants, phenoxthin and phenothioxin, exist), dibenzo-1:4-oxathiadiene or dibenzo-1:4-oxthiin. Phen-oxathiin is a colourless solid, m.p. 61°, with a pleasant lemon-like odour. It is prepared by heating diphenyl ether with sulphur and aluminium chloride (Suter and Maxwell, 1938).

Carbonation of the 1- and 3-lithium derivatives gives the 1- and 3-carboxylic acids, sulphonation with chlorosulphonic acid gives the 3-sulphonic acid, but nitric acid gives the sulphoxide, and then 3:6-dinitrophenoxathiin-10-sulphone. 2-Acyl-derivatives are formed in the Friedel-Crafts reaction. Phenoxathiin has insecticidal properties.

For further reading on six-membered rings containing two sulphur (or one sulphur and an oxygen) atoms, see Elderfield (1957). Phenoxathiin is also reviewed by Deasy (1943).

| LXVI | LXVII | LXVIII |
| | (alternative systems of numbering are also in use) | |

(c) *Six-membered Rings containing Oxygen and Nitrogen*

1:4-Oxazine (LXVIII) is known only in the form of derivatives of 3-hydroxy-1:4-oxazine (Newbold, Spring and Sweeny, 1950). 1:2- and 1:3-oxazines are known only as still more complex derivatives. For a review of the monocyclic oxazines, see Cromwell (1957).

There are eight possible isomeric benzoxazines. The action of acetic anhydride on *o*-hydroxybenzylamine gives 2-methyl-1:3-benzoxazine (LXIX). A large number of 2:3-dihydro-1:3-benzoxazines has been produced by a modified Mannich reaction, viz. the condensation of a *p*-substituted phenol with formaldehyde (2 mols.) and a primary amine (Burke, 1949). These dihydro-compounds are stable to hot alkali but are hydrolysed by hot dilute acid with liberation of formaldehyde.

When *o*-aminobenzyl bromide is boiled with hydrogen bromide in acetic anhydride, 2-methyl-3:1-benzoxazine is formed, which is cleaved to *o*-acetamidobenzyl alcohol by cold water in a few minutes. 1:2-Dihydro-3:1-benzoxazines are formed by cyclizing the anils of 2-aminobenzyl alcohol with aldehydes. 2:4-Diketo-1:2-dihydro-3:1-benzoxazine (LXX), known as isatoic anhydride, is obtained by oxidizing isatin with chromic acid, or passing phosgene into a solution of anthranilic acid in dilute hydrochloric acid (Wagner and Fegley, 1947).

No simple 1:4-benzoxazines are known, but 2:3-dihydro-1:4-benzoxazine, known as phenomorpholine (b.p. 268°), is made by the action of ethylene chlorhydrin on o-aminophenol (chloroacetic acid and o-aminophenol give the 3-oxo-derivative, which has the properties of an acid amide).

LXIX   LXX   LXXI

The other families of benzoxazines are, on the whole, even less well characterized.

For further reading, see Elderfield, Todd and Gerber (1957).

Phenoxazine (LXXI), or dibenzo-1:4-oxazine, is a colourless solid, m.p. 156°. It may be prepared by heating o-aminophenol with its hydrochloride (Gilman and Moore, 1957). Substituted phenoxazines can also be prepared by the Turpin-Ullmann reaction: 2-nitro-2'-hydroxydiphenylamines having a further substituent in the 6-position, are heated with alkali, whereby nitrous acid is eliminated.

Phenoxazine is not easily N-alkylated: it requires sodamide and an alkyl iodide in liquid ammonia (Gilman and Moore, 1957). Phenoxazine is oxidized by bromine, ferric chloride or hydrogen peroxide to the orange, *ortho*-quinonoid phenoxazonium salt (LXXII) which has tricovalent oxygen. It is unstable and highly reactive, being hydroxylated to 3-phenoxazone (LXXIII) by treatment with alkali: this is *para*quinonoid and its formation is similar to pseudobase formation in the pyrylium salts (p. 266). Aromatic amines similarly give '3-phenyl-phenoxazime'. These are the parent substances of the phenoxazine dyes, which are further substituted by a hydroxy- or amino-group.

The phenoxazine dyes are analogues of the indamines ($HN:C_6H_4:N\cdot C_6H_4NH_2$) and indophenols ($O:C_6H_4:N\cdot C_6H_4OH$) which are much used as oxidation-reduction indicators. These dyes are usually prepared by condensing an *o*-hydroxyquinone, a nitroso-phenol, or a nitrosoaniline, with *o*-aminophenols. Thus *m*-diethylamino-*p*-cresol and *p*-nitrosodimethylaniline give Capri blue, 2-diethylamino-3-methyl-7-dimethylaminophen-oxazonium chloride (LXXIV). Meldola's blue is similarly produced from 2-naphthol and *p*-nitrosodimethylaniline. Nile blue is similar, but further substituted with a 7-amino-group and is used as a differential stain in microscopy. These basic dyes are little used for textiles. Some, like brilliant cresyl blue (as (LXXIV) but primary in the 7-position), are useful oxidation-reduction indicators.

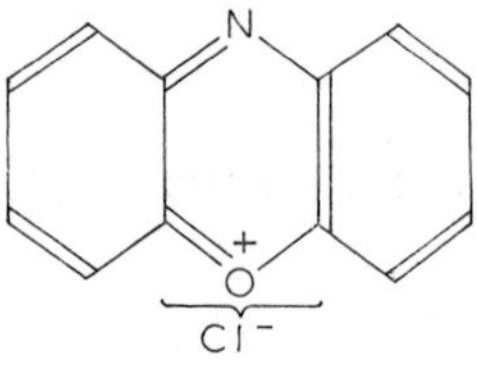

LXXII

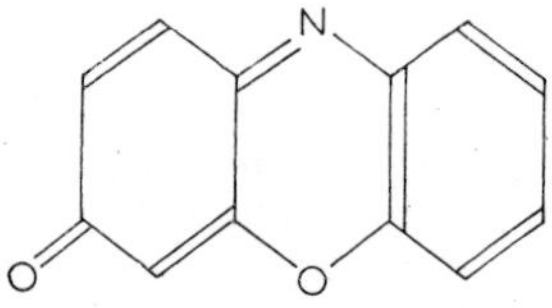

LXXIII

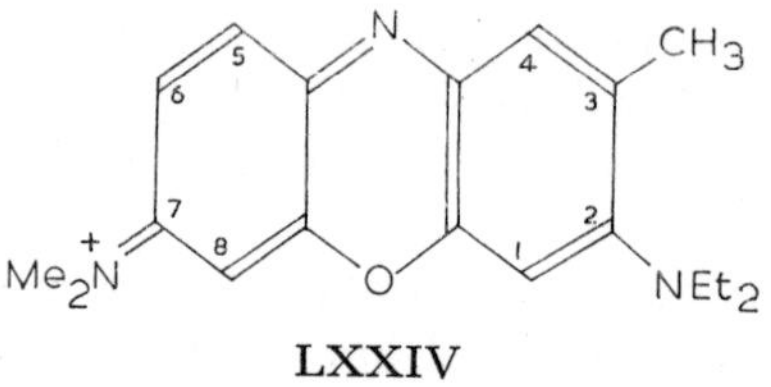

LXXIV

When heated with aniline, the phenoxazine basic dyes are converted to phenazines (p. 124). This is evidence that the phenoxazonium nucleus is unstable, and hence has little aromaticity.

Gallocyanine (LXXV), obtained by boiling nitrosodimethyl-aniline and gallic acid, is much used as a cheap navy-blue dye for chrome-mordanted cotton-and-wool mixtures. Modern Violet and anthracyanine are derivatives, also used with a chrome mordant. The Sirius brilliant blues, introduced in 1928, are direct dyes for cotton of excellent fastness. They are derivatives of triphendioxazine, a five-ring system obtained by condensing one molecule of chloranil and two of an aromatic amine: the product is then sulphonated.

For further reading on phenoxazines see Pearson (1957), Coffey (1949).

LXXV   LXXVI

(d) Six-membered Rings containing Sulphur and Nitrogen

The thiazines resemble the oxazines, but the rings are a little more stable to cleavage.

1:4-Thiazine (LXXVI) was first prepared in 1948. It was obtained by passing thio*di*glycollic imide over alumina at 450°, and the yield was only 13%. It is a colourless liquid, b.p. 76°, which resists acylation.

1:2-Thiazine is unknown, and only one derivative has been described.

1:3-Thiazine is not known. Typical derivatives are 2-methyl-5:6-dihydro-1:3-thiazine (from trimethylene chlorobromide and thio-acetamide) and 2-methylimino-3-methyl-5:6-dihydro-1:3-thiazine.

2:3-Benzo-1:4-thiazine is unknown. Benzothiamorpholine (2:3-dihydrobenzothiazine, b.p. 210° (20 mm.)), is formed by condensing ethylene oxide with *o*-aminothiophenol (Culvenor, Davies and Heath, 1949). It seems to be a stronger base than benzomorpholine and gives N-alkyl-derivatives and quaternary salts. It does not give a sulphone on oxidation. The 3-keto-benzothiamorpholines have been much investigated and prove to be typical lactams, opening in alkali to *o*-aminophenyl-thioglycollic acid.

o-Aminobenzyl chloride and thioformamide give 4:5-benzo-1:3-thiazine; *o*-acetamidobenzyl chloride and phosphorus pentasulphide give the 2-methyl-derivative, also obtainable by heating the corresponding benzoxazine with phosphorus pentasulphide. The methyl-group is activated and condenses with benzaldehyde.

For further reading on thiazines and monobenzothiazines, see Elderfield and Harris (1957).

LXXVII   LXXVIII

The dibenzothiazines are known as phenothiazines. Phenothiazine (LXXVII), or 'thiodiphenylamine', is a colourless solid, m.p. 180°, prepared by heating diphenylamine, sulphur and a trace of iodine. It is neutral, and poorly soluble in water (for purification, see Baker and Brickman, 1945). It is an important larvicide for mosquitos, and is considered a valuable insecticide for spraying fruit trees and vegetables. It is also used extensively in treating worm infections in sheep, cattle, swine and horses, as it has a low toxicity to warm-blooded creatures.

When boiled with copper, phenothiazine gives some carbazole, a rare example of ring-contraction. Phenothiazine is easily acylated and N-alkylated. Alkylation is most readily accomplished in liquid ammonia in the presence of sodamide. Several useful drugs are N-alkylated phenothiazines, (*a*) the tranquilizer, chlorpromazine (Largactil), which is 3-chloro-10(3'-dimethylamino-*n*-propyl)phenothiazine; (*b*) the long-acting anti-histaminic, promethazine (Phenergan), which is 10(2'-dimethylaminopropyl)phenothiazine (Charpentier, 1947); (*c*) the anti-cholinergic Diparcol which is 10(2'-diethylaminoethyl)-phenothiazine, used in parkinsonism; and (*d*) Stemetil, which is 1-[3-]3-chloro-10-phenothiazinyl)propyl-4-methylpiperazine, an oral remedy for migraine.

Upon nitration, phenothiazine gives at first 2-nitro-, and then 2:7-dinitro-, phenothiazine sulphoxide. The latter can be reduced to 2:7-diaminophenothiazine, the leucobase of Lauth's violet (see below). Nitrophenothiazines are prepared from *o*-nitro-*o'*-mercaptodiphenylamines by elimination of nitrous acid (the Turpin reaction), or the sulphoxides can be reduced by refluxing in acidified alcohol. The Friedel-Crafts C-acylation of phenothiazine is difficult unless N-acylation has first been carried out, and 3- and 3:6-acyl-derivatives are then, rather surprisingly, obtained (Baltzly, Harfenist and Webb, 1946; Michels and Amstutz, 1950). Formylation of 10-methyl-phenothiazine with N-methylformanilide and phosphorus oxychloride gives the 2-aldehyde (Buu-Hoï and Hoan, 1951), and methylation gives 2-chloro-N-methylphenothiazine. The direct chlorination of phenothiazine yields 'perchlorides' of undetermined constitution and unseparated mixtures of chlorinated sulphoxides.

Phenothiazine is converted to its sulphoxide with hydrogen peroxide. In acid solution, phenothiazine is oxidized (e.g. by bromine or ferric chloride) to a phenazothionium (phenothiazonium) salt, analogous to phenoxazonium chloride (LXXII). These salts are unstable in solution, and either rearrange to 2-halo-derivatives of phenothiazine, or oxidize to 2-hydroxyphenazothionium salts which are more stable. Oxidation in the presence of amines gives 2-amino-derivatives, as with phenoxazonium salts. The hydroxy- and amino-derivatives are interconvertible, using amines and hydroxyl-ions respectively. These derivatives are easily reduced to amino- and hydroxyphenothiazines, which re-oxidize to the amino- and hydroxyphenazothionium salts, even on standing in air. The phenothiazine dyes are diamino-phenazothionium salts. Thus thionine (Lauth's violet) is 2:7-diaminophenazothionium chloride, and methylene blue (LXXVIII) is its tetramethyl-derivative.

Lauth's violet is made by heating *p*-phenylenediamine with sulphur, and oxidizing the 2:7-diaminophenothiazine thus formed. It is used only as an oxidation-reduction indicator. Methylene blue is made by mixing together *p*-aminodimethylaniline, sodium thiosulphate and potassium dichromate to give 4-aminodimethylaniline-3-thiosulphonic acid. This acid gives methylene blue when heated with dimethylaniline and potassium dichromate. Methylene blue is usually marketed as the

U

double salt with zinc chloride, but a zinc-free product is available upon request.

The cation of methylene blue is a powerful base ($pK_a = >12$): this is ascribed to the contributions to the resonance hybrid of the cation, of forms carrying the positive charge on either nitrogen, plus a small contribution from a form where sulphur is positively charged. This cation is unstable and readily loses one or two methyl groups to give azure B and azure A respectively: air and alkali accelerate this change, and a partly demethylated product is valued in microscopy for certain types of differential staining (Haynes, 1927). Used alone, or mixed with eosin (Giemsa's stain), methylene blue is one of the most used of all microscopical stains. As with all basic dyes, the industrial use of methylene blue is restricted to the cheapest textiles, because of its instability to light. It is used on jute, coir, raffia and crepe paper. The methylene blue test for milk is used to detect bacterial contamination which causes reduction of the dye to the colourless tetramethyldiaminophenothiazine. There is also a methylene blue test for oxidation in cotton: oxidized cellulose takes up the dye without the usual mordant (antimony tannate).

For further reading on phenothiazines, see Pearson (1957), Massie (1954).

CHAPTER VIII

Spectra

SPECTRA are of value in determining the constitution of an unknown substance, particularly in deciding between alternative structures. They are also valuable for establishing the identity of a (known) substance, and in assaying the amount present in a given preparation. The use of spectra for these purposes has some limitations: the nature of the substance can sometimes preclude one or more of the above uses. However, experience and the discovery of new techniques are overcoming some of the limitations.

When a molecule absorbs light, its energy is momentarily increased by an amount equal to that of the photon absorbed. This increase is accommodated as extra vibrational, rotational and electronic energy. Vibrational and rotational transitions are produced by infrared light, electronic transitions by ultraviolet light.

A. Infrared and Raman Spectra

The majority of the vibrations in organic molecules interact with electromagnetic energy so as to absorb it in the infrared region, principally between 2·5 and 25 μ (4000 to 400 cm.$^{-1}$). The utility of infrared spectroscopy depends on the fact that pairs of atoms, and small groups, give rise to absorption bands at characteristic frequencies which are usually only a little affected by other parts of the molecule. Thus hydroxyl-groups, whether in alcohols or in acids, absorb in the region 3000–3600 cm.$^{-1}$.

Compared with ultraviolet spectra, infrared spectra are remarkable (a) for the multiplicity of bands shown, and (b) for their clear resolution. As regards (a), this is of the greatest help in deciding whether two specimens are identical or not; but as an aid to discovering the constitution of a complex molecule, not all bands are equally useful. As regards (*b*), the resolution is not so good in the low-frequency region (1200–400 cm.$^{-1}$) where interpretation becomes more difficult.

In general the bands have the same meaning in aliphatic, aromatic and ethylenic chemistry, whether heterocyclic or otherwise. Hence discussion will be limited here to a specifically heterocyclic problem, the tautomerism of heteroaromatic hydroxy-compounds (see p. 57). When these substances are tautomeric with an *ortho*quinoid amide, e.g. (I), N —H stretching vibration causes an absorption band to appear somewhere in the range[1] 3360–3420 cm.$^{-1}$, whereas the corresponding *para*quinonoid forms, e.g. (II), absorb in the range[1] 3415–3445 cm.$^{-1}$ and analogues with a five-membered ring absorb in the range 3440–3485 cm.$^{-1}$. Some examples of these N —H stretching frequencies are (in carbon tetrachloride):

ortho		*para*	
2-Hydroxyquinoline	3394	4-Hydroxyquinoline	3442
3-Hydroxycinnoline	3371	4-Hydroxycinnoline	3427

Each extra ring-nitrogen slightly lowers the N —H frequency (Mason, 1957).

I   II

Substances which assume either *o*- or *p*-quinonoid forms prefer the *ortho*quinoid, e.g. 4-hydroxypyrimidine prefers (I) to (II); other examples are 4-hydroxyquinazoline, 4-hydroxy-pteridine and 6-hydroxypurine (Mason, 1955, 1957). These conclusions based on infrared spectra are supported by the ultraviolet evidence, including comparison with substances

---

[1] These ranges do not overlap when the number of OH-groups and N-atoms is taken into account, using subsidiary rules.

where the tautomerism is immobilized by substituting methyl for the wandering hydrogen (Brown, Hoerger and Mason, 1955, a; Brown and Mason, 1956, 1957; Hearn, Morton and Simpson, 1951, b).

A further infrared check on tautomerism of this type is provided by the amide $C=O$ stretching band which lies at higher frequencies (1655–1690) in the *ortho* than in the *para* (1630–1645 cm.$^{-1}$) types. Measurements are best conducted in solution because the frequency of this $C=O$ band is sometimes lower in the solid state. If an OH-group is neither α- nor γ- to a ring-nitrogen, there is no absorption in the amide $C=O$ range, but a sharp band can be seen (in chloroform solution) at 3590–3650 cm.$^{-1}$ due to a free hydroxy-stretching vibration. However, when an OH-group is *peri* to a ring-nitrogen (e.g. 8-hydroxy-quinoline), a broad band appears in the range 3395–3470 cm.$^{-1}$), due to intramolecular hydrogen bonding (OH . . . N-stretching vibration). Such bands have widths of 60–100 cm.$^{-1}$ at half-extinction, and hence are distinct from amide $N-H$ bands which have widths at half-extinction of only 15–30 cm.$^{-1}$ (Mason, 1957).

To distinguish between imino- and amino-tautomeric forms of α- and γ-amino-derivatives of nitrogenous heterocyclics, the spectra of deuterated and non-deuterated specimens must be compared (Mason, 1957).

For further reading on infrared spectroscopy, see Jones and Sandorfy (1956); Duncan (1956); Gore (1955); Randall, Fowler, Fuson and Dangl (1949).

Raman spectra give information similar to that afforded by infrared spectra but by a totally different, and somewhat more difficult, technique. Their great value, particularly to those with biological interests, is that they can be used in aqueous solutions, whereas infrared spectra can only be studied in a very limited range of solvents or in the solid state.

For further reading on raman spectra see Jones and Sandorfy (1956); Cleveland (1955).

Microwave and radiofrequency spectra are newer developments. They give information about bond-lengths and bond-angles. Developments in this field include electronic magnetic resonance (a very sensitive detector of free radicals) and nuclear magnetic resonance (which has proved useful in studies of isomerism and prototropy). These techniques are now being applied to heterocyclic chemistry (Gordy, 1956).

B. Ultraviolet Spectra

(a) *General.* In contrast to the types discussed above, ultraviolet spectra are concerned mainly with conjugated pathways in the molecule, or of very considerable parts of it. Commercial photoelectric spectrophotometers permit mapping of (a) the visible region (which is often relatively featureless and may contain little of value) and (b) ultraviolet down to about 215 mμ (the cut-off depends on the percentage of stray light, which can be considerable in this region, and on the absorption of the solvent). Determination of spectra at lower wavelengths (the Schumann or vacuum region) requires the use of an evacuable instrument because of the absorption caused by the components of air; also a calcium fluoride (or similar prism) must replace quartz. This is a difficult technique to which relatively few substances have yet been submitted.

The energy taken up by an illuminated molecule is accommodated mainly as increased electronic energy, often largely confined to one electron which is raised from its ground level to an excited level. The wavelength of the absorbed light is determined by the energy of the transition, and the extinction coefficient by its probability. The electronic transition is usually polarized in one direction (e.g. along a particular molecular axis).

Probability has not proved a convenient practical unit. In its place use is made of (a) *oscillator strength*, ranging from 10^{-4} or less for very weak transitions to 3 for the very strong ones; or (b) *transition moment*, varying (for commonly observed spectra) from 0·01 to 3 in units of electronic charge multiplied by Ångstrom units. Although the dimensions of the transition moment are the same as those of the ordinary (i.e. permanent) dipole moment, the former has no reference to permanent effects, but only to the process of change from one state to another. It follows that molecules in their excited states must have dipole moments very different from those recorded for their ground state.

In the case of a very simple gas, the absorption consists of groups of lines or very narrow peaks, each representing a transition from a particular combination of vibrational and rotational levels in the electronic ground state to some combination of levels in an excited electronic state. In such groups of peaks, the highest peak represents the most probable transition, and it is flanked on each side by less probable ones, of ever-diminishing height. In molecules containing more than a few atoms, the separate peaks tend to coalesce into one band-envelope, a tendency which is greatly increased in the liquid state, and in solution. Separation of peaks in the liquid state can be achieved by working at very low temperatures such as $-195°$. This is a difficult technique, and relatively few substances have been submitted to it. Most spectra are obtained in solution at $20°$, in spite of the loss of detail.

The figures used in illustrating this chapter have also been obtained at room temperature and in various solvents. The most highly resolved spectra are to be obtained in saturated hydrocarbons, and these (e.g. hexane, *iso*octane, *cyclo*hexane) may be considered interchangeable. Dioxane is usually interchangeable with the hydrocarbons, being of low dielectric constant, but its ability to be a receptor to molecules with bondable hydrogen can make a small difference. Most of the other solvents have higher dielectric constants and many, such as alcohol and water, can both give and receive hydrogen bonds. These properties of the non-hydrocarbon solvents lower the resolution, separate peaks often being gathered into one band or envelope. However, the poor solubility of many substances in hydrocarbons can make the use of other solvents inescapable.

The effect of non-hydrocarbon solvents on the spectra of hydrocarbons is slight, resulting at most in a slight shift to longer wavelengths and a coarsening of the outline (Friedel, Orchin and Reggel, 1948). Substances with bondable hydrogen (or substances capable of binding the hydrogen of a solvent that has bondable hydrogen) usually show a greater shift and coarsening. Finally some substances carrying a large separation of charge, or capable of tautomerizing, can show a large displacement of absorption. One of the most striking effects obtained by raising the dielectric constant is given by 4-hydroxy-acridine which is blue in alcohol, green in methanol and yellow in water; 2-hydroxyacridine goes through a parallel change at a lower dielectric constant, namely between that of ether and alcohol (Albert and Short, 1945). 2-Hydroxyphenazine behaves similarly (Badger, Pearce and Pettit, 1951). An example of the opposite effect, a profound bathochromic shift with *increasing* dielectric constant, is seen in 7-amino-5:5-diphenyl-3-oxo-3:5-dihydroacridine (III), also known as 7-amino-9:9-diphenyl-carbazon (Goldstein and Vaymatchar, 1928). This substance is yellow in aliphatic hydrocarbons, scarlet in aromatic hydro-carbons, purple in ether, violet in pyridine and blue in alcohol.

In the sets of curves (Figures 3–25 of this chapter), care has been taken to see that variation in the nature of solvents is minimal in any one figure, and that where they do occur the solute: solvent interaction is not likely to be considerable.[1] These solvent variations stem from the preferences of the various authors whose work has been drawn upon.

III   IV

Non-conjugated organic substances seldom show absorption of high intensity at easily measurable wavelengths, i.e. above 200 mμ. Thus substances with only one double-bond are typified by ethylene which has a λ_{max} (peak of longest wave-length) of only 175 mμ (log ε_{max} 3·9), and acetone, λ_{max} 188 mμ (2·9). The insertion of aliphatic substituents into these sub-stances makes little difference to the spectrum, but simple con-jugation (as in butadiene and the α:β-unsaturated ketones) moves λ_{max} along to about 215 mμ. In conjugated substances, transitions between π-orbitals become important. If the number of double-bonds reaches 5, the peak of longest wavelength usually falls in the visible region, and hence the substance is coloured. Even a substance absorbing as low as 300 mμ will appear pale yellow if the lowest fringe of the envelope crosses into the visible (i.e. about 400 mμ).

[1] Except in Figure 8 where the solvents are purposely varied.

The spectra of heteroaromatic and aromatic substances are closely related. The spectra of aromatic hydrocarbons are divided into three bands or regions: I, II and III (also known as E_1, E_2 and B, or Y_3, Y_2 and Y_1, respectively). These bands are given, for the commoner aromatic hydrocarbons, in Table 12. It is thought that the I and II bands arise from transitions to dipolar excited states, such as (IV) for anthracene,[1] and some success has attended attempts to identify II with such transitions across the shorter of the two axes of the molecule, as shown in (IV). The III bands, which lie at longer wavelengths and absorb with less intensity, are thought to arise from transitions to a non-ionic excited state (Sklar, 1942; Forster, 1947).

TABLE 12. The Ultraviolet Absorption of Aromatic Hydrocarbons (Braude, 1955)

Aromatic hydrocarbon	I		II		III	
	λ_{max}	$\log \varepsilon$	λ_{max}	$\log \varepsilon$	λ_{max}	$\log \varepsilon$
Benzene	184	4·7	202	3·8	255	2·35
Naphthalene	220	5·1	275	3·8	312	2·4
Phenanthrene	252	4·7	295	4·1	330	2·4
Anthracene	252	5·3	375	3·9	—	—

All three bands are due to $\pi \rightarrow \pi$ transitions. It can be seen that the addition of each benzene ring increases λ_{max}. In anthracene, and other linearly annelated naphthalenes, the III band has become lost in the II band[2] which the process of linear annelation has advanced to a greater degree (Clar's rule). The higher λ_{max} of anthracene (as compared to phenanthrene) is typical of linear (as compared to angular) hydrocarbons.

Reference to Figure 4 demonstrates the three regions in phenanthrene, by way of example. The I band is an envelope through which the highest peak protrudes at 252 mμ, with associated peaks at 220 and 275 mμ; the II band is a solitary peak at 295 mμ, and the III band consists of six well-resolved, but not very intense peaks centred about the highest one at 330 mμ.[1]

[1] Assignments such as these are made by physicists from quantum mechanical calculations, and applied to sharp spectra determined in the gas phase, or at low temperatures. [2] From measurements in polarized u.v. light.

The principal key to the study of heteroaromatic substances is that each spectrum resembles that of the corresponding aromatic hydrocarbon. This resemblance is greatest when the hetero atom is nitrogen, less when it is sulphur, least when it is oxygen. These resemblances are most easily studied in the tricyclic substances, where a considerable width of spectrum is available for detailed comparison; the resemblance is less in monocyclic substance, where the change of, say, nitrogen for carbon obviously alters a large proportion of the molecule. When a hetero atom is present, the transitions in region (III) involve a *charged* (ionic) excited state, an important difference from the hydrocarbons (Platt, 1951).

(*b*) *The π-deficient heteroaromatics* have similar spectra to those of the aromatic hydrocarbons (Badger, Pearce and Pettit, 1951). Thus acridine (Figure 3B) is similar to anthracene (Figure 3A), but some of the fine structure has been lost, as always happens when a hetero atom replaces a carbon atom; also the leading edge (the low-intensity portion of longest wavelength) has shifted to slightly longer wavelengths. Phenazine (Figure 3C), which has one more ring-nitrogen atom than acridine, also resembles anthracene but has still less fine structure and the leading edge has progressed a little further towards the visible. Similar effects can be seen by comparing phenanthridine with the hydrocarbon phenanthrene (Figure 4): the important difference here is an increase in intensity of the region centred on 330 mμ (this is the III region, not visible in anthracene).

The bicyclic structures show similar features but necessarily in a more compressed form. Thus *iso*quinoline (Figure 6B) shows the three regions of naphthalene (Figure 5A, see also Table 12), with some loss of detail, and a great intensification of the III region. The III region in quinoline (Figure 6A) is not so clearly separated from the II region of this substance; nevertheless the spectrum of quinoline is similar to that of naphthalene (Figure 5A). The insertion of two ring-nitrogen atoms into naphthalene (Figure 7) makes a greater change than in anthracene (Figure 3). Cinnoline (Figure 7A) and quinazoline (Figure 7B) preserve the three regions of naphthalene, with the expected elevation of the III region. In quinazoline, the λ_{max}

values of naphthalene are not greatly altered, but in cinnoline they have also moved to considerably longer wavelengths. In both cases, all fine detail has been lost. Quinoxaline (Figure 7C) resembles cinnoline, but the II region has moved more than the III region and become telescoped with it. Phthalazine resembles naphthalene more than any of these isomers (Amstutz, 1952).

Pteridine, a tetrazanaphthalene or diazaquinoxaline, has a quinoxaline-like spectrum particularly lacking in detail (Figure 8A). When pteridine is dissolved in a hydrocarbon (Figure 8B) some of the lost detail is recaptured as would be expected, and a new feature is brought to light, namely an extensive band of low intensity at 350–420 mμ. This has been traced to an n to π transition[1] (the spectral features discussed so far have been due to π to π transitions). These transitions occur from the lone pair of electrons (on the nitrogen atom) to the π-electron layer which covers the pteridine nucleus. The n → π transitions are present, but barely recognizable, in substances with only one ring-nitrogen atom, but they can easily be demonstrated in π-deficient heteroaromatics with two or more nitrogen atoms (Badger and Walker, 1956; Mason, 1955).

The spectra of benzene and pyridine are compared in Figure 9, and as so little exists above 210 mμ, the opportunity has been taken of adding information obtained from the 'vacuum ultraviolet', below 200 mμ. Pyridine and benzene are seen to have similar spectra: the I region (see Table 12) is moved to lower wavelengths in pyridine, the II region is similar in both instances, and the III region agrees in wavelength, but the absorption is more intense in pyridine, and the fine detail has been lost (however, other authors have been able to demonstrate four peaks on the long-wave side of the 240–260 mμ band (see Figure 22, also Menczel, 1927).

Also diazabenzenes (pyrimidine, pyridazine and pyrazine, Figure 10) all show a prominent envelope at 240–260 mμ, corresponding to the III region of pyridine. Each diazine shows, in addition, a prominent envelope at longer wavelengths. These are in the positions calculated for n → π transitions (Halvorsen and Hirt, 1951), and are less prominent in non-hydrocarbon solvents. They serve as a reminder of the large spectral changes

[1] Also known as a p → π transition.

that can be brought about by an apparently small change in a monocyclic nucleus.

However there are many substituents which cause only a small change in spectra when inserted into aromatic nuclei. These, the simple bathochromic substituents (Jones, 1945), do not conjugate with the nucleus, and they move the absorption maxima to longer wavelengths by a small, fixed amount without any significant change in the outline or details of the spectrum. Information on these substituents is summarized in Table 13. Thus it becomes possible, for example, to make use of the spectrum of the C-methyl-derivative of a substance, when the spectrum of that substance is unknown (this had to be done in Table 15). Comparison of the spectra of aniline and *p*-toluidine in Figure 11 shows how small the influence of a C-methyl-group is.

TABLE 13. Simple Bathochromic Substituents
Displacement of the III band (the 255 mμ band) of benzene
to longer wavelengths
(Jones, 1945; Braude, 1945, 1955; Morton and Stubbs, 1940)

Substituent	Displacement mμ
– CH$_3$	5
– F	10
– Cl	10
– Br	10
– I	3
– CN	15
– $^+$NH$_3$	0

The effect of these simple bathochromic substituents is the same in heteroaromatic and aromatic nuclei alike. The cyano- and guanidino-groups, curiously enough, fail to conjugate to any extent with an aromatic ring. The phenyl-group shows a variable conjugative effect which is large only when steric hindrance is minimal. Thus it is large in 8-phenylpurine (Mason, 1954), quite small in diphenyl (Friedel and Orchin, 1951), and non-existent in 5-phenylacridine and 9-phenyl anthracene (Jones, 1945).

When π-deficient N-heterocycles are acidified in solution, and thus converted to the cation, the *change* in spectrum is very different from that shown by aromatic bases. The amino-group in aniline conjugates with the benzene ring (see below for conjugation) thus displacing λ_{max} by 28 mμ to longer wave-lengths and completely changing the shape of the curve. But when aniline is acidified, this process is reversed because the acceptance of a proton by the nitrogen atom breaks the con-jugation. In other words, the electrons which the nitrogen atom had released into the ring (see p. 33) are withdrawn to bind the proton. Thus the spectrum of the aniline cation is almost identical with that of benzene, but somewhat less resolved (see Figure 11). It may come as a surprise that a charged group like $-NH_3{}^+$ can have even less effect on a spectrum than an uncharged group like $-CH_3$, but we shall meet other examples which make it clear that charge (in the ground state) does not *of itself* affect spectra, although it may do so if it affects con-jugation between a substituent and the nucleus.

When a proton is added to a π-deficient N-heterocycle, the λ_{max} is usually left unchanged (pyridine, quinoline, 1:8-naph-thyridine), or it is broadened to slightly longer wavelengths (*iso*quinoline, quinoxaline, acridine). Acridine, a striking example of the latter effect, is illustrated in Figure 12 (for *iso*quinoline, see Ewing and Steck, 1946). The clear-cut difference between the behaviour of aromatic amines and π-deficient heterocycles has helped to establish the rule that amino-derivatives of the latter almost invariably add the first proton to the *ring*-nitrogen atom (Craig and Short, 1945; Steck and Ewing, 1948; Hearn, Morton and Simpson, 1951, a). Only in quinazoline and pteridine is this relationship not found: but these two nuclei apparently add water across a double-bond in the cation, so that two totally different nuclei may be under comparison (see p. 121). When two protons are forced (at very low pH) on to an amino-derivative of π-deficient N-hetero-aromatic substances, the spectrum reverts to that of the cation of the parent substance (Craig and Short, 1945; Hearn, Morton and Simpson, 1951, a). Thus 3-aminoacridine, in 10N-hydro-chloric acid, gives the di-cation, and this has a spectrum almost identical with that of the cation of acridine.

Besides the simple bathochromic substituents shown in Table 13, there are conjugating substituents which are listed in

Table 14. These usually displace Bands II and III to still longer
wavelengths, and by larger amounts than do most of the simple
bathochromic substituents. The displaced band is usually of
increased absorption and shows less fine structure. In aniline
(Figure 11) the displaced Band II is seen at 230 mμ. But in
some cases, principally on account of instrumental limitations,
only the enhanced III band is seen, e.g. in phenol, where the
peak of benzene at 255 (log ε = 2·35) has been shifted to 270
(log ε = 3·3).

TABLE 14. Conjugating Substituents
Displacement of the 255 mμ band of benzene (i.e. the III
band) to longer wavelengths
(Jones, 1945; Braude, 1945, 1955; Morton and Stubbs, 1940)

Substituent	Displacement mμ
– SO₃H and – SO₂NH₂	5
– SH	25[a]
– SCH₃	30[a]
– S⁻	45[a]
– OH and – OMe	18[b]
– O⁻	28
– NH₂	28
– NH·CH₃	39
– N(CH₃)₂	45
– CHO and – COCH₃	23
– CO₂H and – CO₂⁻	13
– CO₂CH₃	13
– CH:CH₂	26

a. Approximate (inflection) (cf. Böhme and Wagner, 1942).
b. 10 and 16 for α- and β-naphthol respectively.

It will have been realized that the conjugation of −OH,
−NH₂ and −SH groups involves the sharing of their lone pairs
of electrons with the aromatic ring. β-Naphthol (Figure 14) is
an example of the introduction of a conjugating substituent
into naphthalene (Figure 5). It can be seen that the I and II
bands of naphthalene (at 220 and 275 mμ) are virtually unchanged but the small III band of naphthalene is replaced in
β-naphthol by an intense band at 331 mμ. In α-naphthol
(Figure 13), the I, II and III bands of naphthalene have all
advanced by about 15 mμ each.

The effect of inserting a conjugating substituent into a N-heteroaromatic molecule is often best approached by asking the question: what is the effect of inserting a ring-nitrogen atom into an aromatic hydrocarbon already bearing the substituent in question? The answer is that the ring-nitrogen atom has usually very little effect. Thus the spectrum of β-naphthol is recreated, in almost all its complexity, in 2-, 3-, 6- and 7- hydroxy-quinolines, which are monoaza-β-naphthols (see Figure 14).

This resemblance is surprising in 2-hydroxyquinoline which has been shown to be largely in the form of the amide tautomer; this is a resonance hybrid with a large contribution from (V) (see p. 57). We know the spectrum of the enol tautomer of 2-hydroxyquinoline would be the same as the spectrum (Morton and Rogers, 1925) of 2-methoxyquinoline. This assumption is legitimate because the spectra of phenol, the naphthols and many hydroxy-polycyclic hydrocarbons have been found to be identical with their methyl ethers (Jones, 1945; Friedel and Orchin, 1951), and this identity has been demonstrated for 8-hydroxy- and -methoxy- quinoline (Ewing and Steck, 1946), and also for their 3-isomers (cf. p. 56). Now, the spectrum of 2-methoxyquinoline has a band III of lowered λ_{max} and intensity: it is bifurcated with peaks at 322 (3·57) and 309 (3·65); moreover the II peak is almost suppressed. This difference between 2-methoxy- and 3-methoxy- quinoline suggests that the methoxy-group in the 2-position exerts its aliphatic (electron-attracting), rather than its aromatic (electron-releasing), character.

The insertion of a ring nitrogen-atom into α-naphthol, giving 5- and 8-hydroxyquinoline, and 5-hydroxy*iso*quinoline, shifts the spectrum to slightly longer wavelengths, and fine structure is lost (see Figure 13). Thus an inserted ring-nitrogen affects α- and β-naphthol similarly. As with 2-hydroxyquinoline, the resemblance of the spectrum of 4-hydroxyquinoline to that of its isomers is something of a coincidence: 4-methoxyquinoline (and hence the enolic tautomer of 4-hydroxyquinoline) absorbs at 290 mμ, and less intensely (Ewing and Steck, 1946). But 4-hydroxyquinoline is known to consist principally of the amide tautomer, a resonance hybrid with a large contribution from (VI). It is noteworthy that 1-hydroxy*iso*quinoline (another potential aza-α-naphthol) has a very different spectrum from 5-hydroxy*iso*quinoline (Ewing and Steck, 1946): evidently here the compensating factors have not balanced as in 2- and 4-hydroxyquinoline.

That the spectra of various α- and γ-hydroxy-N-heterocycles differ so much from those of their O-derivatives, and resemble so much those of their N-derivatives, has been most helpful in elucidating their true nature (see p. 60). A typical set of curves illustrating this point is shown in Figure 15.

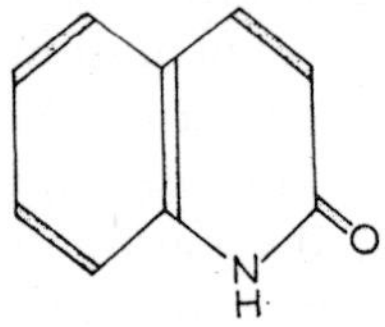

V 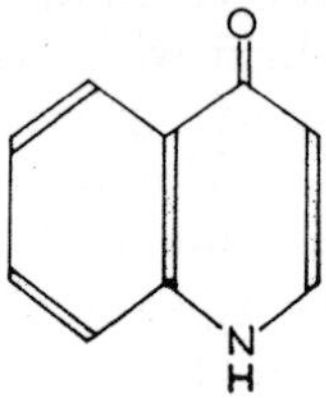   VI 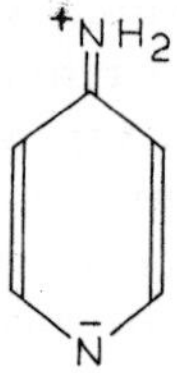   VII

Like α- and β-naphthol and phenol, most of the hydroxy-quinolines and 3-hydroxypyridines show an increase in λ_{max} of 10 mμ (or more) on being made alkaline. However 2- and 4-hydroxyquinoline and -pyridine show little or no shift (Ewing and Steck, 1946). Again, the hydroxyquinolines and 3-hydroxy-pyridine show a similar bathochromic shift in acid, but with increased resolution. Although it might appear that the α- and γ-hydroxy-derivatives did not undergo a shift in acid (Ewing and Steck, 1946), the poorly basic properties of these substances had not been put on a quantitative footing. It is now evident from the ionization constants (Albert and Phillips, 1956) that Ewing and Steck did not use acid strong enough to obtain the cations.

Returning to Table 14, some other points of interest, applicable to heteroaromatic spectra, can be gleaned. The lack of spectral change produced on methylating a hydroxyl-group was commented on at length above. The mono- and di-methylation of an amino-group produces a small, cumulative shift to longer wavelengths without alteration of the outline. This is illustrated for aniline and its two N-methyl-derivatives in Figure 16. The methylation of an aldehyde to a ketone

usually produces no change in spectrum. Further, the methylation, and also the ionization, of a carboxylic acid group produces little or no change in spectrum (Jones, 1945). The
ionization of a hydroxy-group increases conjugation to a degree
equal to that produced by an amino-group. Thus, although
amines usually have λ_{max} about 10 mμ longer than the corresponding phenols, and have a less resolved spectrum, the *anions*
of these phenols usually have spectra identical with those of
the amines. This not only applies to polycyclic hydrocarbons
(Jones, 1945), but has been demonstrated in some π-deficient
N-heteroaromatics (Albert, 1952).

Just as it has been possible to demonstrate by reference to the
spectra of N- and O-methyl-derivatives (e.g. Figure 15) that the
hydrogen of α- and γ-hydroxy-N-heteroaromatics is on the ring-
nitrogen, analogous comparisons have shown that the α- and
γ-amino-N-heteroaromatics have both hydrogen atoms on the
*exo*cyclic nitrogen atom, i.e. that they are primary amines.
Figure 17 is typical of many sets of spectra which exist to
demonstrate this point. It can be seen that the effect of converting $-NH_2$ to $-N(CH_3)_2$ is very similar both for 2-amino-
pyridine and aniline (Figure 16).

Although the insertion of a ring-nitrogen into aniline and α-
and β-naphthylamine gives the expected shift to longer wavelengths in most positions, 4-amino-pyridine and 2- and 4-
aminoquinoline show only very small shifts (Steck and Ewing,
1948). This may be attributable to the high proportion of
dipolar forms (e.g. VII) in their resonance hybrids (see p. 54).
These three substances, and 2-aminopyridine also, show little or
no shift to longer wavelengths when acidified, whereas their
isomers have the expected large shifts.

(*c*) *The π-excessive heteroaromatics* have spectra similar to those
of the corresponding hydrocarbons. Carbazole, not being linear,
is compared to phenanthrene and not anthracene (Badger and
Christie, 1956). The three main regions of absorption of carbazole (240, 280–295, and 320–340 mμ) should be compared
with the similar regions of phenanthrene in Table 12. The
spectra can then be compared in Figure 18, where the similarity
is seen to be considerable, but the intensity of the 320–340 mμ
region is much greater for carbazole than for phenanthrene.

x

Similarly, the spectrum of indole (absorbing at 220 and 250–280 mμ) is comparable with that of naphthalene (cf. Table 12, then Figure 20). The isolated peak at 288 mμ in indole seems to correspond with one about 310 mμ in naphthalene. Comparison of the spectra of 1-azacarbazole with carbazole (Figure 18), and 7-azaindole with indole (Figure 20), shows that the introduction of doubly-bound nitrogen ($=N-$) is not so disturbing as that of singly-bound nitrogen ($-NH-$). It is noteworthy that both 1- and 2-azacarbazole have spectra that are almost identical (Horner, 1939). Thus the *positional* influence of the doubly-bound nitrogen is slight. Compared to carbazole, these azacarbazoles have less fine structure, and the 320–340 mμ band is slightly intensified and broadened to longer wavelengths: these effects are closely similar to those described above for acridine, quinoline and the other π-deficient N-heterocycles.

When both kinds of nitrogen atom ($=N-$ and $-NH-$) are in the *same* ring, the correlation of spectra is less predictable because of mutual electronic disturbance. Whereas indole absorbs at 250–280 mμ in a broad band with λ_{max} at 280 mμ, and has a sharp outlying peak at 288 mμ, benziminazole (Figure 21) is more highly resolved and has sharp peaks, all of comparable intensity at 242, 274 and 279 mμ (Steck *et al.*, 1948). However, the insertion of a further nitrogen atom between these two (giving benzotriazole, i.e. 2:3-diaza-indole) has the usual effect: the spectrum still resembles that of benziminazole, but fine detail has disappeared and only two peaks (at 249 and 279 mμ) are to be seen (Fagel and Ewing, 1951). Finally, in purine (3:5:7-triaza-indole), the region under discussion is still further self-integrated so that only one peak (at 263 mμ) is to be seen. It was hoped that 9-methylpurine, which is soluble in *cyclo*hexane, would reveal extra detail in that solvent, but none could be seen (Mason, 1954).

The spectrum of pyrrole (Figure 23) is rather formless,[1] but it can at least be said that its band III absorption is in the region of the band III of benzene and is more intense. The N-alkylpyrroles absorb ten times as strongly as pyrrole. This is attributed to an increase in aromatic character caused by

---

[1] A well-formed peak near 210 mμ is seen in the vacuum u.v. (Klevens and Platt, 1953).

decreased electro-negativity of the nitrogen atom after alkylation: this permits fuller conjugation of the $2p$ orbital of
nitrogen with those of carbon (Walsh, 1948). In iminazole, the
reverse effect is seen, the absorption in the 240–250 mμ region
being about one-fifth of that of pyrrole (see Figure 23: it is
regrettable that no more of this spectrum has been explored
even though the results may be surmised). This suppression in
iminazole is due principally to the electron-attracting power of
the doubly-bound nitrogen atom which can exert a large
unconjugating effect in so small a molecule. Tetrazole also has
only end-absorption of this kind.

The spectra of furan, thiophen and their benzologues are
related to the spectra of the aromatic hydrocarbons in the same
way as those of pyrrole and its benzologues (Badger and Christie,
1956). However the resemblance is less close for the furans than
for the thiophens and pyrroles. The relevant spectra are shown
in Figure 19 (dibenzofuran and dibenzothiophen), Figure 22
(benzofuran and benzothiophen), Figure 23 (furan) and Figure
24 (thiophen).

The insertion of a doubly-bound nitrogen atom ($=N-$) has
no more effect on these O- and S-heterocycles than on their
nitrogen analogues. Thus benzothiazole has almost exactly the
same spectrum as benzothiophen (Cerniani and Passerini,
1954), and benzoxazole as benzofuran (Passerini, 1954). Indeed, the spectrum of benzoxazole diverges less from that of
naphthalene than does the spectrum of benzofuran. Again
thiazole has a spectrum like that of thiophen (Figure 24), and
oxazole like that of furan (Cornforth and Cornforth, 1947). For a
fuller discussion of the spectra of O- and S-heterocycles, see p. 209.

VIII   IX

(d) *Coloured substances.* Lewis (1945) showed that dyes of the
structure (VIII), where X is S, O or NR″ (i.e. thiopyronine,
pyronine and acridine dyes, respectively), have λ_{max} values

calculable by the summation of a small number of empirically-derived constants. Dyes of the type (IX), where X is S, O or NR" (i.e. thiazine, oxazine and phenazine dyes, respectively), behave similarly. The results have an average deviation of ± 3 mμ. In these formulae R is $-NH_2$, or $-NMe_2$, or $-OH$, and R' is $=NH$, or $=O$ in the neutral molecule. That R' can be $=N^+Me_2$ in the cation, and R can be O^- in the anion, permits a heightened resonance in some ionic species of these molecules, and Lewis's calculations do not apply when R and R' are in other positions. Some less empirical calculations for these substances have been put forward more recently (Dewar, 1950).

X   XI

For correlation between constitution and spectra in cyanine dyes, see Brooker *et al.* (1941).

Porphyrins have spectra showing high resolution in the visible region (see Figure 26), a most unusual property for coloured organic substance (see p. 181 for further information on porphyrin spectra).

XII

(*e*) *Pyrones.* A striking resemblance exists between the spectra of pyrones and pyridones, commonly depicted as (X) and (XI) respectively (Berson, 1953). The relevant figures are in Table 15. As is usually found in comparing O- and N-heterocycles, the oxygen analogues absorb at somewhat lower wavelengths.

However, the differences are not great, and the curves have similar shapes (cf. Figure 25).

(*f*) *General*. Suppression of a predicted spectral shift following the insertion of a substituent can usually be traced to steric hindrance (Jones, 1945). The spectrum of the cation of 1-amino-9-methylacridine (XII) is almost identical with that of acridine (neutral molecule). This shows that the methyl-group hinders the approach of the proton to the ring-nitrogen (Craig, 1946).

TABLE 15. Comparison of the Spectra of Pyrones
and their Nitrogen-analogues

Substance	λ_{max} (mμ)	log ε_{max}	
γ-Pyrone (X)	246	4·42	Gibbs, Johnson and Hughes, 1930
4-Hydroxypyridine ("4-pyridone") (XI)	256	4·15	Specker and Gawrosch, 1942
5-Methyl-α-pyrone	295	3·70	Fried and Elderfield, 1941
2-Hydroxypyridine	297	3·80	Specker and Gawrosch, 1942
γ-Benzopyrone (chromone)	300⎫ 296⎭	3·85	
	241[a]	4·00	Gibbs, Johnson and Hughes, 1930
4-Hydroxyquinoline	332⎫ 315⎭	4·15	
	230	4·25	Ewing and Steck, 1946
α-Benzopyrone (coumarin)	311	3·77	
	275	3·06	Mattoo, 1956
2-Hydroxyquinoline	329	3·70	
	270	3·80	Ley and Specker, 1939

a. Shoulder only.

IMPORTANT. When the ultraviolet spectra of *ionizable* substances are measured in water, the pH must be adjusted so that only one ionic species can be present. This is accomplished by choosing a buffer with a pH at least two units away from any pK of the substance being measured. Thus, determination of ionization constants is an essential first step in the examination of spectra. If this precaution is not taken (and it was not often taken in the past) impure spectra are formed from the superposition of the spectra of two different ionic species, e.g. neutral molecule and cation.

For further reading on ultraviolet spectroscopy see Braude (1955); Matsen (1956); West (1956).

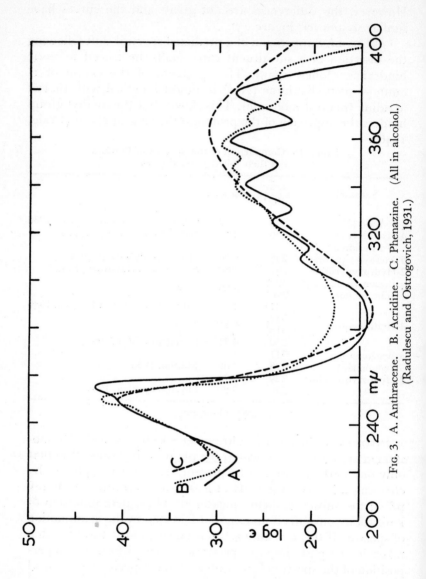

FIG. 3. A. Anthracene. B. Acridine. C. Phenazine. (All in alcohol.)
(Radulescu and Ostrogovich, 1931.)

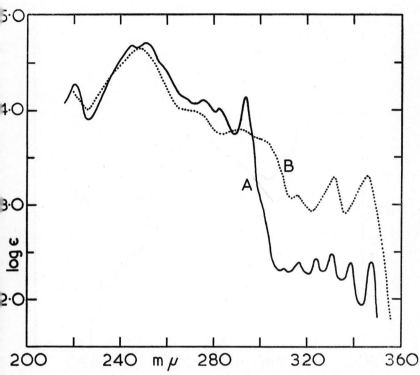

FIG. 4. A. Phenanthrene (in 95% ethanol) (Badger and Christie, 1956).
B. Phenanthridine (in ethanol) (Badger, Pearce and Pettit, 1951).

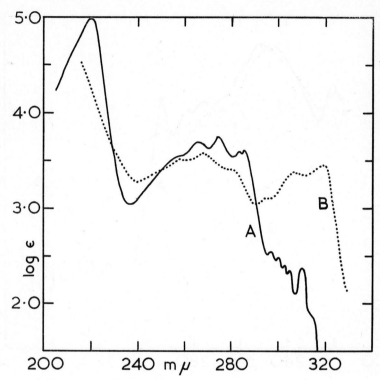

FIG. 5. A. Naphthalene (in 95% ethanol) (Friedel, Orchin and Reggel, 1948).
B. Quinoline (in water, pH 6·3: neutral molecule) (Albert, Brown and Cheeseman, 1951).

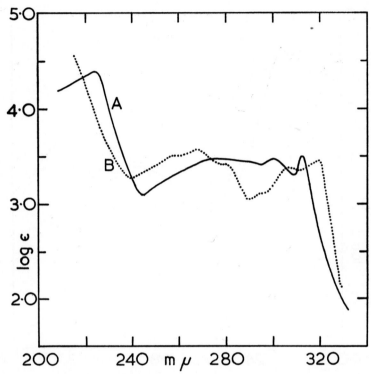

FIG. 6. A. Quinoline (in water at pH 7: neutral molecule) (Albert, Brown
              and Cheeseman, 1951).
         B. *Iso*quinoline (in 95% ethanol) (Ewing and Steck, 1946).

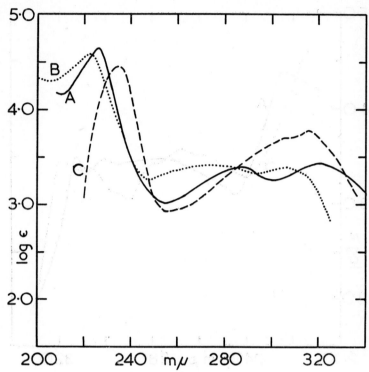

FIG. 7. A. Cinnoline (in water at pH7)
B. Quinazoline (in water at pH7)
(Osborn, Schofield and Short (1956)).
C. Quinoxaline (in ethanol) (Badger and Walker, 1956).

(All neutral molecules)

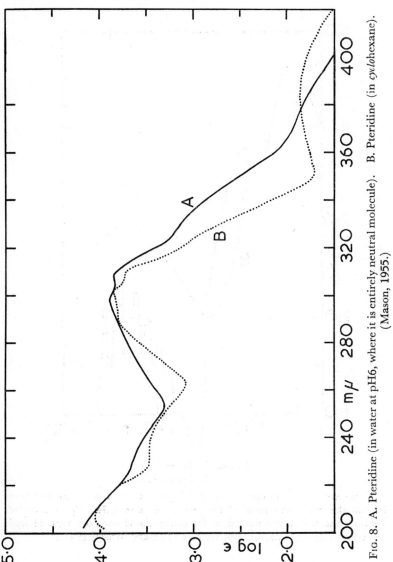

FIG. 8. A. Pteridine (in water at pH6, where it is entirely neutral molecule). B. Pteridine (in *cyclohexane*). (Mason, 1955.)

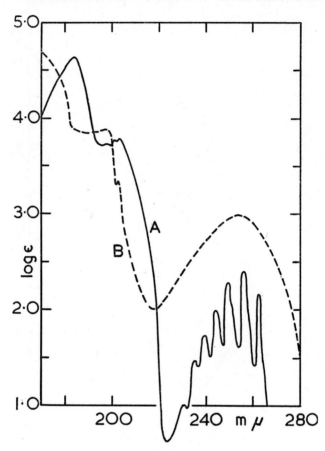

FIG. 9. A. Benzene.
B. Pyridine.

These are composite curves and differ from other curves presented here in that the 'vacuum-region' of the ultraviolet is included. For spectra of benzene and pyridine obtained in the conventional way, see Figs. 11 and 24 respectively). (Matsen, 1956; see also Price and Walsh, 1947.)

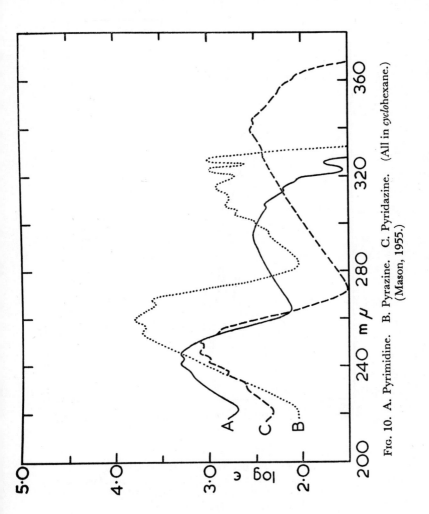

FIG. 10. A. Pyrimidine.   B. Pyrazine.   C. Pyridazine.   (All in *cyclo*hexane.)
(Mason, 1955.)

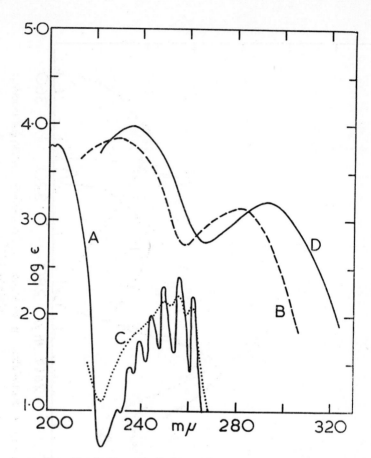

FIG. 11. A. Benzene (in hexane).
B. Aniline, neutral molecule (in ethanol).
C. Aniline, cation (in dilute hydrochloric acid).
D. p-Toluidine, neutral molecule (in ethanol).
(Waterman and Harberts, 1936.)

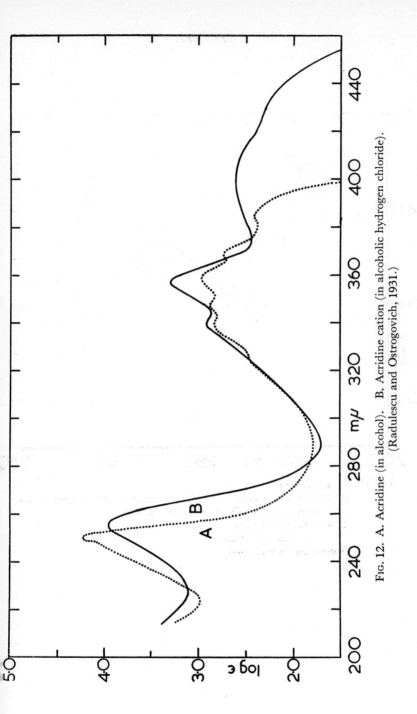

Fig. 12. A. Acridine (in alcohol). B. Acridine cation (in alcoholic hydrogen chloride). (Radulescu and Ostrogovich, 1931.)

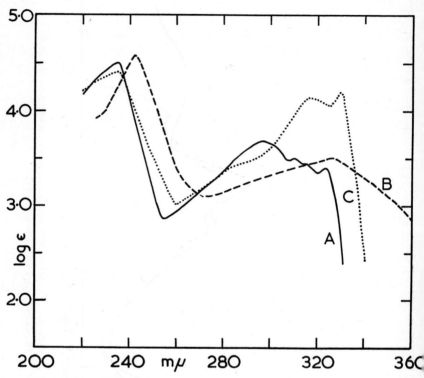

FIG. 13. A. α-Naphthol.
B. 5-Hydroxyquinoline (8-hydroxyquinoline and 5-hydroxy*iso*-
quinoline have almost identical spectra).
C. 4-Hydroxyquinoline.
(All in 95% ethanol.)
(Ewing and Steck, 1946.)

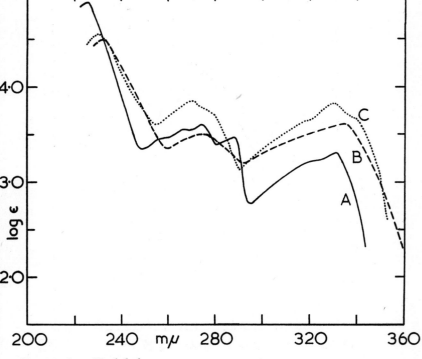

Fig. 14. A. β-Naphthol.
   B. 6-Hydroxyquinoline (3-hydroxyquinoline has almost the same
        spectrum).
   C. 2-Hydroxyquinoline.
        (All in 95% ethanol.)
   (Ewing and Steck, 1946.)

Y

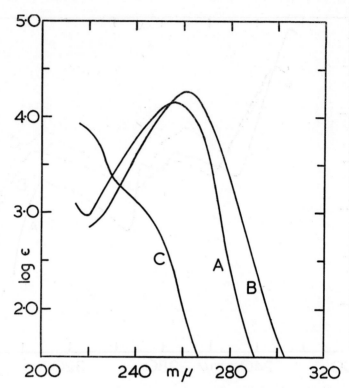

FIG. 15. A. 4-Hydroxypyridine.
　　　　B. N-Methyl-derivative of A.
　　　　C. O-Methyl-derivative of A.
　　　　　　(All in methanol.)
　　　(Specker and Gawrosch, 1942.)

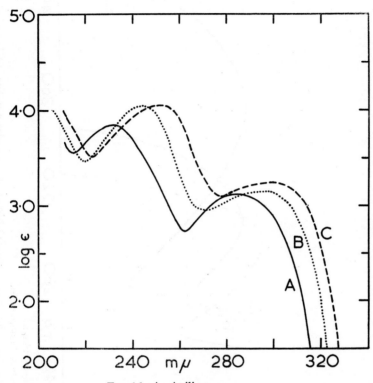

Fɪɢ. 16. A. Aniline.
         B. Methylaniline.
         C. Dimethylaniline.
              (All in methanol.)
         (Ley and Specker, 1939.)

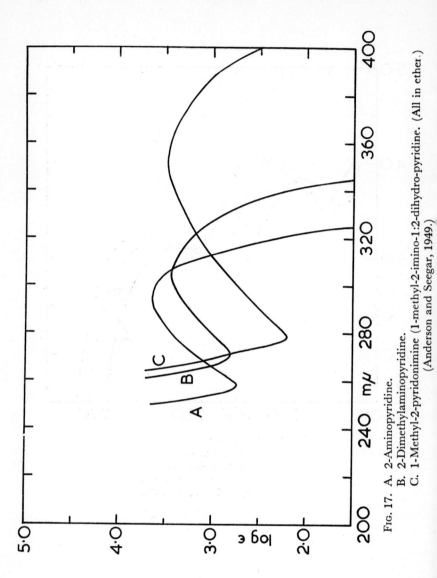

Fig. 17. A. 2-Aminopyridine.
           B. 2-Dimethylaminopyridine.
           C. 1-Methyl-2-pyridonimine (1-methyl-2-imino-1:2-dihydro-pyridine. (All in ether.)
                                                              (Anderson and Seegar, 1949.)

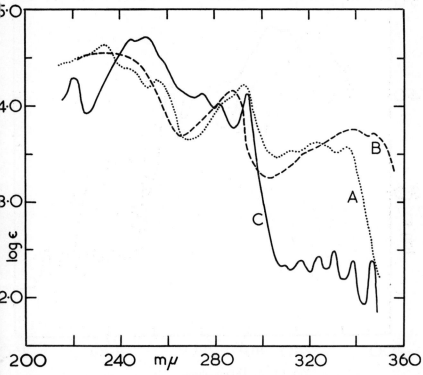

FIG. 18. A. Carbazole (in 95% ethanol) (Friedel and Orchin, 1951).
      B. 1-Azacarbazole (in dioxan) (Horner, 1939).
      C. Phenanthrene (in 95% ethanol) (Badger and Christie, 1956).

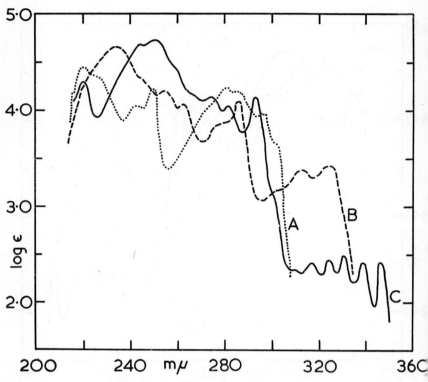

Fig. 19. A. Dibenzofuran.
B. Dibenzothiophen.
C. Phenanthrene.
(All in 95% ethanol.)
(Badger and Christie, 1956.)

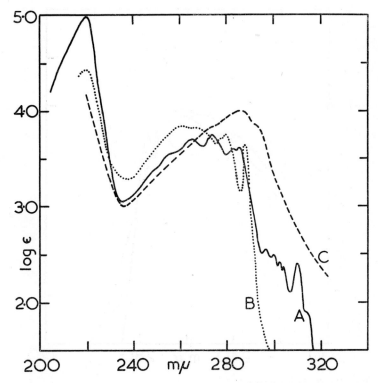

Fig. 20. A. Naphthalene (in 95% ethanol) (Friedel, Orchin and Reggel, 1948).
     B. Indole (in *cyclo*hexane) (Friedel and Orchin, 1951).
     C. 7-Azaindole (in *cyclo*hexane) (Robison and Robison, 1955).

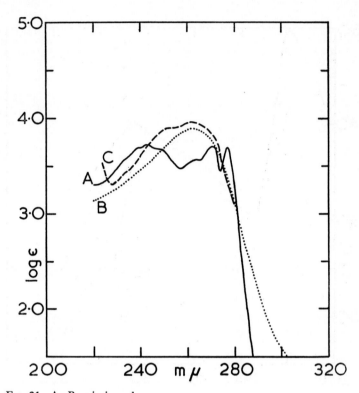

Fig. 21. A. Benziminazole.
B. Purine.
C. Adenine.
(All as neutral molecules in aqueous buffers.)
(Measured in Department of Medical Chemistry, Australian National University.)

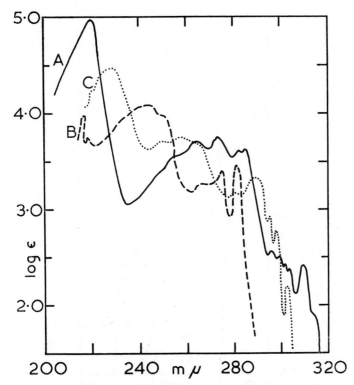

Fig. 22. A. Naphthalene (Friedel, Orchin and Reggel, 1948).
B. Benzofuran (Badger and Christie, 1956).
C. Benzothiophen (thionaphthene) (Badger and Christie, 1956).
(All in 95% ethanol.)

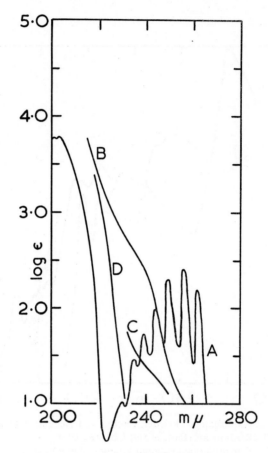

FIG. 23. A. Benzene (in hexane) (Waterman and Harberts, 1936).
B. Pyrrole (in hexane) (Menczel, 1927).
C. Iminazole, neutral molecule (in water, at pH7·9) (McFarlane, 1936).
D. Furan (in hexane) (Menczel, 1927).

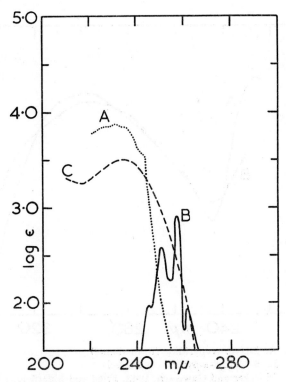

Fig. 24. A. Thiophen (in *iso*octane) (Hartough, 1952).
  B. Pyridine (neutral molecule in water) (Herington, 1950).
  C. Thiazole (neutral molecule in water) (specially determined for
     the present work).

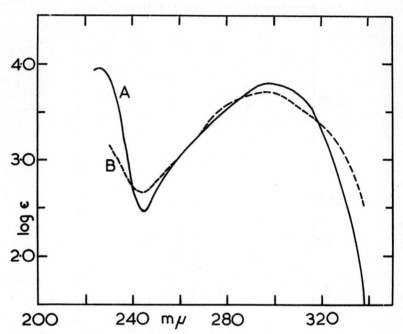

Fig. 25. A. 2-Hydroxypyridine (in methanol).
B. 5-Methyl-α-pyrone (in alcohol).
(Specker and Gawrosch, 1942; Fried and Elderfield, 1941.)

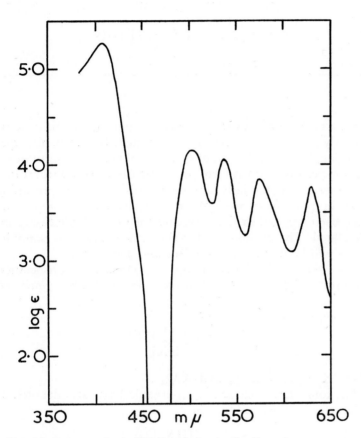

FIG. 26. Protoporphyrin IX dimethyl ester (in dioxan).
(Kindly prepared from human blood, and measured by Dr. J. E. Falk.)

CHAPTER IX

Ionization Constants

IONIZATION CONSTANTS are useful criteria of identity, particularly for substances which do not melt. But their principal use is for the establishment of structure of unknown substances, e.g. for deciding which form predominates at equilibrium in a tautomeric, or potentially tautomeric, substance. The prevailing forms in many hydroxy- and amino-derivatives of heterocycles have been decided in this way, and the ratios of the two forms calculated. The pyridine carboxylic acids provide an example, which will be discussed below (see also Table 17).

The term ionization constant is preferred to 'dissociation constant' which is a vague expression, not necessarily connected with ionization. The ionization constant of an acid (K_a) refers to the equilibrium:

$$K_a = \frac{[H^+]\,[X^-]}{[HX]}$$

where X^- is, for example, $CH_3CO_2^-$.

The ionization constant of an organic base, also denoted as (K_a), refers to the equilibrium:

$$K_a = \frac{[HX^+]}{[H^+]\,[X]}$$

where X may be, for example, CH_3NH_2.

The older expression K_b is dying out because the ionizations of acids and bases are now usually expressed on the same scale. Ionization constants are most conveniently expressed as pK_a values, i.e. as their negative logarithms. At 20°,

$$pK_b = 14 \cdot 17 - pK$$

Strong *acids* have low pK_a values, strong *bases* have high pK_a values.

The ionization constants of acids are most conveniently determined by potentiometric titration with a glass electrode using carbonate-free potassium (or trimethylammonium) hydroxide. The constant is calculated after each tenth equivalent of alkali is added, and the values should agree to within ± 0.05 if the substance is pure. The following equation is used:

$$pK_a = pH + \log([AH] + [OH^-]/[A^-] - [OH^-])$$

The constants of bases are calculated, after similar titration by acid, from the following equation:

$$pK_a = pH - \log([B] + [H^+]/[BH^+] - [H^+])$$

where $[BH^+]$ and $[AH]$ are the concentrations of protonated species that would be present if hydrolysis corrections (which are taken care of by the rest of the formulae) were neglected.

Ionization constants determined in mixed solvents should be avoided when possible: they are not strictly comparable, because lipophilic molecules change the dielectric constant in their vicinity by surrounding themselves with the more lipophilic solvent.

Constants obtained at various dilutions may be interconverted by the approximation:

$$pK_a \text{ (thermodynamic)} = pK_a \text{ (as determined)} + 0.5\sqrt{I}$$

where I is the ionic strength at half-neutralization.

Thus an acid titrated at the following molarities should have the quantity in parentheses added to the pK_a values:

0.05M (0.08); 0.02M (0.05); 0.01M (0.03); 0.0005M (0.01)

For bases, these quantities should be subtracted. It is evident that the thermodynamic pK_a is invariable with dilution, but it is not widely quoted because of the approximations so often used in its calculation.

For carboxylic acids, no temperature corrections apply. For the large corrections for bases see Hall and Sprinkle (1932).

When substances are too insoluble for potentiometric titration (say, less soluble than 0.001M, but the figure depends upon where the pK_a lies), ultraviolet spectrometry affords a possible alternative (the method is summarized by Albert and Phillips, 1956).

The effect of substituents on the pK's of acids and bases is now almost quantitatively predictable. In aliphatic compounds, the inductive effect predominates and almost every group is electron-withdrawing (hence acid-strengthening, and base-weakening). The two exceptions are the methyl-group, and any group which is ionized as an anion: these are acid-weakening (and hence base-strengthening). When a substance has two substituents which can ionize to give the same kind of charge (e.g. a dicarboxylic acid), the ionization of the first group causes the second group to ionize with more difficulty, as demanded by

TABLE 16. The effect of Substituents on the Ionization of *non-Heterocyclic* Substances (in water at 20–25°)[a]

Acid	pK_a	Base	pK_a
Aliphatic		*Aliphatic*	
Formic acid	3·8	(Ammonia)	9·2
Acetic acid	4·8	Methylamine	10·6
Hexanoic acid	4·9	Ethylamine	10·7
Nonanoic acid	4·9	Butylamine	10·6
Acrylic acid	4·2	Heptadecylamine	10·6
Oxalic acid	1·2, 4·2	Allylamine	9·7
Malonic acid	2·8, 5·7	Ethylenediamine	10·0, 7·0
		Benzylamine	9·4
Nitroacetic acid	1·7	Carbomethoxymethylamine	
Glycine		(glycine methyl ester)	7·8
(aminoacetic acid)	2·3	Glycine aminoacetic acid)	9·9
Cyanacetic acid	2·4	Aminomethanesulphonic acid	5·7
Chloracetic acid	2·9	Ethanolamine	9·5
Glycollic acid		β-Methoxyethylamine	9·4
(hydroxyacetic acid)	3·8	Dimethylamine	10·9
Acetoacetic acid	3·6	Trimethylamine	9·8
Ethyocyacetic acid	3·6	Triethanolamine	7·8
Thioglycollic acid		*Cyclo*hexylamine	10·6
(mercaptoacetic acid)	3·7		
Methylthioacetic acid	3·7		
Phenylacetic acid	4·3		
Methanol	16		
Ethanol	18		
Ethyl mercaptan	12·0		

[a] Mainly from Hall and Sprinkle (1932); Brown, McDaniel and Häfliger (1955).

TABLE 16—*continued*

Acid	pKa	Base	pKa
Aromatic		*Aromatic*	
Benzoic acid	4·2	Aniline	4·6
Phthalic acid	3·0, 5·3	Nitroanilines (*o*, *m*, *p*)	0·3, 2·4, 1·1
Cinnamic acid	4·4	Hydroxyanilines	4·7, 4·2, 5·5
α-Naphthoic acid	3·7	Chloroanilines	2·6, 3·3, 3·8
β-Naphthoic acid	4·2	Methoxyanilines	4·5, 4·2, 5·3
Anthracene carboxylic		Phenylanilines	3·8, 4·2, 4·3
acids (1, 2, 9)	3·7, 4·2, 3·6	Methylanilines	
Nitrobenzoic acids		(toluidines)	4·4, 4·7, 5·1
(*o*, *m*, *p*)	2·2, 3·5, 3·4	Aminoanilines	4·5, 4·9, 6·1
Chlorobenzoic acids	2·9, 3·8, 4·0	Aminoanilines (second	
Methoxybenzoic acids	4·1, 4·1, 4·5	constant)	1·3, 2·6, 3·3
Aminobenzoic acids	5·0, 4·8, 4·9		
Trimethylammonium-		N-Methylaniline	4·8
benzoic acids	1·4, 3·4, 3·4	Dimethylaniline	5·1
		α-Naphthylamine	3·9
Phenol	9·9	β-Naphthylamine	4·1
α-Naphthol	9·9		
β-Naphthol	9·9		
Nitrophenols (*o*, *m*, *p*)	7·2, 8·3, 7·1		
Chlorophenols	8·5, 9·0, 9·4		
Hydroxyphenols	9·5, 9·4, 10.0		
Methylphenols			
(cresols)	10·2, 10·1, 10·2		
Methoxyphenols	9·9, 9·6, 10·2		
Aminophenols	9·7, 9·9, 10·3		
Phenylphenols	9·9, 9·6, 9·5		

statistics: and Coulomb's law operates to make ionization still harder if the two groups are near together.

A selection of pK_a's from aliphatic and aromatic chemistry are assembled in Table 16. In aromatic chemistry, the inductive effect operates just as described above; in addition to this a mesomeric effect operates in the *o*- and *p*-positions. The mesomeric effect of the nitro-group intensifies the inductive effect, but that of the amino-, hydroxy-, and methoxy-groups opposes the inductive effect. The results are most clearly assessed in *para*-substituted compounds, because *ortho*-substituents can show, in addition, an '*ortho*-effect' due to steric hindrance or hydrogen-bonding.

z

Heteroparaffinic substances obey the same rules as ordinary aliphatic substances, and a selection of their values is given at the head of Table 18.

The pK_a's of *heteroaromatic* substances are influenced by substituents very much as ordinary aromatic substances are.[1] But the parent substances themselves are in a class apart. The ionization of π-deficient N-heterocycles (e.g. pyridine) has been discussed in general terms on p. 47, which should be re-read at this point. More data have been obtained for such substances than for all other heterocyclic compounds. A selection of values is given in Table 18. The following further sources should be noted:

Alkaloids (Kolthoff, 1925).
Methylpyridines (Ikekawa, Sato and Maeda, 1954).
Other substituted pyridines (McDaniel and Brown, 1955).
Pyridine-N-oxides (Jaffé and Doak, 1955).
Halogenated quinolines (Knight, Wallich and Balch, 1955).
Poly-methylated quinolines (Felsing and Biggs, 1933; Knight, Wallich and Balch, 1955).
Substituted acridines (Albert and Goldacre, 1946; Albert, 1951).
Substituted pteridines (Albert, Brown and Wood, 1954; Albert, Brown and Cheeseman, 1951, 1952).
Substituted benzoquinolines, phenanthridines and benzacridines (Albert, Goldacre and Phillips, 1948).
Barbiturates (Bush, 1937; Butler, 1955).

The π-excessive heterocycles have been dealt with in detail on pp. 141, 208 and the accompanying Table 10. Additional values will be found in Table 18.

Heteroethylenic substances have not been systematically examined for pK values and few are known. Most of these are listed at the end of Table 18. In addition reference has been made to the (slight) basic properties of various pyrones on pp. 270 and 281. The explanation of the very different pK_a's of tetrahydroquinoline and tetrahydro*iso*quinoline, discussed on p. 248, gives

---

[1] So much so, that the steric nature of the ortho-effects in benzene have only become properly understood by studying the 2-substituted pyridines (McDaniel and Brown, 1955). However amino-, mercapto, or hydroxy-groups in the α- or γ-positions behave differently (see pp. 52–62).

a clue to predicting the ionization of other partly hydrogenated rings.

Up to this point, only heterocyclic *bases* have been discussed. Among the few pK_a values available for heterocyclic non-amphoteric *acids* are thiophen-2-carboxylic acid (3·5), and its 3-isomer (4·1); furan-2-carboxylic acid (3·1), and its 3-isomer (3·9).

When a molecule contains both an acidic and a basic group, it is possible for each to ionize separately, and for there to be a wide pH zone within which neither group is ionized. A familiar example of this kind is *p*-aminobenzoic acid. It is much more common for amphoteric heterocyclic substances to be largely ionized at all pH values. This happens thus: the cation, by attracting electrons, is able to bring about the ionization of the acid at higher hydrogen ion concentrations than would permit this in the absence of the cation. And the anion is similarly able, by repelling electrons, to bring about the ionization of the base at lower hydrogen ion concentrations than would be possible in the absence of the anion. This mutual strengthening has already been discussed in connexion with the hydroxy-derivatives of π-deficient N-heteroaromatics (see pp. 56, 58). The pyridine carboxylic acids (picolinic, nicotinic and *iso*nicotinic acid) provide a neat illustration of the techniques used to decide whether the principal species in neutral solution is a neutral molecule or a zwitterion (an ion bearing two full charges, opposite in sign). They also illustrate the calculation of the ratio of these two forms at equilibrium (Green and Tong, 1956).

$$\text{I} \qquad\qquad \text{II}$$

The ultraviolet spectra of the three pyridine monocarboxylic acids were compared, in neutral aqueous solution, with those of their O-methyl- and N-methyl-derivatives, (I) and (II) respectively. It was found that there were large differences from the spectra of the O-methyl-derivatives, whereas those of the N-methyl-derivatives almost coincided. The conclusion that all three carboxylic acids were mainly in the zwitterionic state in neutral solution, was confirmed and put on a quantitative basis by carrying out potentiometric titration, and submitting the pK_a's thus obtained (Table 17) to the simple calculation used by Edsall and Blanchard (1933) for glycine and other aliphatic amino-acids.

This calculation makes use of the assumption that the inductive effect of $-CO_2Me$ and $-CO_2H$ (non-ionized) groups are practically identical, as dipole moment measurements have shown in unambiguous molecules. Thus, the pK_1 of pyridine-4-carboxylic acid, if non-ionized, should be approximately 3·26, the same as the basic constant of the methyl ester. But the pK governing loss of the first proton is 1·84. Thus the tautomeric ratio of zwitterion to neutral molecule in the acid is given by the expression:

$$R = \text{antilog } (pK_1 \text{ (ester)} - pK_1 \text{ (acid)}) - 1$$
$$= \text{antilog } (3·26 - 1·84) - 1$$
$$= 25$$

Hence there are 25 doubly charged ions to each uncharged molecule.

TABLE 17. The Tautomeric Ratio of Zwitterion to Neutral Molecule in Pyridine-carboxylic Acids

Pyridine	pK_1	pK_2	Tautomeric Ratio
2-Carboxylic acid	1·01	5·32	16:1
(Methyl ester)	2·21		
3-Carboxylic acid	2·07	4·81	11:1
(Methyl ester) (I)	3·13		
(Methyl betaine) (II)	2·04		
4-Carboxylic acid	1·84	4·86	25:1
(Methyl ester)	3·26		

The relevant ionization constants and tautomeric ratios are given in Table 17. Had the answer been required at a pH lying nearer than 2 units to any pK_a, a simple adjustment for mono-ions would be made.

Many other amphoteric π-deficient heterocycles are described in the literature, notably the hydroxy-derivatives. Because the pK values mean little without comparison with N- and O-methylated derivatives, hydroxy-derivatives have been inserted only sparingly into Table 18; it is better to consult Table 6 (p. 57), and Albert and Phillips (1956). Apart from the acids in Table 17, carboxylic acids have been examined in the quinoline and acridine series, and a further (miscellaneous) collection has been made by Luz and Fallab (1956), including some π-excessive amphoteric carboxylic acids.

Many π-excessive N-heterocycles are amphoteric (see Table 10, p. 143), including the purines (for an extensive list of purines, see Albert and Brown, 1954; but for methylated xanthines see Taylor, 1948; Turner and Osol, 1949), and the indazoles (Sureau, 1956) and benziminazoles (Davies *et al.*, 1951).

For further reading on ionization constants, see Brown, McDaniel and Häfliger (1955).

TABLE 18. The Ionization of Heterocyclic Bases
(In water at 20–25°)[a]

Base	pK_a	Base	pK_a
Heteroparaffinic[b]		2-chloro-	0·7
Aziridine (ethylenimine)	8·0	3-chloro-	2·8
Azetidine		2-bromo-	0·9
(trimethylenimine)	11·3	3-bromo-	2·8
Pyrrolidine		2-iodo-	1·8
(tetramethylenimine)	11·3	3-iodo-	3·2
N-Methylpyrrolidine	10·4	2-methyl-	6·0
Piperidine		3-methyl-	5·7
(pentamethylenimine)	11·2	4-methyl-	6·0
N-Methylpiperidine	10·1	2-*iso*propyl	5·8
Piperazine	9·8	2:6-dii*so*propyl-	5·3[c]
Hexamethylenetetramine	6·4	2-*t*-butyl-	5·8
Morpholine	8·7	2:6-di-*t*-butyl-	3·6[c]
N-Ethylmorpholine	7·6	3-phenyl-	4·9
2-Hydroxy-3-		2-(2′-pyridyl)-	4·4
ethylpiperidine	9·1	3-acetyl-	3·2
		2-amino-	6·9
		3-amino-	6·0
Heteroaromatic:		4-amino-	9·2
π-*deficient N-heterocycles*		hydroxy-, and their	
Pyridine	5·2	O- and N-methyl	
2-fluoro-	−0·4	derivatives (see	
3-fluoro-	3·0	Table 6, on p. 57)	

TABLE 18—continued

Base	pKa	Base	pKa
Heteroaromatic:		3-amino-	5·9
π-deficient N-heterocycles—cont.		4-amino-	6·0
carboxy- and carbo-		5-amino-	10·0
methoxy- (see		2:5-diamino-	11·5
Table 17)		2:7-diamino-	8·1
2-imino-N-methyl-		2:8-diamino-	9·6
1:2-dihydro-	12·2	3:7-diamino-	6·2
4-imino-N-methyl-		5-methoxy-	7·0
1:4-dihydro-	12·5	5-hydroxy-	−0·3
Quinoline	4·9	Acridine methochloride[e]	9·8
2-methyl-	5·4	2-amino-	12·0
3-methyl-	5·1(?)	3-amino-	9·8
4-methyl-	5·2	4-amino-	10·0
5-methyl-	4·6	5-amino-	11·1
6-methyl-	4·9	2:8-diamino-	>12
7-methyl-	5·1	Phenanthridine	4·6
8-methyl-	4·6	6-amino-	6·9
3-chloro-	2·4[d]	9-amino-	7·3
4-chloro-	3·4	9-methoxy-	2·3
7-chloro-	3·6	2-hydroxy-	4·8
2-amino-	7·3	6-hydroxy-	5·3
3-amino-	4·9	9-hydroxy-	< −1·5
4-amino-	9·2	Phenanthridine	
5-amino-	5·5	methochloride[e]	10·4
6-amino-	5·6	Pyridazine	2·3
7-amino-	6·6	3-amino-	5·2
8-amino-	4·0	4-amino-	6·7
hydroxy-, and their		3-methoxy-	2·5
O- and N-methyl		4-methoxy-	3·7
derivatives (see		Pyrimidine	1·3
Table 6, on p. 57)		4-methyl-	2·0
4-imino-N-methyl-		2-amino-	3·5
1:4-dihydro	12·4	2-dimethylamino-	4·0
*Iso*quinoline	5·4	4-amino-	5·7
1-amino-	7·6	4-dimethylamino-	6·3
3-amino-	5·0	5-amino-	2·8
4-amino-	6·3	2:4-diamino-	7·3
5-amino-	5·6	2:4:6-triamino-	6·8
6-amino-	7·2	2-methoxy-	<1
7-amino-	6·2	4-methoxy-	2·5
8-amino-	6·1	2-amino-4-hydroxy	4·1
1-methoxy-	3·0	4-amino-2-hydroxy-	
1-hydroxy-	−1·2	(cytosine)	4·6
(N-methyl-derivative)	−1·8	2-imino-N-methyl-	
Acridine[h]	5·6	1:2-dihydro-	10·7
1-amino-	4·4	4-imino-1-methyl-	
2-amino-	8·0	1:4-dihydro-	12·2

TABLE 18—*continued*

Base	pK_a	Base	pK_a
Pyrazine	0·6	Pteridine	4·1[f]
2-methyl-	1·4	2-methyl-	4·9
2:3:5:6-tetramethyl-	3·7	4-methyl-	2·9
2-amino-	3·1	7-methyl-	3·5
2-methoxy-	0·7	2-amino-	4·3
Cinnoline	2·3	4-amino-	3·6
3-amino-	3·7	6-amino-	4·1
4-amino-	6·8	7-amino-	3·0
5-amino-	2·7	2-methoxy-	2·1
6-amino-	5·0	4-methoxy-	1·0
7-amino-	4·8	6-methoxy-	3·6
8-amino-	3·7	7-methoxy-	1·6
4-hydroxy-	−0·3	2-methylthio-	2·2
6-hydroxy-	3·6	4-methylthio-	2·6
4-methoxy-	3·2	7-methylthio-	2·5
Phthalazine	3·5		
1-amino-	6·6	*Heteroaromatic:*	
1-hydroxy-	−2	*π-excessive heterocycles*	
Quinazoline	3·5[f]	Pyrrole	∼0·4
2-amino-	4·8	Pyrazole	2·5
4-amino-	5·8	1-methyl-	2·1
5-amino-	3·6	3-methyl-	3·6
6-amino-	3·3	Iminazole	7·2
7-amino-	4·6	1-methyl-	7·4
8-amino-	2·8	2-methyl-	7·9
4-methyl-	2·5	4-methyl-	7·5
2-methoxy-	1·3	Indazole	1·3
4-methoxy-	3·1	3-amino-	3·1
Quinoxaline	0·7	4-amino-	3·3
2-methyl-	1·0	5-amino-	5·1
2-amino-	4·0	6-amino-	4·0
5-amino-	2·6	7-amino-	3·0
6-amino-	2·9	Benziminazole	5·5
2:3-diamino-	4·7	2-amino-	7·5
1:5-Naphthyridine	2·9	5-amino-	6·1
1:8-Naphthyridine	3·4	1-methyl-	5·7
Phenazine	1·2	2-methyl-	6·2
2-amino-	4·7	4-methyl-	5·7
2:7-diamino-	4·6	5-methyl-	5·8
3:4-Benzocinnoline	2·2	2-phenyl-	4·5
2-amino-	6·7	Purine	2·4
Phenanthrolines		6-methyl-	2·6
ortho	4·9	8-methyl-	2·8
meta	3·9	9-methyl-	2·4
para	3·9	8-phenyl-	2·7
1:4:5-Triazanaphthalene	1·2	6-chloro-	<2
1:4:6-Triazanaphthalene	2·5	2-hydroxy-	**1·7**

TABLE 18—continued

Base	pK_a	Base	pK_a
Heteroaromatic: π-excessive heterocycles		*Heteroethylenic*	
Purine—*cont.*	—*cont.*	2-Methyl-Δ²-	
6-hydroxy-		tetrahydropyridine	9·6
(hypoxanthine)	2·0	1:2-Dimethyl-Δ¹-	
8-hydroxy-	2·6	tetrahydropyridine	
2-methoxy-	2·4	(see p. 247)	11·4
6-methoxy-	2·2	1:2:3:4-	
8-methoxy-	3·1	Tetrahydroquinoline	5·0
2-amino-	3·8	1:2:3:4-	
6-amino-(adenine)	4·2	Tetrahydro*iso*quinoline	9·4
8-amino-	4·7	1:2:3:4-	
2:6-diamino-	5·1	Tetrahydroquinoxaline	4·8; 1·2
2:6:8-triamino-	6·2	3:4-Dihydroquinazoline[g]	>8·6
2-dimethylamino-	4·0	1:2:3:4-	
6-dimethylamino-	3·9	Tetrahydropteridine	6·6
8-dimethylamino-	4·8	5-Formyl-	5·0
2-amino-6-hydroxy-		4-Methyl-	6·7
(guanine)	3·3	5-Formyl-	5·4
6-amino-2-hydroxy-	4·5	5-Acetyl-	5·3
2-mercapto-	0·5	5:8-Diacetyl-	2·1
2-methylthio-	1·9	1-Methyl-Δ³-	
6-methylthio-	0	dihydropyrrole	9·9
8-methylthio-	2·9	2-Ethyl-Δ²-dihydropyrrole	7·4
Thiazole	2·5	1:2-Dimethyl-Δ¹-	
2-amino-	5·4	dihydropyrrole (see	
2-imino-N-methyl-		p. 257)	11·9
2:3-dihydro-	9·6	2-Methyl-Δ²-	
Benzothiazole	—	dihydrothiazole	5·4
2-amino-	4·5	1:4-Thiazine	5·6
Benzoxazole	—	Thionine (Lauth's violet)	11·0
2-amino-	3·7	Methylene blue	>12

a. This wide temperature range is necessary in order to include the results of various authors, but it has the disadvantage that variations of ±0·2 are not significant.

b. Values taken mainly from Searles *et al.* (1956).

c. Note the crowding possible before the approach of a hydrated hydrogen ion is sterically hindered.

d. 2-Chloroquinoline is much weaker than this, but the exact value is not known.

e. In heterocyclic quaternary salts, the pK represents an equilibrium between the true quaternary cation and the pseudobase (e.g. 5-hydroxy-10-methyl-5:10-dihydroacridine) with which it is in slow equilibrium. Equilibrium may take one minute in some cases, and several days in others.

f. It is believed that covalent hydration of the cation is responsible for the unexpectedly high values of the parent substances quinazoline and pteridine (see pp. 121 and 85). Pteridine is also a weak acid of pK_a 12·2 thanks to a covalently hydrated anion.

g. Determined in dilute alcohol, hence the figure in water must be higher.

h. Many other acridine values are known (Albert, 1951).

CHAPTER X

Oxidation-reduction Potentials. Dipole Moments

THIS CHAPTER deals with two important sections of electro-chemistry additional to that discussed in Chapter IX.

Oxidation-reduction potentials. The transfer of electrons from one substance to another is a process termed 'oxidation-reduction': the substance gaining electrons becomes reduced and the substance losing electrons becomes oxidized. When these transfers are thermodynamically reversible, the oxidation-reduction potential is best obtained by potentiometric titration with a reducing agent such as titanous chloride, or an oxidizing agent, such as benzoquinone. In other cases, valuable information concerning at least the reduction potential (irreversible) can be obtained from polarography.

Michaelis showed that most organic chemicals are reduced in two separate stages, each equivalent to the transfer of one electron (and usually one hydrogen ion as well). Thus if the oxidized form is called O, the reduced (dihydro-) form R, and the semi-reduced form S, the overall process ($R \rightleftharpoons O + 2\varepsilon$) usually consists of these two steps:

$$R \rightleftharpoons S + \varepsilon \qquad (1)$$
$$S \rightleftharpoons O + \varepsilon \qquad (2)$$

The semi-reduced form S is a free radical (an older name was 'semiquinone') which can be exceedingly reactive in some cases, whereas in others it is stabilized by resonance. If it decomposes it may do so in two ways; by a slow dimerization, or instantly by dismutation, according to the equation:

$$2S \rightleftharpoons R + O$$

If S is stable, as in monohydrophenazine, the equilibrium will favour S. The presence of S forms is often recognized by their absorbing at longer wavelengths than either the R or O form, or by some other spectral peculiarity; they are best characterized by the inflection seen during potentiometric titration between platinum electrodes.

The most useful oxidation-reduction potential is E_0 (pronounced e-zero). It is the potential compared to that of the hydrogen half-cell (or 'electrode') at pHo (e.g. N-hydrochloric acid at one atmosphere).[1] Polarographers, however, usually refer potentials to the saturated calomel electrode (SCE), and $0 \cdot 246$ volt must be added to such results to refer them to the normal hydrogen electrode.

In the course of a titration, the E_0 should be calculated after every tenth equivalent of oxidant or reductant is added. The following equation forms the basis of these calculations.

$$E_0 = E_h - \frac{RT}{nF} \ln \frac{[Ox]}{[Red]} \tag{3}$$

where E_h is the potential recorded by the galvanometer, R is the gas constant, T is the absolute temperature, F is the faraday, n the number of electrons concerned, ln is the natural logarithm, $[Ox]/[Red]$ is the ratio of concentrations of oxidized to reduced forms. When equal concentrations of oxidized and reduced forms are present, the expression after the minus sign vanishes: hence $E_0 = E_h$ under these conditions.[2] Equation (3) may be written in the following form for the use of logarithms to the base 10, and for n = 1.

$$E_0 = E_h - 0 \cdot 0581 \log \frac{[Ox]}{[Red]}, \text{ at } 20° \tag{4}$$

$$= E_h - 0 \cdot 0591 \log \frac{[Ox]}{[Red]}, \text{ at } 25° \tag{5}$$

E_0' is the symbol for oxidation-reduction potentials at a stated pH value other than o.

---

[1] Thus the hydrogen electrode has the value: $E_0 = O$ at pHo, and decreases by $0 \cdot 06$ for each unit rise in pH, reaching $- 0 \cdot 42$ volt at pH7.

[2] Just as $pK = pH$ at half neutralization.

Oxidation-reduction potentials are of theoretical interest, being related to the constitution. They give an indication of the ease of oxidation or reduction of the substance concerned. Values at pH7 are of special interest to biological workers. Many of the processes by which nutritive material is 'oxidized' in the living cell have been shown to be electron, or hydrogen-and-electron, transfer reactions, occurring stepwise in order of increasing potential.

As an approximation, oxidation-reduction potentials lying between the oxygen and hydrogen electrodes (i.e. between +0·8 and −0·4 at pH7) may be considered ideally reversible; that is to say, adjustment is instantaneous and no energy barrier has first to be surmounted. In some cases, equilibrium between oxidized and reduced forms is attained more slowly, e.g. methylene blue and its dihydro-derivative. In this instance, equilibrium is not instantaneous if all traces of copper are removed from the solution, although such a condition seldom arises in practice (Reid, 1930).

Measurement of thermodynamically reversible potentials by potentiometry is confined in practice to the region between the oxygen and hydrogen electrodes (see last paragraph). Special techniques, such as polarography, enable values to be obtained outside this range.

Table 19, which is intended to help in orientating the values in Table 20, consists of common oxidizing and reducing agents. Most of these values have been determined only at pH0, but where values at pH7 are also known, these have been inserted. In general, E_0' values do not change with pH if substances are only undergoing an electron change. Thus ferric sulphate has the same value at pH2 as at pH0 (above pH2 it precipitates), and potassium ferricyanide has the same value between pH4 and 9. When a hydrogen ion is added as well, the E_0' falls off by 0·06 volt for each unit rise in pH (and twice as much for two hydrogens). This relationship is disturbed (i.e. the straight line plot of E_0' against pH undergoes a sharp bend) upon passing through a pH value which happens to be a pK_a value of the oxidized (or reduced) forms.

Table 20 contains most of the known reduction potentials of heterocyclic substances. The substances most studied are (a) normal constituents engaged in hydrogen transport in living cells, or (b) coloured indicators used for studying the E_h of biological systems.

TABLE 19. Oxidation-reduction Potentials (E_0)
(The more positive values represent the more oxidizing ability)
(20–25°)

Equilibrated pair	pH0	pH7
	volts	volts
Cobaltic ion—cobaltous ion	1·8	
Permanganate ion—manganese dioxide	1·52	
Hypochlorous acid—chloride ion	1·50	
Chlorine—chloride ion	1·36	
Dichromate anion—chromic cation	1·36	
Oxygen electrode ($O_2 + 4H^+ + 4\varepsilon \rightleftharpoons 2H_2O$)	1·23	0·81
Bromine—bromide ion	1·07	
Silver ion—silver	0·80	
Ferric ion—ferrous ion	0·77	
Methylene blue—dihydro analogue	0·52	0·01
Iodine—iodide ion	0·53	
Ferricyanide ion—ferrocyanide ion	0·61	0·43
Quinone—hydroquinone	0·70	0·27
Dichlorophenolindophenol—dihydro analogue	0·66	0·22
Stannic ion—stannous ion	0·15	
Hydrogen electrode ($2H^+ + 2\varepsilon \rightleftharpoons H_2$)	0	−0·42
Stannous ion—tin	−0·14	
Acetaldehyde—ethanol	—	−0·20
Zinc ion—zinc	−0·76	
Sodium ion—sodium	−2·71	

Of the π-deficient N-heterocycles with only one ring-nitrogen atom, acridine has been most studied, and although agreement is not complete, the E_0' at pH7 seems to be about −0·3 for the first step and −1·1 for the second, with 5:10-dihydroacridine as the final product (Breyer, Buchanan and Duewell, 1944; Kaye and Stonehill, 1951). The insertion of electron-releasing groups (such as $-NH_2$) makes the potential considerably more negative, as would be expected.

Toluene-4-thiol reduces acridine to acridan, but does not affect pyridine, quinoline or *iso*quinoline. From this it may be inferred that these three substances have lower E_0 values than acridine, and in fact no reproducible polarographic values have been obtained for them. However, some substituted quinolines have proved amenable to polarographic study, particularly those with electron-attracting substituents, which necessarily raise the E_0 (Stock, 1949; Casimir and Lyons, 1950). In the pyridine series, the E_0 of $-1 \cdot 57$ has been obtained for nicotinamide, but quaternization raises this to $-0 \cdot 24$ (two steps) (Leach, Baxendale and Evans, 1953). The latter value has also been obtained for the coenzymes, di- and tri-phosphopyridine

TABLE 20. Reduction Potentials
of Heteroaromatic Substances[a] at pH7
(20–25°)

	volts
Cytochrome a (a porphyrin)	0·29
Cytochrome c	0·26
Phenazine methosulphate (mono-)	0·08
Thionine (Lauth's violet, a diaminothiazine)	0·06
Alloxan (a pyrimidine-quinone)	0·06
Cresyl blue (a diamino-oxazine)	0·05
Methylene blue (a diaminothiazine)	0·01
Oxonine (a diamino-oxazine)	$-0 \cdot 02$
Pyocyanin (a quaternized hydroxyphenazine)	$-0 \cdot 03$
Cytochrome b	$-0 \cdot 04$
Ethyl capri blue (a diamino-oxazine)	$-0 \cdot 07$
Triphenyltetrazolium chloride	$-0 \cdot 08$
Nile blue (a diaminobenzoxazine)	$-0 \cdot 12$
Phenazine	$-0 \cdot 13$
Riboflavine	$-0 \cdot 19$[b]
2-Hydroxyphenazine	$-0 \cdot 23$
Nicotinamide methochloride	$-0 \cdot 24$
Phenosafranine (a diaminophenazine)	$-0 \cdot 25$
Neutral red (a diaminophenazine)	$-0 \cdot 32$
Benzyl viologen (a dipyridyl)	$-0 \cdot 36$
(Hydrogen electrode)	$(-0 \cdot 42)$
Methyl viologen	$-0 \cdot 44$
Pteroylglutamic acid (folic acid)	$-0 \cdot 63$[c]
Quinoxaline	$-0 \cdot 90$
Pyrimidine	$-1 \cdot 05$[d]
Acridine	$-1 \cdot 1$
6-Aminoquinoxaline	$-1 \cdot 1$
Nicotinamide	$-1 \cdot 6$

a. Only the name of the more oxidized member of the pair is given: the reduced form has two more hydrogen atoms. The values between 0·8 and $-0 \cdot 4$ are likely to be true $E_0{}'$ values, i.e. refer to thermodynamically reversible equilibria.

b. Several riboflavine-containing 'yellow enzymes' have values between $-0 \cdot 06$ and $-0 \cdot 42$.

c. For other pteridines see Allen, Pasternak and Seaman (1952).

d. Further pyrimidines, see Cavalieri and Lowy (1952).

nucleotides, and shows the powerful effect of quaternization which can bring a low potential within the biological range.

Of π-deficient heterocycles with two nitrogens in the one (necessarily six-membered) ring, it is known that a 1:4-arrangement is far more conducive to reduction than a 1:3-arrangement. The potentials are far higher than in analogues with only one nitrogen atom. Comparison of quinoxaline and phenazine suggests that the addition of a benzene ring is conducive to reduction (see Table 20).

Heterocycles with two fused rings offer interesting comparisons. In pteridine (fused pyrazine and pyrimidine rings), the pyrazine ring is easily reduced, but the pyrimidine ring remains unaffected (see Albert, Brown and Cheeseman, 1952, for a summary). In purine (fused iminazole and pyrimidine rings), the iminazole ring is even more difficult to reduce than the pyrimidine (Bendich, 1957): 1:6-dihydropurine is eventually obtained.

Very little work has been done on the potentials of π-excessive heterocycles, but on general principles they would be expected to have even lower potentials than the π-deficient heterocycles. The tetrazolium salts are easily reduced (Jerchel and Möhle, 1944), but the process involves ring-opening.

The reduction of the N-oxides of π-deficient N-heterocycles has more recently been studied (Varyukhina and Pushkareva, 1956; Ochiai, 1953). The potentials are higher than those of the parent substances and are raised by (a) annelation, and (b) inclusion of two nitrogens in the one ring.

For further reading, see Clark (1948), Evans and de Heer (1950), Michaelis (1940), Hewitt (1950).

Dipole Moments. The dipole moment of a substance is a measure of its electrical asymmetry. Thus, although a molecule may contain many atoms with a partial negative charge, and many with a partial positive charge, it may be considered as having one negative centroid (cf. the concept of centre of gravity), and one positive centroid. Thus the molecule is subjected to a couple determined by the product of the total charge, and the distance between the centroids. This product is called the electric dipole moment (μ), and the values are expressed in Debye units ($D = 10^{-18}$ e.s.u.).

In simple cases, the moment of the molecule is the vector sum of the moments of individual bonds or groups. However, the existence of inductive and conjugative effects complicates this relationship. Hence, in the determination of structure, it is better to consider the dipole moments *only after other physical data have led to a choice of first alternatives*. The wisdom of this principle is illustrated by an investigation designed to find whether 4-aminopyridine exists mainly as (I) or as (II).

NH$_2$ NH $\overset{+}{\text{N}}$H$_2$

          N   N $\overset{-}{\text{N}}$
                  H

     I   II   III

Because the dipole moment was high, it was concluded that (II) predominated (Leis and Curran, 1945). Nevertheless this conclusion was incorrect. Much more fundamental properties (infrared and ultraviolet spectra, ionization constants) clearly showed that (I) was almost exclusively present (see p. 52). The source of the heightened moment was then traced to a small contribution from (III) in the resonance hybrid of (I) (Angyal and Angyal, 1952).

The dipole moment of a substance is ideally measured in the vapour, but it is usually more convenient to measure it in solution. In the latter case, the solvent should have (*a*) zero moment, and (*b*) no groups capable of forming bonds with a bondable hydrogen should one be present in the solute. For such purposes benzene, hexane, and carbon tetrachloride are ideal solvents. Dioxan, although much used, gives erroneous results whenever hydrogen-bonds can be formed (Kumler and Halverstadt, 1941) (see 4-aminopyridine, 3-hydroxypyridine, 4-aminoquinoline and iminazole in Table 21).

Table 21 contains a selection of known dipole moments. It shows, as has been assumed in earlier chapters, that π-deficient N-heterocycles have negative heteroatoms, whereas their π-excessive analogues have positive heteroatoms. In pyrrole the moment is mainly derived from the positions taken up by the π-electrons (i.e. it is a 'π-moment'), because the nature of the —NH — group does not permit of a 'lone-pair moment', and in heteroaromatic substances the 'σ-moments' are trivial (Dr. R. D. Brown, personal communication). In pyridine the moment is largely derived from the lone-pair, the remainder consisting of a small π-moment.

It will be seen from Table 21 that most heterocycles, like most other weak (or non-) electrolytes, have moments under 3D. Values exceeding 4D denote a considerable degree of polarization, as in *p*-nitroaniline (6·3D): 1 methyltetrazole is such a substance. However even N-phenylsydnone (see p. 237), for which the term 'mesoionic' has been coined, has a moment of only 6·5D, whereas true zwitterions, such as glycine, reach values around 15D.

Several instances of dipole moments contributing to the solution of constitutional problems have been noted in previous chapters, notably problems concerning the hydroxypyridines (p. 61), pyrones (p. 270), xanthones (p. 281), and pyridine-N-oxides (p. 88).

For further reading on dipole moments, see Smith (1955), Sutton (1955), Le Fèvre (1948). For an interesting discussion of π-excessive heterocycles, see Jensen and Friediger (1943).

TABLE 21. Dipole Moments[a]
(20–30°)

Substance	Solvent	μ
Heteroparaffinics		D
Ethylene oxide	(vapour)	1·88
Trimethylene oxide	benzene	2·01
Propylene oxide	benzene	1·88
2-Methyl-1:3-dioxolan	benzene	1·21
1:3:5-Trioxan	benzene	2·18
1:4-Dioxan	(vapour)	0
γ-Butyrolactone	(benzene)	4·12
Tetrahydrofuran	(benzene)	1·71
Tetrahydrothiophen	(benzene)	1·87
Tetrahydropyran	(benzene)	1·87
Pyrrolidine	(benzene)	1·57
2-oxo-	(benzene)	2·3

TABLE 21—*continued*

Substance	Solvent	μ
		D
Morpholine	(benzene)	1·48
Succinimide	(benzene)	1·54
Succinic anhydride	dioxan	4·20
Piperidine	benzene	1·17
N-methyl-	benzene	0·91
Hexamethylenetetramine	chloroform	0
Paraldehyde	benzene	1·92
Heteroaromatics (π-*deficient*)		
Pyridine	benzene	2·20
Pyridine	dioxan	2·22
2-chloro-	benzene	3·22
2-bromo-	benzene	2·98
3-bromo-	benzene	1·93
4-chloro-	benzene	0·84
2:6-dibromo-	benzene	3·43
2-methyl-	benzene	1·96
3-methyl-	benzene	2·30
4-methyl-	benzene	2·57
2:6-dimethyl-	benzene	1·65
2-amino-	benzene	2·17
3-amino-	benzene	3·19
4-amino-	benzene	3·79
4-amino-	dioxan	4·36
2-hydroxy-	benzene	1·95
N-methyl-derivative	benzene	4·15
3-hydroxy-	benzene	2·00
3-hydroxy-	dioxan	2·95
4-hydroxy-	dioxan	6·30
N-methyl-derivative	benzene	6·9
2-methoxy-	benzene	1·15
3-methoxy-	benzene	2·75
4-methoxy-	benzene	3·00
Ethyl *iso*nicotinate	benzene	2·49
Quinoline	benzene	2·18
2-methyl-	benzene	1·95
4-methyl-	benzene	2·52
2-chloro	benzene	3·26
2-amino-	benzene	2·22
3-amino-	benzene	3·07
4-amino-	benzene	3·97
4-amino	dioxan	4·38
4-methoxy-	benzene	2·94
8-hydroxy-	benzene	2·70
*Iso*quinoline	benzene	2·52

2A

TABLE 21—*continued*

Substance	Solvent	μ
Heteroaromatics (π-*deficient*)—*cont.*		**D**
Acridine	benzene	1·95
5-amino-	benzene	4·13
5-chloro-	benzene	0
N-Methylacridone	benzene	3·0
Phenanthridine	benzene	1·50
Pyridazine	benzene	4·32
Pyrazine	(vapour)	0
2:5-dimethyl-	benzene	0
2:6-dimethyl-	benzene	0·53
Pyrimidine	dioxan	2·42
2:5-dichloro-	dioxan	2·27
Cinnoline	benzene	4·14
4-methyl-	benzene	4·53
Quinoxaline	—	?
2-methyl-	benzene	2·2
2:3-dimethyl-	benzene	0
Quinazoline	—	?
2-methyl-	benzene	2·2
Phenazine	benzene	0
Pyocyanin (anhydride of		
1-hydroxyphenazine-9-methochloride)	benzene	7
Heteroaromatics (π-*excessive*)		
Pyrrole	benzene	1·80
N-methyl	?	1·94
Indole	benzene	2·05
1-methyl-	benzene	2·16
2-methyl-	benzene	2·47
3-methyl- (scatole)	benzene	2·08
2-phenyl-	benzene	2·01
Isatin	benzene	5·72
Carbazole	benzene	2·09
Pyrazole	benzene	1·47
1-methyl-	benzene	2·28
3-methyl-	benzene	1·43
1:5-Dimethyl-2-phenyl-3-pyrazolone		
(phenazone)	benzene	5·48
Iminazole	benzene	3·84[b]
	dioxan	4·84
1-methyl-	benzene	3·63
4-methyl-	benzene	6·4
Benziminazole	dioxan	3·93
Indazole	benzene	1·83
1:2:3-Triazole	benzene	1·77[c]
1-phenyl-	benzene	4·08
2-phenyl-	benzene	0·97

TABLE 21—*continued*

Substance	Solvent	μ
		D
1:2:4-Triazole	dioxan	3·17
1-phenyl-	benzene	2·88
4-phenyl-	benzene	5·63
Tetrazole	dioxan	5·11
1-methyl-	benzene	5·38
1-Ethyltetrazole	benzene	5·46
2-Ethyltetrazole	benzene	2·65
Phenyl-sydnone	benzene	6·50
Furan	benzene	0·71
2-methyl-	benzene	0·74
Furfural	benzene	3·57
Thiophen	benzene	0·54
2-methyl-	benzene	0·67
2-nitro-	benzene	4·12
2-bromo-	benzene	1·39
3-mercapto-	benzene	1·07
Oxazole	benzene	1·4
Isoxazole	benzene	2·81
Thiazole	benzene	1·64
2-amino-	benzene	1·75
3:4-Benzisoxazole (anthranil)	benzene	3·06
4:5-Benzisoxazole	benzene	3·03
Benzoxazole	benzene	1·47
Benzothiazole	benzene	1·45
2-mercapto-	benzene	4·00
Methylthio-diphenyl thiadiazolinium iodide	chloroform	13·1
Heteroethylenics		
2:5-Dihydrofuran	benzene	1·53
Pyrroline	benzene	1·42
2:6-Dimethyl-γ-pyrone	benzene	4·05
Phenoxthiin	benzene	1·09
Thianthrene	?	1·57
Dibenzodioxan	benzene	0
Xanthone	benzene	3·11
Thioxanthone	dioxan	5·4

a. Many of these values are taken from Wesson (1948), the remainder from more recent work.

b. Jensen and Friediger (1943) obtained this value at infinite dilution, but because this substance is so strongly associated in benzene, the moment is 5·62 in 0·08M solution.

c. Because the moment resembles that of pyrazole rather than that of iminazole, the mobile hydrogen is thought to be principally on $N_{(2)}$.

CHAPTER XI

Interpretation of Complex Formulae
in terms of
Physical and Chemical Properties

THOSE who have read the preceding chapters of this book, where connexions between structure and properties are kept to the fore, should have little difficulty with the more complex formulae of alkaloids, vitamins and other natural products. By considering separately the heteroparaffinic, heteroaromatic and heteroethylenic portions of a structural formula, a first approximation to the physical and chemical properties can be achieved. Some examples will demonstrate this process at work.

I   II

Example 1. *Atropine* (I). This is seen at once to be heteroparaffinic (see Chapter II). It is obviously an ester of a secondary alcohol (II) (tropine) with an aromatic acid (III) (tropic acid). The bicyclic ring-system, nortropane, of which tropine (II) is a hydroxy-, N-methyl-, derivative, was discussed on p. 23. Like all N-heteroparaffinics, it has essentially the properties of a saturated aliphatic amine. The bridge across the ring has little effect on the properties, and tropine may be thought of simply as β-ethanolamine, with inert alkyl substituents (see p. 4 for an explanation of this simplifying process). This idea has led to the discovery of non-heterocyclic drugs with an atropine-like action, made by esterifying hydroxylated tertiary amines, such as N:N-diethylethanolamine (V) (or the similar pentanolamine

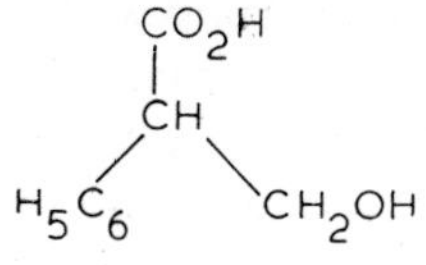

$$
\begin{array}{cc}
\text{III} & \text{IV}
\end{array}
$$

III (tropic acid type structure): CO$_2$H—CH(C$_6$H$_5$)—CH$_2$OH

IV: OH—CH$_2$—C(CH$_3$)$_2$—CH$_2$—C($_2$H$_5$)—N—C$_2$H$_5$

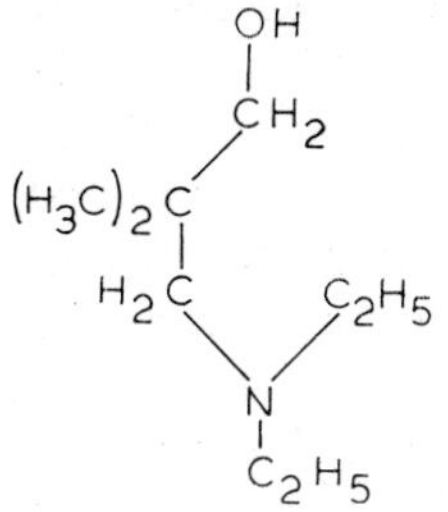

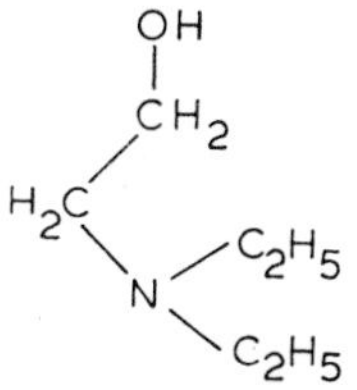

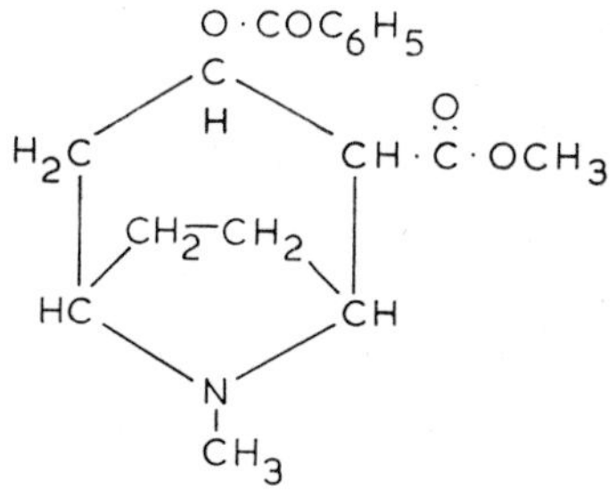

$$
\begin{array}{cc}
\text{V} & \text{VI}
\end{array}
$$

V: OH—CH$_2$—CH$_2$—N(C$_2$H$_5$)$_2$

VI: O·COC$_6$H$_5$ ... CH·C·OCH$_3$ (O) ring with N—CH$_3$

(IV)) with tropic acid or diphenylacetic acid. Thus (IV) and tropic acid give the successful atropine-like drug, 'Syntropan'. Inspection of the formula of atropine reveals only one ionizable group: the ring-nitrogen. From Table 16 (p. 338), the pK_a of trimethylamine is seen to be 9·8, and atropine should be a similarly strong base. This prediction is confirmed by reference to Kolthoff (1925), where the pK_a is seen to be 10·0, which is unusually high for an alkaloid, but is quite in order for one with this structure. No ultraviolet spectrum, other than that of the benzene ring in the acid group, can be expected (for heteroparaffinic substances have almost no spectrum), and the principal chemical reaction of such an inert structure should be the hydrolysis of the ester linkage, as is indeed the case.

Example 2. *Cocaine* (VI). This is seen to be an ester (twice over) of the heteroparaffinic substance (VII), known as ecgonine, which is a secondary alcohol, a tertiary amine and a carboxylic acid. In cocaine, the alcoholic group of ecgonine is esterified with benzoic acid, and the acidic group with methanol. Ecgonine (VII) is simply a carboxy-derivative of (II). The presence in cocaine of an ester group that is *beta* to the basic group should lower the pK_a by approximately one unit of pK. Reference to Kolthoff (1925), shows 8·7 as the pK_a of cocaine. It has been found that simple aromatic esters of diethylaminoethanol (V) have an anaesthetic action like cocaine, and the *p*-aminobenzoyl ester is the familiar dental anaesthetic, procaine. Being heteroparaffinic, cocaine is chemically fairly inert, apart from hydrolysis to (VII).

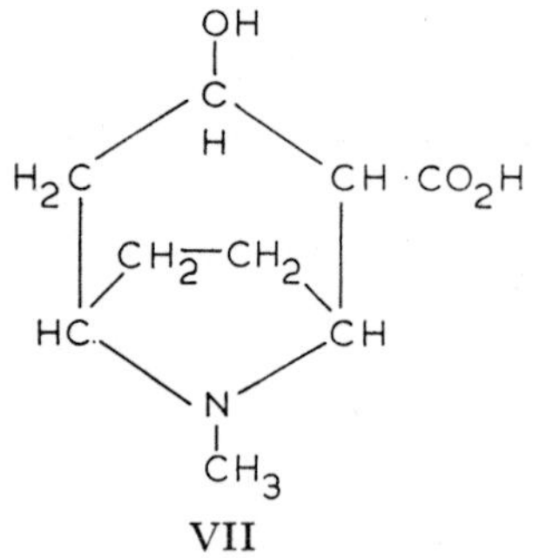

VII

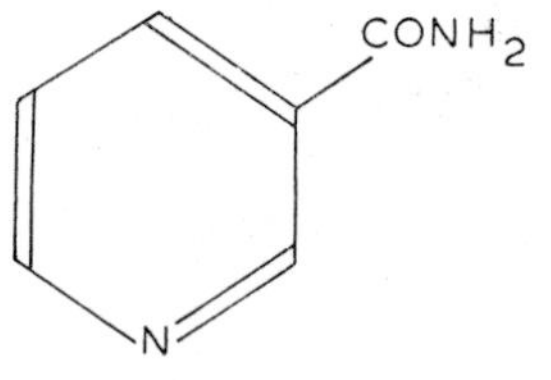

VIII

Example 3. *Nicotinamide* (VIII). This vitamin is obviously a completely heteroaromatic substance, and a π-deficient one (see Chapter IV). The π-deficiency is enhanced by an electron-withdrawing substituent ($-CONH_2$). With this diagnosis, it can safely be predicted that nicotinamide is stable to acid and alkali (but under severe conditions the amide-group will become hydrolysed), unreactive to electrophilic reagents and reactive to nucleophilic reagents. It should be difficult to reduce, unless first quaternized (see Chapter X) and stable to mild oxidizing agent (Chapter IV). The ultraviolet spectrum should resemble that of pyridine, i.e. conventional instruments should reveal only one band. This band should be moved to somewhat longer wavelengths (say 265 mμ), and show much less detail than pyridine (see Chapter VIII). Nicotinamide should be a weaker base than pyridine, which has pK_a = 5·2. As the electron-attracting powers of $-CONH_2$ and $-COOMe$ are so similar, the pK_a should be close to that of 3-carbomethoxy-pyridine, which is 3·2 (see Table 17, p. 342): in fact it is known to be 3·4.

IX   X

Example 4. *Pyridoxal* (IX). Like the last example, this is evidently a π-deficient heteroaromatic substance, but it has three electron-releasing and only one electron-attracting substituent. This would make it open to electrophilic substitution in the 6-position which is the only one free (but the yields would probably not be high). Nucleophilic substitution in this position would probably not occur. The hydroxy-group, not being α- or γ-, cannot have the special properties associated with these positions (see p. 55), but the molecule will undoubtedly be partly in the zwitterionic state, as 3-hydroxy-pyridine is (see p. 56, also Metzler and Snell, 1955). Thus, it should absorb both at about 280 (neutral molecule) and 315 μ (zwitterion), and have pK's roughly at 5 and 8·5 (actually they are at 4·2 and 8·7). The propinquity of the phenolic and the aldehyde groups permits a cyclic acetal to be formed (see ring-chain tautomerism, Chapter II, p. 13), but this should not greatly affect chemical properties. This same propinquity should permit the formation of stable chelate complexes with metals, like those formed by salicylaldehyde, e.g. (X).

Example 5. *Quinine* (XI). This is one of several natural products having two distinct ring systems. On the left is a π-

deficient heteroaromatic nucleus which closer inspection shows
to be simply quinoline with a 6-methoxy-substituent. The upper
right-hand part of the formula is a heteroparaffinic amine,
on whose properties the bridge across the ring can have little
effect. This ring-system (quinuclidine) has been discussed
before (p. 23) and, according to the simplifying rule for hetero-
paraffinics (p. 4), it must have essentially the inert properties
of triethylamine. These two nuclei are joined by being both

XI

inserted into *methanol*, giving a secondary alcohol. This substituent and the vinyl-group will combine to lower slightly the
basic strength of a tertiary amine (pK_a about 10), and in fact
the first ionization constant of quinine is 8·4. A second, but
weaker, basic centre is present in the quinoline part of the
formula, and although this should be slightly weakened by the
coulombic effect (i.e. the repulsive effect on protons caused by
ionization of the first nitrogen atom), the two basic centres are
just too far apart for much interaction of this kind. The pK_a of
quinoline is 4·9, hence it is not surprising that the second
constant of quinine is 4·7. The ultraviolet spectrum of quinine
should be that of quinoline displaced to slightly longer wavelengths (Chapter VIII) because no other groups absorbing
above 210 mμ are present. The general chemical reactions will
be primarily those of quinoline (e.g. the tendency to nucleophilic substitution in the 2-position), and it should be noted
that the carbon atom which carries the alcoholic group is
activated, just as the methyl-group is in 4-methyl-quinoline.

This means that the hydrogen on this carbon is mobile, and, as a result, alkalis cause isomerism to quinotoxin (cf. Manske and Holmes, 1952). In other ways, the secondary alcoholic group is normal, being readily oxidized to the corresponding ketone, or changed by phosphorus halides to the corresponding chloro-compound, which readily splits off HCl and so forms a new double-bond (conjugating with those of the quinoline nucleus). The vinyl-group undergoes the usual additive reactions of ethylene.

XII   XIII

Example 6. *Nicotine* (XII). This is another alkaloid in which a heteroaromatic nucleus (pyridine in this case) is joined to a heteroparaffinic nucleus (N-methylpyrrolidine), but in this case the nuclei are joined directly, without a bridge. As there is no conjugation outside the pyridine ring, and the substituent is not a conjugating one, the ultraviolet spectrum of nicotine should be almost identical with that of pyridine. Of the two nitrogen atoms, the heteroparaffinic must be the stronger base (see Chapter IX). Its pK_a will be that of a tertiary aliphatic amine (*ca.* 10) weakened by the insertion, near to the nitrogen, of an electron-attracting ring (pyridine is considered to be about as electron-attracting as a nitro-group). The first pK_a of 8·2 agrees with this estimate, and the second pK (3·4) is that of pyridine (5·2) reduced by the coulombic effect discussed above. On oxidation, nicotine gives pyridine-3-carboxylic acid, as would be expected from the known high stability of π-deficient N-heterocyclic rings.

Myosmine (XIII), a related alkaloid isolated from tobacco smoke, differs only in the five-membered ring which is a secondary base and (more important) has an ethylenic bond.

As may be predicted from the known chemistry of Δ^2-dihydro-pyrroles (p. 256), myosmine is unstable and easily dispropor-tionates to analogues with a pyrrole, and a pyrrolidine, nucleus respectively. As would be assumed from Table 18 (p. 343), it is a weaker base than nicotine.

Example 7. *Heteroauxin* (XIV). This growth-factor for plants has a π-excessive heteroaromatic nucleus (indole), not appre-ciably lowered in π-electron-content by the carboxylic acid group, which is almost insulated from the ring by a methylene bridge. (Parenthetically, a paraffinic side-chain of two or more carbon atoms exerts the same complete barrier to the passage of electrons as does the layer of paraffin or polythene so often used for electrical insulation: whether on the molecular or the macro-scale, the reason is the same.) Thus heteroauxin would be expected to give all the reactions of indole except polymeriza-tion (the side-chain should sterically hinder addition across the 2:3-double-bond). The acid strength should lie very close to that of acetic acid.

Example 8. *Thiamine* (XV). This vitamin is seen to consist of a π-deficient heteroaromatic nucleus (pyrimidine) united by a methylene bridge to another heteroaromatic nucleus (thiazole) the π-excessive character of which is slightly reinforced by two alkyl-substituents, but considerably diminished by the positive charge on the nitrogen atom. Because of the substantial insulating effect of the methylene bridge, the two nuclei can be considered separately. In the pyrimidine nucleus can be seen an activated methyl-group (see p. 97) and an α-amino-group (see p. 52), both with their usual special properties. The thiazolium ring, as explained in Chapter VI (2 (*h*)) (see p. 223), reacts with alkali by becoming nucleophilically substituted by hydroxyl in the 2-position: this is followed by ring-opening which exposes a mercapto-group, and the latter auto-oxidizes in air. Thus, treatment of thiamine with alkali causes far-reaching, and eventually irreversible, changes. Like other thiazolium compounds, in which the quaternizing group is 'methylene attached to an electron-attracting nucleus', thiamine is cleaved by sodium sulphite, giving 2-methyl-4-amino-5-pyrimidinemethane-sulphonic acid and 4-methyl-5-(β-hydroxyethyl)thiazole.

Example 9. *Pilocarpine* (XVI). This is another alkaloid in which two very different kinds of rings are joined together. It consists essentially of an iminazole ring, the mobile hydrogen of which is substituted by methyl and bearing a lactone ring in the 2-position. The properties of iminazoles are discussed in Chapter V, and of saturated lactones along with other hetero-paraffinics in Chapter II. Pilocarpine does not depart from the sum of these properties, and has the expected pK of 7·2, and a lack of ultraviolet spectrum above 220 mμ.

Example 10. *Physostigmine* (eserine) (XVII). This alkaloid has a complex nucleus, not hitherto encountered and consisting of three fused rings. The benzene ring on the left bears a phenolic group, esterified with methylaminoformic acid. It will be recalled that urethane is the aminoformate of ethanol, hence physostigmine is the methylurethane of the complex phenol. Of the two hetero-rings, that on the right is heteroparaffinic, an N-methylpyrrolidine as in nicotine (XII). The middle ring is a dihydropyrrole, as in myosmine (XIII), but with the difference that its double-bond is stabilized by forming part of the benzene ring (we have already met this phenomenon in phthalic anhydride and isatin). Thus the central ring is only nominally heteroethylenic and would not be expected to show double-bond additivity. The expected spectrum of physostigmine should be very simple, i.e. that of an ester of p-aminophenol. The principal basic group is in the right-hand ring: the pK_a should be that of a tertiary aliphatic amine (pK_a about 10), but weakened by the propinquity of the amino-group in the middle ring which would be base-weakening, not only by simple induction, but by carrying a small positive charge owing to the aniline-like structure which it forms with the benzene ring. As it happens, the pK_a values of the right-hand and central rings are 8·2 and 2·1 respectively. Physostigmine is easily hydrolysed by alkali to carbon dioxide, methylamine and the phenol, discussed above, which is subject to autoxidation and turns pink in air. It gives both a mono- and a di-quaternary salt.

XVIII

Example 11. *Kinetin* (XVIII). This substance increases cell-division in plants, whereas the action of indoleacetic acid (XIV) consists mainly of lengthening existing cells. A purine nucleus (p. 195) is conspicuous on the left-hand side of (XVIII), and, as there is an amino-group in position 6, the molecule is a substituted adenine. The substituent in question is a furfuryl group (i.e. furylmethylene) (see p. 228). Both nuclei, particularly the furan, are capable of electrophilic substitution; nucleophilic substitution is not at all likely. The tendency of furans to polymerize is offset by the size of the molecule, which would make it difficult for two molecules both to present unsubstituted α:β-positions to one another. Because of the γ-position of the amino-group, adenine has a pK_a of 4: this should remain practically the same in kinetin. Because furan has little ultraviolet absorption, and in the present case the furan ring bears no conjugating substituent, the spectrum should be like that of purine. The usual instability of furans to acid should be encountered in this molecule.

XIX

Example 12. *Rotenone* (XIX). This slow-acting but highly lethal insecticide consists of five fused rings which, reading from left to right, we may call A, B, C, D and E. Of these, A is a benzene ring bearing two methoxy substituents placed *ortho* to one another, as in many other natural products. It is in keeping with the known stability of aromatic rings, that violent oxidation of rotenone leaves this ring intact, and it is isolated in the form of 2-hydroxy-4:5-dimethoxybenzoic acid. Mild oxidation of rotenone gives 'dehydrorotenone' by removing the two hydrogen atoms indicated by the arrows. This oxidation brings ring C into the quasi-aromatic state for which γ-pyrones are noted (see p. 269); but in rotenone C is a dihydropyrone ring, and typically unstable (see p. 267). Ring B is technically a dihydropyran ring, but the double-bond is shared with the benzene ring, and hence has aromatic instead of ethylenic character. This remark also applies to the apparently hetero-ethylenic ring E, which at first sight may seem to be a dihydro-furan. Thus, as would be expected, the only bond that gives the reactions of an ethylenic bond is in the *iso*allyl side chain. For a discussion of the chemistry of rotenone, see Robertson (1932).

CHAPTER XII

Notes on some Rational Approaches to New Syntheses

THERE are no simple, infallible rules for devising a new synthesis. The organic chemist, after years of experience in the preparation of substances both new and old, often possesses a seemingly intuitive knowledge of the best reagents and conditions to employ; he appears to be capable of unconsciously summoning up the knowledge that the situation requires from all that he has ever read or done.

However, less experienced workers can be helped by general principles when a new synthesis has to be undertaken. Mainly, the synthetic chemist must work by analogy, trying to compensate as well as he can for the differences between his starting materials and the ones used in the older analogue. Thus, if the two starting materials differ only in substituents, the different electronic disturbances in the two molecules caused by these substituents have to be taken into account in choosing the reagent, the time, and the temperature. It goes without saying that lengthy education in theoretical and practical chemistry is needed before this can be accomplished.

In the synthesis of heterocyclic substances, a special shortcut is available for six-membered rings containing a —NH-group. These may be prepared by gently warming the corresponding —O-heterocycles with ammonia. Thus the γ-pyrone known as diethyl chelidonate (I) gives the pyridone (II) known as diethyl chelidamate. α-Pyrones react similarly, and 1-hydroxy*iso*quinolines have been made from *iso*coumarins in this way. The course of these reactions depends upon the relatively poor aromatic properties of oxygen-, compared to nitrogen-, heterocycles (see p. 200), so that (I) is opened by alkali to give a suitable intermediate for making (II), whereas (II) is stable to alkali.

Five-membered rings also give this reaction, but severer conditions are necessary (see p. 179 for the preparation of pyrroles from furans, and p. 192 for the transformation of oxazoles into iminazoles).

$$EtO_2C \quad O \quad CO_2Et$$

$$\text{I}$$

$$EtO_2C \quad \underset{H}{N} \quad CO_2Et$$

$$\text{II}$$

Another approach to synthesis is to try to visualize the nature of the last intermediate, by deciding where the last join will have to be made. When the molecule has both heterocyclic and benzene rings, it is almost inevitable that the benzene ring will be intact in the previous intermediate, and hence the join will occur in the heterocyclic portion. It will usually, but not always, occur next to a hetero-atom, but this hetero-atom may be *external* to the ring. Thus the formula of acridone (III) should at once suggest the two most likely intermediates, either diphenylamine-2-carboxylic acid (IV), or 2:2′-diaminobenzo-phenone (V). This is so because $-CO-$ in a ring usually has its origin in $-COOH$, and $-NH-$ often arises from two amino-groups. The conversion of (IV) to (III) obviously involves the loss of water under conditions where the acid group is made into a cation, for it has to react as an electrophilic reagent. Therefore this reaction would be carried out with concentrated sulphuric acid, polyphosphoric acid, or aluminium chloride at about 100°. The conversion of (V) to (III), on the other hand, involves the loss of a molecule of ammonia, which usually proceeds best under more mildly acidic conditions at 150–180°, and is sometimes helped by a copper catalyst.

Another common ring-closure is the formation of an azo-methine link between an aldehyde- and an amino-group. Thus quinoxaline (VI) is obviously best made from *o*-phenylene-diamine and glyoxal (VII) at 20°. Closely related to this and to the first of the acridone syntheses, is the formation of an amide link between an ester and an amino-group, as in the synthesis of 6-hydroxypteridine (VIII) from 4:5-diaminopyrimidine and ethyl glyoxylate (IX) in cold 2N-sulphuric acid. In this, as in so many cyclizations, two isomers can be obtained depending on the direction of ring-closure: thus at pH9, where neither of the reactants is ionized, only 7-hydroxypteridine (X) is produced. The synthetic chemist, always aware of such alternative closures, is learning how to make them produce the desired isomer.

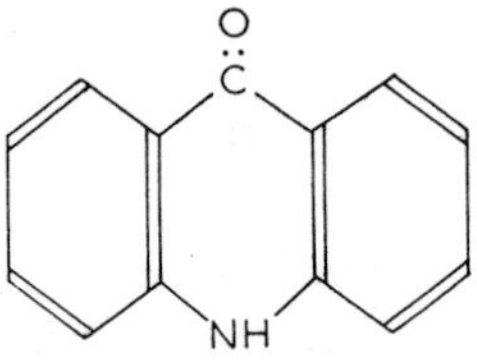

III 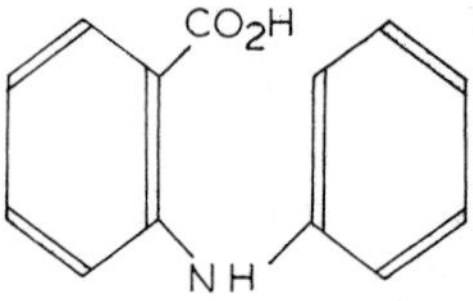   IV

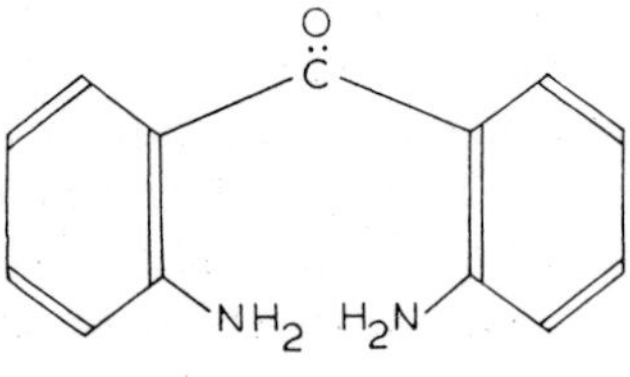

V

The occurrence in a ring of two nitrogens next to one another suggests an intermediate in which they were also vicinal, thus cinnolines can be obtained from a diazotized anilino-group if it is placed *ortho* to an activated[1] methylene group (see p. 119). Similar reactions are the preparation of benzotriazole, by the action of nitrous acid on *o*-phenylene-diamine (p. 194), the preparation of indazole from *o*-hydrazinobenzoic acid (p. 193), and of 1:2:3-triazole from hydrazoic acid and acetylene (p. 193).

[1] i.e. one made electron-deficient by an electron-attracting substituent.

It should be noted that the use of acetylene derivatives for heterocyclic syntheses is fast increasing now that they are becoming more readily available. Their highly reactive character makes them versatile intermediates. In this connexion, it must be pointed out that a feebly reactive intermediate requires high temperatures, which are often injurious to some constituent of the reaction. Highly reactive intermediates, on the other hand, require mild conditions and often a protecting group must first be inserted, and then removed when the desired reaction has taken place. Conversely the insertion of an activating group into the molecule of a feebly-reacting intermediate can facilitate a reaction.

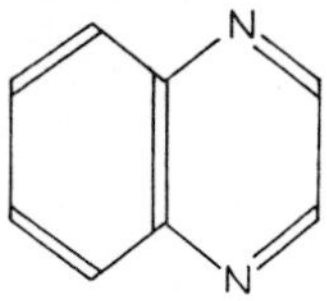

VI 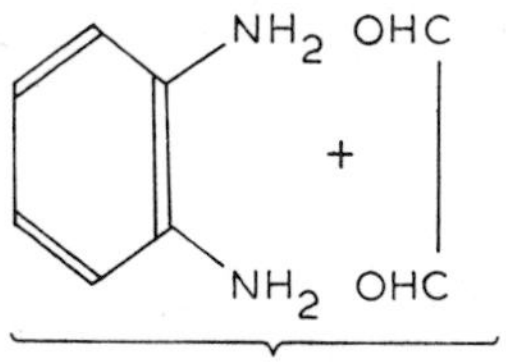   VII 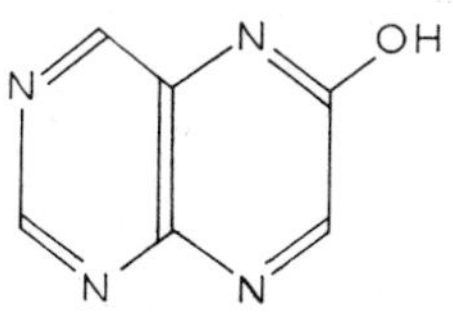   VIII

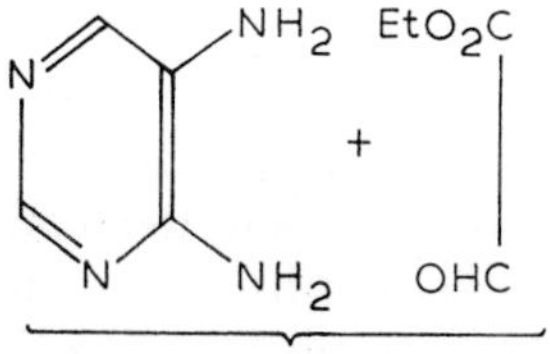

IX 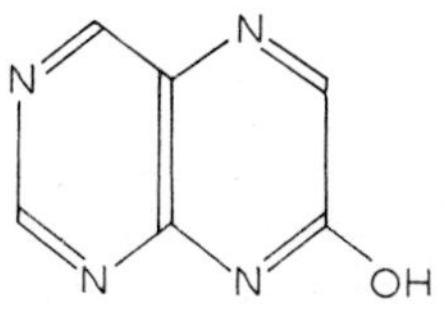   X

Thus 2-nitro-2'-hydroxydiphenylamine (XI) cannot be closed to oxazine (XII), but if an electron-attracting group is present in the 6-position as well, the corresponding oxazine is easily produced by elimination of nitrous acid. Reluctant reactions can also be helped by catalysts, where these are known. Thus the Knorr synthesis of 2-hydroxyquinolines needs a trace of acid, and usually a trace of copper as well (p. 107).

The above reaction (elimination of nitrous acid) is one of the less usual ways of forming an oxygen link. More commonly water is eliminated from two hydroxyl-groups, as in the preparation of dioxan from ethylene glycol (see p. 12). For an oxygen linkage in an unsaturated setting, two aldehydo-groups may be condensed together (they behave as enols), as in the preparation of γ-pyrone from acetone dialdehyde (XIII). Sulphur bridges are similarly formed, and often the dimercaptan is created *in situ* from the dienol by the action of phosphorus pentasulphide. For example 2:5-hexanedione reacts (as its dienol) with phosphorus pentasulphide to give the dimercaptan (XIV) which at once cyclizes to 2:5-dimethylthiophen.

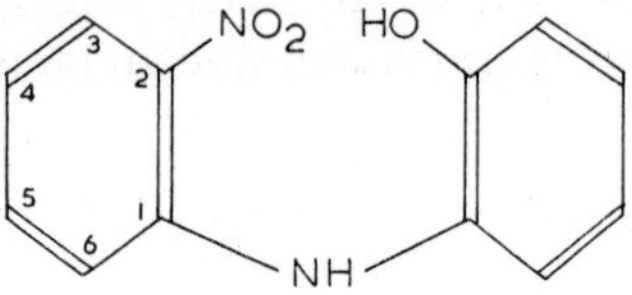

XI 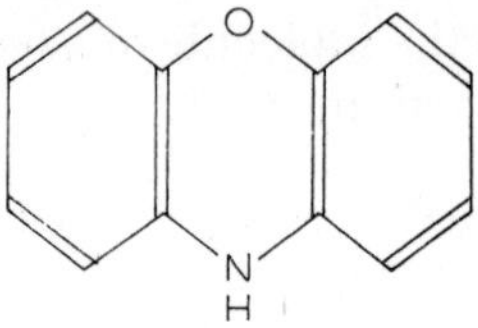   XII

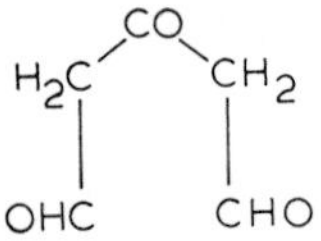

XIII 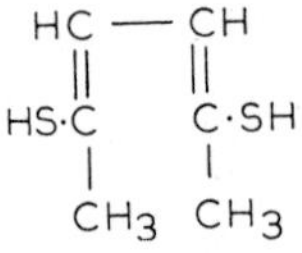   XIV

The reaction just discussed is only one of many given by 1:4-dicarbonyl-compounds (XV) and their derivatives, each leading to a different heterocyclic family. In general, such intermediates react with ammonia to give a nitrogen-heterocycle, or they react with phosphorus pentasulphide to give a sulphur-heterocycle, or they are simply dehydrated to give an oxygen-heterocycle. In each case the product is a five-membered ring.[1] Thus 1:4-diketones (or di-aldehydes) give pyrroles, thiophens and furans respectively.

In a modification of this reaction, β-ketoamides (XVI) react with phosphorus pentasulphide, or by dehydration, to give the azalogues: thiazoles and oxazoles respectively. This reaction has not yet been successfully applied to iminazoles. In a further development, dihydrazides (XVII) give higher azalogues. Thus

[1] Few similar reactions leading to six-membered rings are known, apart from the γ-pyrone synthesis just described.

ammonia gives 1:2:4-triazoles, phosphorus sulphides give 1:3:4-thiadiazoles, whereas 1:3:4-oxadiazoles are obtained by dehydration.

$$\begin{array}{cccc}
\text{CH}_2\text{—CH}_2 & \text{CH}_2\text{—NH} & \text{NH—NH} & \text{CH}_2\text{—CH}_2 \\
| \quad\quad | & | \quad\quad | & | \quad\quad | & | \quad\quad | \\
\text{RCO} \quad \text{COR} & \text{RCO} \quad \text{COR} & \text{RCO} \quad \text{COR} & \text{RCO} \quad \text{C:NOH} \\
 & & & \quad\quad\quad \text{R} \\
\text{XV} & \text{XVI} & \text{XVII} & \text{XVIII}
\end{array}$$

All the reactions in the last paragraph give rings where two carbon atoms are linked by a hetero-atom. By using the mono-oximes of the 1:4-diketones, it is possible to link carbon and nitrogen by a hetero-atom. For example, the mono-oximes (XVIII) on dehydration give isoxazoles, and the corresponding mono-hydrazones give pyrazoles. Similarly the (mono) oximes derived from the ketonic function in β-ketoamides (XVI) give 1:2:4-oxadiazoles on dehydration, and the corresponding hydrazones give 1:2:4-triazoles. Finally, the use of dioximes and dihydrazides enables the linkage of two nitrogens by a hetero-atom. Thus the dioximes of (XV) give 1:2:5-oxadiazoles, and the dihydrazones of (XV) give 1:2:3-triazoles.

Many of the reactions described in the last three paragraphs also take place when R is $-OH$, $-OCH_3$, or $-NH_2$ (i.e. one or more aldehyde or ketone group can be replaced by an acid, ester, or amide group): in such cases, the product bears the corresponding $-OH$, $-OCH_3$, or $-NH_2$ groups.

$$\begin{array}{ccc}
\begin{array}{c} \text{H} \\ \text{C} \\ \text{H}_2\text{C} \quad \text{O} \\ | \\ \text{HC} \\ \text{O} \end{array} & + & \begin{array}{c} \text{NH}_2 \\ | \\ \text{CH} \\ \text{HN} \end{array} \quad \begin{array}{c} \text{6} \quad \text{1 N} \\ \text{5} \\ \text{4} \quad \text{3} \quad \text{2} \\ \text{N} \end{array} \\
\text{XIX} & & \text{XX} \quad\quad \text{XXI}
\end{array}$$

For planning the synthesis of a six-membered ring with *two* hetero-atoms, a useful beginning is to draw the formula, assume that the join will occur at the hetero-atom, and to decide what reactive fragments must be united to obtain the required structure. Thus pyrimidine (XXI) could be made from malon-dialdehyde (XIX) and formamidine (XX). Analogously, malonaldehydic acid (XXII) gives 4-hydroxypyrimidine, and cyanacetaldehyde (XXIII) gives 4-aminopyrimidine. Again diethyl malonate readily gives 4:6-dihydroxypyrimidine. The formamidine (XX) may also be substituted: thus acetamidine gives 2-methylpyrimidines, guanidine gives 2-aminopyrimidines, urea gives 2-hydroxypyrimidines and thiourea gives 2-mercapto-pyrimidines.

In an alternative type of approach, both hetero-atoms can be given to the major fragment. Thus malondiamide (XXIV) can be condensed with ethyl formate to give 4:6-dihydroxy-pyrimidine (see p. 116).

Finally, it is sometimes possible to effect a join not involving any hetero-atom: for example a $-CH=CH-$ linkage can be created. The increasing availability of acetylenic intermediates is drawing more attention to this kind of reaction, but several examples are known where a higher degree of saturation has proved adequate. For example in the Madelung synthesis, N-formyl-*o*-toluidine (XXV) gives indole (XXVI) on strong heating with a base (see p. 184). Again, the Skraup synthesis of quinoline has (XXVII) as the ultimate intermediate (p. 105). Friedländer's quinoline synthesis almost certainly has (XXVIII) as the ultimate intermediate (p. 107). The principal *iso*quinoline syntheses are also carbon-to-carbon joins.

Those who feel strongly attracted to the synthetic side of organic chemistry may find it useful to abstract all the syntheses described in Chapters II to VII of this book, and to classify them (possibly along the lines discussed in the present chapter). This operation could profitably be followed by a literature search for the effects of electron-withdrawal, electron-release, and steric hindrance on the severity of the conditions required to effect each reaction.

REFERENCES

ABRAHAMS (1956). *Quart. Revs.*, **10**, 419.
ACHESON, BURSTALL, JEFFORD AND SANSOM (1954). *J. Chem. Soc.*, p. 3742.
ACHESON, HOULT and BARNARD (1954). *J. Chem. Soc.*, p. 4142.
ACHESON and ROBINSON (1953). *J. Chem. Soc.*, p. 232.
ADAMS and MAHAN (1942). *J. Amer. Chem. Soc.*, **64**, 2588.
ADAMS and SCHRECKER (1949). *J. Amer. Chem. Soc.*, **71**, 1186.
ADAMS and SLACK (1956). *Chem. & Ind.*, p. 1232.
ADAMSON and KENNER (1935). *J. Chem. Soc.*, p. 286.
ADKINS and COONRADT (1941). *J. Amer. Chem. Soc.*, **63**, 1563.
ALBERT (1947). *J. Chem. Soc.*, p. 244.
ALBERT (1948). *J. Chem. Soc.*, p. 1225.
ALBERT (1951). *The Acridines*, London: Arnold.
ALBERT (1952). *Quart. Revs.*, **6**, 197.
ALBERT (1953). *Biochem. J.*, **54**, 646.
ALBERT (1954). *Fortschritte Chem. Org. Natur.*, **11**, 350.
ALBERT (1955). (a) *Naturally occurring nitrogen heterocyclic compounds*, Special
    Publication No. 3 of the Chemical Society (London), p. 124; (b) *J. Chem.
    Soc.*, p. 2690; (c) *Chem. & Ind.*, p. 202.
ALBERT (1956). *Nature*, **178**, 1072.
ALBERT (1957). *Biochem. J.*, **65**, 124.
ALBERT (1958). *Chem. & Ind.*, p. 582.
ALBERT and BARLIN (1958). *Heterocyclic Chemistry*, London: Butterworth.
    (see also *J. Chem. Soc.*, 1958.
ALBERT and BROWN (1954). *J. Chem. Soc.*, p. 2060.
ALBERT, BROWN and CHEESEMAN (1951). *J. Chem. Soc.*, p. 474.
ALBERT, BROWN and CHEESEMAN (1952). *J. Chem. Soc.*, pp. 1620, 4219.
ALBERT, BROWN and DUEWELL (1948). *J. Chem. Soc.*, 1284.
ALBERT, BROWN and WOOD (1954). *J. Chem. Soc.*, p. 3832.
ALBERT, BROWN and WOOD (1956). *J. Chem. Soc.*, p. 2066.
ALBERT and DUEWELL (1947). *J. Soc. Chem. Ind.*, **66**, 11.
ALBERT and GLEDHILL (1945). *J. Soc. Chem. Ind.*, **64**, 169.
ALBERT and GOLDACRE (1946). *J. Chem. Soc.*, p. 706.
ALBERT, GOLDACRE and HEYMANN (1943), *J. Chem. Soc.*, p. 651.
ALBERT, GOLDACRE and PHILLIPS (1948). *J. Chem. Soc.*, p. 2240.
ALBERT and HAMPTON (1952). *J. Chem. Soc.*, p. 4985.
ALBERT and HAMPTON (1954). *J. Chem. Soc.*, p. 505.
ALBERT, LISTER and PEDERSEN (1957). *J. Chem. Soc.*, p. 4612.
ALBERT and PEDERSEN (1956). *J. Chem. Soc.*, p. 4683.
ALBERT and PHILLIPS (1956). *J. Chem. Soc.*, p. 1294.

ALBERT and RITCHIE (1943). *J. Chem. Soc.*, p. 458.
ALBERT and ROYER (1949). *J. Chem. Soc.*, p. 1148.
ALBERT and SHORT (1945). *J. Chem. Soc.*, p. 760.
ALBERT and WILLIS (1946). *J. Soc. Chem. Ind.*, **65**, 26.
ALDER and STEIN (1932). *Annalen*, **496**, 204.
ALFORD and SCHOFIELD (1953). *J. Chem. Soc.*, p. 1811.
ALLEN (1950). *Chem. Revs.*, **47**, 275.
ALLEN, GILBERT and YOUNG (1937). *J. Org. Chem.*, **2**, 227.
ALLEN, PASTERNAK and SEAMAN (1952). *J. Amer. Chem. Soc.*, **74**, 3264.
ALLEN and THIRTLE (1946). *Org. Synth.*, **26**, 16.
ALLEN and WILSON (1943). *J. Amer. Chem. Soc.*, **65**, 611.
ALLEN and WILSON (1947). *Org. Synth.*, **27**, 33.
AMERICAN CYANAMID CO. (1948). Brit. Pat. 598,175 (per *Chem. Abs.*, 1949, **43**, 698).
AMERICAN CYANAMID CO. (1950). U.S. Pat., 2,524,431 (per *Chem. Abs.*, 1951, **45**, 2513, cf. *ibid.*, 1950, **44**, 1537).
AMSTUTZ (1944). *J. Org. Chem.*, **9**, 310.
AMSTUTZ (1952). *J. Org. Chem.*, **17**, 1508.
ANDERSON (1933). *J. Amer. Chem. Soc.*, **55**, 2094.
ANDERSON and SEEGAR (1949). *J. Amer. Chem. Soc.*, **71**, 340.
ANDREWS, ANAND, TODD and TOPHAM (1949). *J. Chem. Soc.*, p. 2490.
ANGYAL (1952). *Aust. J. Sci. Res.* (1952), **A**, **5**, 374.
ANGYAL and ANGYAL (1952). *J. Chem. Soc.*, p. 1461.
ANGYAL, BARLIN and WAILES (1953). *J. Chem. Soc.*, p. 1740.
ANGYAL and WERNER (1952). *J. Chem. Soc.*, p. 2911.
APPLEBY, SARTOR, LEE and KAPRANOS (1948). *J. Amer. Chem. Soc.*, **70**, 1552.
ARCHER and PRATT (1944). *J. Amer. Chem. Soc.*, **66**, 1656.
ARCUS and COOMBS (1954). *J. Chem. Soc.*, p. 4319.
ARCUS and EVANS (1958). *J. Chem. Soc.*, p. 789.
ARCUS and MESLEY (1953). *J. Chem. Soc.*, p. 178.
ARMIT and ROBINSON (1925). *J. Chem. Soc.*, **127**, 1604.
ARNDT (1940). *Org. Synth.*, **20**, 26.
ARNDT (1953). *Organic Analysis*, **1**, 197 (New York: Interscience).
ARNDT (1956). *Berichte*, **89**, 730.
ARNDT and BEKIR (1930). *Berichte*, **63**, 2393.
ARNDT, LOEWE, ÜN and AYÇA (1951). *Berichte*, **84**, 319.
ARNDT, MARTIN and PARTINGTON (1935). *J. Chem. Soc.*, p. 602.
ARNDT and PUSCH (1925). *Berichte*, **58**, 1644.
ARONOFF (1950). *Chem. Revs.*, **47**, 175.
ASTWOOD, GREER and ETTLINGER (1949). *J. Biol. Chem.*, **181**, 121.
ATKINSON, BROWN and SIMPSON (1956). *J. Chem. Soc.*, p. 1081.
ATKINSON and TAYLOR (1955). *J. Chem. Soc.*, p. 4236.
v. AUWERS (1915). *Annalen*, **408**, 270.
v. AUWERS (1923). *Berichte*, **56**, 1672.

BACHMAN and COOPER (1944). *J. Org. Chem.*, **9**, 302.
BACHMAN and SCHISLA (1957). *J. Org. Chem.*, **22**, 858.

BACKEBERG and MARAIS (1942). *J. Chem. Soc.*, p. 381.

BADDILEY, LYTHGOE and TODD (1943). *J. Chem. Soc.*, p. 386.

BADDILEY and TOPHAM (1944). *J. Chem. Soc.*, p. 678.

BADGER (1954). *Structures and Reactions of Aromatic Compounds*, Cambridge.

BADGER and CHRISTIE (1956). *J. Chem. Soc.*, p. 3438.

BADGER, PEARCE and PETTIT (1951). *J. Chem. Soc.*, pp. 3199, 3204.

BADGER and WALKER (1956). *J. Chem. Soc.*, p. 123.

BAK and CHRISTENSEN (1954). *Acta Chem. Scand.*, **8**, 390.

BAKER and BRICKMAN (1945). *J. Amer. Chem. Soc.*, **67**, 1223.

BAKER, JOSEPH and SCHAUB (1954). *J. Org. Chem.*, **19**, 631.

BAKER, LAPPIN and RIEGEL (1946). *J. Amer. Chem. Soc.*, **68**, 1284.

BAKER and OLLIS (1957). *Quart. Revs.*, **11**, 15.

BALLARD and MELSTROM (1950). In Elderfield's *Heterocyclic Compounds*, Vol. 1, New York: Wiley.

BALTAZZI (1955). *Quart. Revs.*, **9**, 150.

BALTZLY, HARFENIST and WEBB (1946). *J. Amer. Chem. Soc.*, **68**, 2673.

BAMBAS (1952). *Five-membered Heterocyclic Compounds with Nitrogen and Sulphur, or Nitrogen, Sulphur and Oxygen (except Thiazole)*, New York: Interscience.

BAMBERGER (1891). *Berichte*, **24**, 1758.

BANKS (1944). *J. Amer. Chem. Soc.*, **66**, 1127.

BARKENBUS and LANDIS (1948). *J. Amer. Chem. Soc.*, **70**, 684.

BARLOW and WELCH (1956). *J. Amer. Chem. Soc.*, **78**, 1258.

BARNES (1957). In Elderfield's *Heterocyclic Compounds*, Vol. 5, New York: Wiley.

BARRETT (1949). In Thorpe's *Dictionary of Applied Chemistry*, under 'Phthalic Acid', London: Longmans.

BAUMGARTEN and ANDERSON (1958). *J. Amer. Chem. Soc.*, **80**, 1981.

BAUMGARTEN and KRIEGER (1955). *J. Amer. Chem. Soc.*, **77**, 2438.

BAUMGARTEN and SU (1952). *J. Amer. Chem. Soc.*, **74**, 3828.

BEAMAN (1954). *J. Amer. Chem. Soc.*, **76**, 5633.

BEER, CLARKE, KHORANA and ROBERTSON (1948), *J. Chem. Soc.*, pp. 1605, 2223.

BEHREND (1887). *Annalen*, **240**, 11.

BEINERT (1956). *J. Amer. Chem. Soc.*, **78**, 5323.

BENDICH (1955). In *The Nucleic Acids*, Vol. I, New York: Academic Press.

BENDICH (1957). In *Chemistry and Biology of Purines*, a Ciba Symposium, London: Churchill.

BENDICH, RUSSELL and FOX (1954). *J. Amer. Chem. Soc.*, **76**, 6073.

BENNETT and HAFEZ (1941). *J. Chem. Soc.*, p. 287.

BENSON (1947). *Chem. Revs.*, **41**, 1.

BENSON and SAVELL (1950). *Chem. Revs.*, **46**, 1.

BENTLEY, CUNNINGHAM and SPRING (1951). *J. Chem. Soc.*, p. 2301.

BERGMANN (1953). *Chem. Revs.*, **53**, 309.

BERGMANN and BURKE (1956). *J. Org. Chem.*, **21**, 226.

BERGSTROM (1937). *J. Org. Chem.*, **2**, 411.

BERGSTROM and McALLISTER (1930). *J. Amer. Chem. Soc.*, **52**, 2845.

BERGSTROM and OGG (1931). *J. Amer. Chem. Soc.*, **53**, 245.

BERNASCONI (1932). *Helv. Chim. Acta*, **15**, 287.

BERNSTEIN, STEARNS, DEXTER and LOTT (1947). *J. Amer. Chem. Soc.*, **69**, 1147.

BERSON (1953). *J. Amer. Chem. Soc.*, **75**, 3521.

BERSON and SWIDLER (1954). *J. Amer. Chem. Soc.*, **76**, 2835.

BEYERMAN, BERBEN and BONTEKOE (1954). *Rec. Trav. Chim. Pays-Bas*, **73**, 325.

BIDDISCOMBE, COULSON, HANDLEY and HERINGTON (1954). *J. Chem. Soc.*, p. 1957.

BINZ and MAIER-BODE (1936). *Angew. Chem.*, **49**, 486.

BIRCH and McALLEN (1950). *Nature*, **165**, 899.

BIRKINSHAW and CHAPLEN (1955). *Biochem. J.*, **60**, 255.

BIRKOVER and KAISER (1957). *Berichte*, **90**, 2933.

BISAGNI, BUU-HOÏ and ROYER (1955). *J. Chem. Soc.*, p. 3688.

BLICKE (1950). In Elderfield's *Heterocyclic Compounds*, Vol. 1, New York: Wiley.

BLICKE and BURCKHALTER (1942). *J. Amer. Chem. Soc.*, **64**, 477.

BLICKE and DOORENBAS. *J. Amer. Chem. Soc.*, 1954, **76**, 2317.

BLICKE and LEONARD (1946). *J. Amer. Chem. Soc.*, **68**, 1934 (cf. *Org. Syntheses*, 1949, **29**, 31).

BOARLAND and McOMIE (1951). *J. Chem. Soc.*, p. 1218.

BOARLAND, McOMIE and TIMMS (1952). *J. Chem. Soc.*, p. 4691.

BOBRANSKI, KOCHANSKA and KOWALEWSKA (1938). *Berichte*, **71**, 2385.

BOEKELHEIDE and FEELY (1957). *J. Org. Chem.*, **22**, 589.

BOEKELHEIDE and GALL (1954). *J. Amer. Chem. Soc.*, **76**, 1832.

BOGERT and McCOLM (1927). *J. Amer. Chem. Soc.*, **49**, 2651.

BOHLMANN (1952). *Berichte*, **85**, 390.

BOHLMANN and RAHTZ (1957). *Berichte*, **90**, 2265.

BÖHME and WAGNER (1942). *Berichte*, **75**, 606.

BOLTON (1954). *Trans. Farad. Soc.*, **50**, 1265.

BOON, CARRINGTON, GREENHALGH and VASEY (1954). *J. Chem. Soc.*, p. 3263.

BOON and JONES (1951). *J. Chem. Soc.*, p. 591.

BOON, JONES and RAMAGE (1951). *J. Chem. Soc.*, p. 96.

BORDNER (1952). U.S. Pat. 2,600,289 (per *Chem. Abs.*, 1953, **47**, 4373).

BORROWS and HOLLAND (1947). *J. Chem. Soc.*, p. 672.

BORROWS and HOLLAND (1948). *Chem. Revs.*, **42**, 611.

BORSCHE and GROTH (1941). *Annalen*, **549**, 238.

BORSCHE and HERBERT (1941). *Annalen*, **546**, 293.

BOTHNER-BY and TRAVERSO (1957). *Berichte*, **90**, 453.

BOWDEN and GREEN (1954). *J. Chem. Soc.*, p. 1795.

BOYD and ROBSON (1935). *Biochem. J.*, **29**, pp. 542, 555, 2256.

BRADFORD, ELLIOTT and ROWE (1947). *J. Chem. Soc.*, p. 437.

BRADLOW and VANDERWERF (1949). *J. Org. Chem.*, **14**, 509.

BRADY and CROPPER (1950). *J. Chem. Soc.*, p. 507.

BRANCH (1916). *J. Amer. Chem. Soc.*, **38**, 2466.

BRANCH and CALVIN (1941). *The Theory of Organic Chemistry*, New York: Prentice-Hall.

BRANDENBERGER and BRANDENBERGER (1954). *Helv. Chim. Acta*, **37**, 2207.

BRAUDE (1945). *Annual Rpts.*, *Chem. Soc.*, **42**, 105.

BRAUDE (1955). In Braude and Nachod's *Determination of Organic Structures by Physical Methods*, New York: Academic Press.

V. BRAUN and GRUBER (1922). *Berichte*, **55**, 1710.

BRAUNHOLTZ and MANN (1957). *J. Chem. Soc.*, p. 4166.

BREDERECK and GOMPPER (1954). *Berichte*, **87**, 700.

BREDERECK, GOMPPER, BANGERT and HERLINGER (1958). *Angew. Chem.*, **70**, 269.

BREDERECK, V. SCHUH and MARTINI (1950). *Berichte*, **83**, 201.

BREDERECK, ULMER and WALDMANN (1956). *Berichte*, **89**, 12.

BREMER (1937). *Annalen*, **529**, 290.

BREYER, BUCHANAN and DUEWELL (1944). *J. Chem. Soc.*, p. 360.

BRINER, MILLER, LIVERIS and LUTZ (1954). *J. Chem. Soc.*, p. 1265.

BROOK and RAMAGE (1955). *J. Chem. Soc.*, p. 896.

BROOK and RAMAGE (1957). *J. Chem. Soc.*, p. 1.

BROOKER, WHITE, KEYS, SMYTH and OESPER (1941). *J. Amer. Chem. Soc.*, **63**, 3192.

BROOKER, WHITE, SPRAGUE, DENT and VAN ZANT (1947). *Chem. Revs.*, **41**, 325.

BROOKES, FULLER and WALKER (1957). *J. Chem. Soc.*, p. 689.

BROWER and AMSTUTZ (1954). *J. Org. Chem.*, **19**, 411.

BROWER, WAY, SAMUELS and AMSTUTZ (1953). *J. Org. Chem.*, **18**, 1648; (1954), **19**, 1830.

BROWN, D. J. (1950). *J. Soc. Chem. Ind.*, **69**, 353; *Nature*, **165**, 1010.

BROWN, D. J. (1952). (a) *J. Appl. Chem.*, **2**, 202; (b) *ibid.*, p. 239.

BROWN, D. J. (1953). *Revs. of Pure and Appl. Chem.* (Australia), **3**, 115.

BROWN, D. J. (1955). *J. Appl. Chem.*, **5**, 358.

BROWN, D. J. (1956). *J. Chem. Soc.*, p. 2312.

BROWN, D. J., HOERGER and MASON (1955). (a) *J. Chem. Soc.*, p. 211 (cf. Brown and Short, *ibid.* (1953), p. 331); (b) *ibid.* (1955), p. 4035.

BROWN, D. J. and MASON (1956). *J. Chem. Soc.*, p. 3443.

BROWN, D. J. and MASON (1957). *J. Chem. Soc.*, p. 682.

BROWN, D. N. and TODD (1955). In Chargaff and Davidson's *The Nucleic Acids*, New York: Academic Press.

BROWN, E. G., GOODWIN and JONES (1956). *Biochem. J.*, **64**, 37 P.

BROWN, H. C. and ADAMS (1942). *J. Amer. Chem. Soc.*, **64**, 2557.

BROWN, H. C., BREWSTER and SHECHTER (1954). *J. Amer. Chem. Soc.*, **76**, 467.

BROWN, H. C. and GERSTEIN (1950). *J. Amer. Chem. Soc.*, **72**, 2926.

BROWN, H. C. and KANNER (1953). *J. Amer. Chem. Soc.*, **75**, 3865.

BROWN, H. C., McDANIEL and HÄFLIGER (1955). In Braude and Nachod's *Determination of Organic Structures by Physical Methods*, New York: Academic Press.

BROWN, R. D. (1952), *Quart. Revs.*, **6**, 65.

BROWN, R. D. (1956). *J. Chem. Soc.*, p. 272.

BROWN, R. D., DUFFIN, MAYNARD and RIDD (1953). *J. Chem. Soc.*, p. 3937.

BROWN, R. D. and HEFFERNAN (1956). *Austral. J. Chem.*, **9**, 83.

BROWNING (1953). *Toxicity of Industrial Organic Solvents*, London: H.M. Stationery Office.

BRUNINGS and CORWIN (1942). *J. Amer. Chem. Soc.*, **64**, 593.
BUCHMAN, REIMS and SARGENT (1941). *J. Org. Chem.*, **6**, 764.
BUNNETT and ZAHLER (1951). *Chem. Revs.*, **49**, 271.
BURKE (1949). *J. Amer. Chem. Soc.*, **71**, 609.
BURTON and KAPLAN (1954). *J. Biol. Chem.*, **211**, 447.
BUSH (1937). *J. Pharmacol.*, **61**, 134.
BUTLER (1955). *J. Amer. Pharm. Assoc.*, **44**, 367.
BUU-HOÏ (1951). *J. Amer. Chem. Soc.*, **73**, 98.
BUU-HOÏ and HOAN (1951). *J. Chem. Soc.*, p. 1834.
BUU-HOÏ and LECOCQ (1946). *Comptes rendus*, **222**, 1441.

CALDIN and LONG (1955). *Proc. Roy. Soc.*, A., **288**, 263.
CALDWELL and KORNFELD (1942). *J. Amer. Chem. Soc.*, **64**, 1695.
CALDWELL, TYSON and LAUER (1944). *J. Amer. Chem. Soc.*, **66**, 1481.
CALDWELL and WALLS (1952). *J. Chem. Soc.*, p. 2156.
CAMPAIGNE and LE SUER (1948). *J. Amer. Chem. Soc.*, **70**, 415.
CAMPAIGNE and MONROE (1954). *J. Amer. Chem. Soc.*, **76**, 2447.
CAMPBELL and SCHAFFNER (1945). *J. Amer. Chem. Soc.*, **67**, 86.
CANTONI (1952). *J. Amer. Chem. Soc.*, **74**, 2942.
CARONNA (1941). *Gazz. Chim. Ital.*, **71**, 475.
CARRINGTON, CURD and RICHARDSON (1955). *J. Chem. Soc.*, p. 1858.
CARTER (1946). *Organic Reactions*, **3**, 198.
CARVALHO (1935). *Ann. Chim.*, **4**, 486.
CASIMIR and LYONS (1950). *J. Chem. Soc.*, p. 783.
CAVA, WILSON and WILLIAMS (1955). *Chem. & Ind.*, p. 17.
CAVA, WILSON and WILLIAMS (1956). *J. Amer. Chem. Soc.*, **78**, 2303.
CAVAGNOL and WISELOGLE (1947). *J. Amer. Chem. Soc.*, **69**, 795.
CAVALIERI (1947). *Chem. Revs.*, **41**, 525.
CAVALIERI and LOWY (1952). *Arch. Biochem. Biophys.*, **35**, 83.
CAVALLITO and HASKELL (1945). *J. Amer. Chem. Soc.*, **67**, 1991.
CERNIANI and PASSERINI (1954). *J. Chem. Soc.*, p. 2261.
CHAKRAVATI (1935). *J. Indian Chem. Soc.*, **12**, 536.
CHALVET and SANDORFY (1949). *Comptes rendus*, **228**, 566.
CHAPMAN and REES (1954). *J. Chem. Soc.*, p. 1190.
CHAPMAN and RUSSELL-HILL (1956). *J. Chem. Soc.*, p. 1563.
CHARPENTIER (1947). *Comptes rendus*, **225**, 306.
CHEESEMAN (1952). *J. Chem. Soc.*, p. 1804.
CHUTE and WRIGHT (1945). *J. Org. Chem.*, **10**, 541.
CLARK (1948). *Topics in Physical Chemistry*, Baltimore: Williams and Wilkins.
CLARK and GEISSMAN (1948). *Third Conference on Biological Antioxidants*, New York, Josiah Macy Foundation, p. 92.
CLAUSON-KAAS and NIELSEN (1955). *Acta Chem. Scand.*, **9**, 475.
CLEMO (1955). *J. Chem. Soc.*, p. 2058.
CLEMO and DRIVER (1945). *J. Chem. Soc.*, p. 829.
CLEMO and MCILWAIN (1934). *J. Chem. Soc.*, p. 1991.
CLEMO and MCILWAIN (1936). *J. Chem. Soc.*, p. 1698.
CLEMO and SWAN (1945). *J. Chem. Soc.*, p. 867.

CLEVELAND (1955). In Braude and Nachod's *Determination of Organic Structures by Physical Methods*, New York: Academic Press.

COFFEY (1949). In Thorpe's *Dictionary of Applied Chemistry*, under 'Oxazin Dyestuffs', London: Longmans.

COFFEY (1950). In Thorpe's *Dictionary of Applied Chemistry*, under 'Pyronine Dyes', London: Longmans.

COFFEY, THOMSON and WILSON (1936). *J. Chem. Soc.* p. 856.

COLONNA (1943). *Pubbl. Ist. Chim. ind. Univ. Bologna*, No. 2, 3 (per *Chem. Abs.*, 1947, **41**, 754).

COLONNA and MONTANARI (1951). *Gazz. Chim. Ital.*, **81**, 744 (per *Chem. Abs.*, 1952, **46**, 7093).

CONANT and CHOW (1933). *J. Amer. Chem. Soc.*, **55**, 3475.

COOK, DOWNER and HEILBRON (1948). *J. Chem. Soc.*, p. 2028.

COOK and HEILBRON (1949). In Clarke, Johnson and Robinson's *The Chemistry of Penicillin*, Princeton: University Press.

COOK and HEILBRON (1950). *Rec. Trav. Chim. Pays-Bas*, **69**, 351.

COOK, HEILBRON and LEVY (1947). *J. Chem. Soc.*, pp. 1954, 1598.

COOK, HEILBRON and LEVY (1948). *J. Chem. Soc.*, p. 201.

COOK, HEILBRON and SMITH (1949). *J. Chem. Soc.*, p. 1440.

COOKSON (1953). *J. Chem. Soc.*, p. 2789.

COOKSON and RIMINGTON (1953). *Nature*, **171**, 875.

COONRADT and HARTOUGH (1948). *J. Amer. Chem. Soc.*, **70**, 1158.

CORNFORTH (1957). In Elderfield's *Heterocyclic Compounds*, Vol. 5, New York: Wiley.

CORNFORTH and COOKSON (1952). *J. Chem. Soc.*, p. 1085.

CORNFORTH and CORNFORTH (1947). *J. Chem. Soc.*, p. 96.

CORNFORTH and CORNFORTH (1949). *J. Chem. Soc.*, p. 1028.

CORNFORTH and HUANG (1948). *J. Chem. Soc.*, p. 1960.

CORNFORTH and ROBINSON (1942). *J. Chem. Soc.*, p. 680.

CORNUBERT and ROBINET (1933). *Bull. Soc. Chim. France*, **53**, 565.

CORWIN (1943). In Gilman's *Organic Chemistry*, 2nd edn., New York: Wiley.

CORWIN (1950). In Elderfield's *Heterocyclic Compounds*, Vol. 1, New York: Wiley.

CORWIN and ANDREWS (1936). *J. Amer. Chem. Soc.*, **58**, 1086.

CORWIN and REYES (1956). *J. Amer. Chem. Soc.*, **78**, 2437.

CORWIN and VIOHL (1944). *J. Amer. Chem. Soc.*, **66**, 1143.

COSULICH, ROTH, SMITH, HULTQUIST and PARKER (1952). *J. Amer. Chem. Soc.*, **74**, 3252.

COULSON (1947). *Quart. Revs.*, **1**, 144.

COULSON and JONES (1946). *J. Soc. Chem. Ind.*, **65**, 169.

COULSON and LONGUET-HIGGINS (1947). *Proc. Roy. Soc.*, A, **191**, 39; **192**, 16.

COWLEY and PARTINGTON (1936). *J. Chem. Soc.*, p. 47.

CRAIG (1933). *J. Amer. Chem. Soc.*, **55**, 295.

CRAIG (1934). *J. Amer. Chem. Soc.*, **56**, 231.

CRAIG (1946). *J. Chem. Soc.*, p. 534.

CRAIG and SHORT (1945). *J. Chem. Soc.*, p. 419.

CRIEGEE and MÜLLER (1956). *Berichte*, **89**, 238.

CROMARTIE and HARLEY-MASON (1952). *J. Chem. Soc.*, p. 2525.

CROMWELL (1957). In Elderfield's *Heterocyclic Compounds*, Vol. 6, New York: Wiley.

CROOK (1948). *J. Amer. Chem. Soc.*, **70**, 416.

CULVENOR, DAVIES and HEATH (1949). *J. Chem. Soc.*, p. 278.

D'ALCONTRES and MOLLICA (1951). *Atti accad. Lincei*, **10**, 52 (per *Chem. Abs.*, 1952, **46**, 495).

DALY and CHRISTENSEN (1956). *J. Org. Chem.*, **21**, 177.

DAUDEL and PULLMAN, A. (1946). *J. Physique*, **7**, 59.

DAVIDSON, WEISS and JELLING (1937). *J. Org. Chem.*, **2**, 319.

DAVIES (1955). *Trans. Farad. Soc.*, **51**, 449; *J. Chem. Soc.*, p. 2412.

DAVIES, MAMALIS, PETROW and STURGEON (1951). *J. Pharm. Pharmacol.*, **3**, 420.

DAVIS and GEISSMAN (1954). *J. Amer. Chem. Soc.*, **76**, 3507.

DAVOLL (1953). *J. Chem. Soc.*, p. 3802.

DAVOLL and LOWY (1952). *J. Amer. Chem. Soc.*, **74**, 1563.

DAVOLL, LYTHGOE and TODD (1948). *J. Chem. Soc.*, p. 1685.

DEASY (1943). *Chem. Revs.*, **32**, 173.

DEDICHEN (1906). *Berichte*, **39**, 1831.

DEINET and LUTZ (1946). *J. Amer. Chem. Soc.*, **68**, 1325.

DE LA MARE, KIAMUDDIN and RIDD (1958). *Chem. & Ind.*, p. 361.

DELÉPINE and HOREAU (1938). *Bull. Soc. Chim. France*, **5**, 339.

DESAI, HUNTER and KHALIDI (1934). *J. Chem. Soc.*, p. 1186.

DEWAR (1949). *Electronic Theory of Organic Chemistry*, Oxford: The University Press.

DEWAR (1950). *J. Chem. Soc.*, p. 2329.

DEWAR and MAITLIS (1957). *J. Chem. Soc.*, pp. 944 and 2521.

DICK and WOOD (1955). *J. Chem. Soc.*, p. 1379.

DIELS and ALDER (1931). *Annalen*, **486**, 221; **490**, 267.

DIELS, ALDER and MÜLLER (1931). *Annalen*, **490**, 257.

DIELS and five others (1933). *Annalen*, **505**, 103.

DIXON (1946). U.S. Pat. 2,400,398 (per *Chem. Abs.*, 1946, **40**, 4748).

DIXON and WIGGINS (1950). *J. Chem. Soc.*, p. 3236.

DOAK and CORWIN (1949). *J. Amer. Chem. Soc.*, **71**, 159.

DOUGHERTY and HAMMOND (1935). *J. Amer. Chem. Soc.*, **57**, 117.

DOVEY and ROBINSON (1935). *J. Chem. Soc.*, p. 1389.

DRESEL and FALK (1953). *Nature*, **172**, 1185.

DREW and HATT (1937). *J. Chem. Soc.*, p. 16.

DRUEY (1958). *Angew. Chem.*, **70**, 5.

DUFRAISSE, ÉTIENNE and TOROMANOFF (1951). *Comptes rendus*, **232**, 2379.

DUFRAISSE, ÉTIENNE and TOROMANOFF (1952). *Comptes rendus*, **235**, 759.

DUNCAN (1956). In West's *Chemical Applications of Spectroscopy* (Vol. IX of Weissberger's *Technique of Organic Chemistry*), New York: Interscience.

DUNLOP (1956). Roy. Inst. Chem. Lectures No. 4.

DUNLOP and PETERS (1953). *The Furans*, New York: Reinhold.
DUNLOP, STOUT and SWADESH (1946). *Indust. Eng. Chem.*, **38**, 705.
DUNLOP and TUCKER (1939). *J. Chem. Soc.*, p. 1945.
DUNN and SMITH (1955). *Nature*, **175**, 336.
DUNNE and seven others (1950). *J. Chem. Soc.*, p. 1252.

EARL (1956). *Rec. Trav. Chim. Pays-Bas*, **75**, 346.
EARL, LEAKE and LE FÈVRE (1948). *J. Chem. Soc.*, p. 2269.
EARL and MACKNEY (1935). *J. Chem. Soc.*, p. 899.
EBERT (1926). *Z. physik. Chem.*, **121**, 385.
EDMAN (1953). *Acta Chem. Scand.*, **7**, 700.
EDSALL and BLANCHARD (1933). *J. Amer. Chem. Soc.*, **55**, 2337.
EFROS (1953). *J. Gen. Chem. U.S.S.R.*, **23**, 842 (per *Chem. Abs.*, 1954, **48**, 4524).
EICHENBERGER, STAEHLIN and DRUEY (1954). *Helv. Chim. Acta*, **37**, 837.
EISNER and LINSTEAD (1955). *J. Chem. Soc.*, p. 3749.
ELDERFIELD (ed.) (1950). *Heterocyclic Compounds*, New York: John Wiley and Sons.
ELDERFIELD (1951). In Elderfield's *Heterocyclic Compounds*, Vol. 2, New York: Wiley.
ELDERFIELD (1952). In Elderfield's *Heterocyclic Compounds*, Vol. 4, New York: Wiley.
ELDERFIELD (1957). In Elderfield's *Heterocyclic Compounds*, Vols. 5 and 6, New York: Wiley.
ELDERFIELD and DODD (1952). In Elderfield's *Heterocyclic Compounds*, Vol. 3, New York: Wiley.
ELDERFIELD, GENSLER and BIRSTEIN (1946). *J. Org. Chem.*, **11**, 812.
ELDERFIELD and HARRIS (1957). In Elderfield's *Heterocyclic Compounds*, Vol. 6, New York: Wiley.
ELDERFIELD and MEYER (1951). In Elderfield's *Heterocyclic Compounds*, Vol. 2, New York: Wiley.
ELDERFIELD and SHORT (1957). In Elderfield's *Heterocyclic Compounds*, Vol. 5, New York: Wiley.
ELDERFIELD, TODD and GERBER (1957). In Elderfield's *Heterocyclic Compounds*, Vol. 6, New York: Wiley.
ELDERFIELD, WILLIAMSON, GENSLER and KREMER (1947). *J. Org. Chem.*, **12**, 405.
ELDERFIELD and WYTHE (1957). In Elderfield's *Heterocyclic Compounds*, Vol. 6, New York: Wiley.
ELION (1954). In *Chemistry and Biology of Pteridines*, a Ciba Foundation Symposium, London: Churchill.
ELION (1956). In *Chemistry and Biology of Purines*, a Ciba Foundation Symposium, London: Churchill.
ELION, BURGI and HITCHINGS (1951). *J. Amer. Chem. Soc.*, **73**, 5235.
ELION, BURGI and HITCHINGS (1952). *J. Amer. Chem. Soc.*, **74**, 411.
ELION and HITCHINGS (1947). *J. Amer. Chem. Soc.*, **69**, 2138.
ELION and HITCHINGS (1956). *J. Amer. Chem. Soc.*, **78**, 3508.

v. Eller (1952). *Acta Cryst.*, **5**, 142.

Elliott (1949). *Biochem. J.*, **45**, 429.

Elvidge (1956). In *Recent Advances in the Chemistry of Colouring Matters*, Special Publication No. 4 of the Chem. Soc. (London).

Elvidge and Linstead (1952). *J. Chem. Soc.*, p. 5000.

Elvidge and Linstead (1954). *J. Chem. Soc.*, p. 442.

Erickson (1952). *J. Amer. Chem., Soc.* **74**, 4706.

Erickson and Spoerri (1946). *J. Amer. Chem. Soc.*, **68**, 400.

Erickson, Wiley, and Wystrach (1956). *The 1,2,3-and 1,2,4-triazines, tetra-zines and pentazines.* New York: Interscience.

Erlenmeyer and Kiefer (1945). *Helv. Chim. Acta*, **28**, 985.

Erlenmeyer and Leo (1933). *Helv. Chim. Acta*, **16**, 1381.

Erlenmeyer and Überwasser (1940). *Helv. Chim. Acta*, **23**, 328.

Erlenmeyer and Überwasser (1942). *Helv. Chim. Acta*, **25**, 515.

Erne (1949). *Helv. Chim. Acta*, **32**, 2205.

Étienne (1946). *Ann. de Chim.* (12), **1**, 5.

Étienne and Staehlin (1954). *Bull. Soc. Chim. France*, p. 743.

Evans (1891). *Z. physik. Chem.*, **7**, 337.

Evans and de Heer (1950). *Quart. Revs.*, **4**, 94.

Evans and Johnson (1930). *J. Amer. Chem. Soc.*, **52**, 4993.

Ewing and Steck (1946). *J. Amer. Chem. Soc.*, **68**, 2181.

Fagel and Ewing (1951). *J. Amer. Chem. Soc.*, **73**, 4360.

Falco and Hitchings (1956). *J. Amer. Chem. Soc.*, **78**, 3143.

Falco, Pappas and Hitchings (1956). *J. Amer. Chem. Soc.*, **78**, 1938.

Falk and Willis (1951). *Austral. J. Sci. Res.*, A, **4**, 579.

Fellion (1957). *Annales de Chimie* (13), **2**, 426.

Felsing and Biggs (1933). *J. Amer. Chem. Soc.*, **55**, 3624.

Felton (1955). In discussion to Albert (1955, a).

Felton, Osdene and Timmis (1954). *J. Chem. Soc.*, p. 298.

Ferguson (1955). *J. Amer. Chem. Soc.*, **77**, 5288.

Ferm and Riebsomer (1954). *Chem. Revs.*, **54**, 593.

Fieser and Fieser (1935). *J. Amer. Chem. Soc.*, **57**, 491.

Files and Challenger (1940). *J. Chem. Soc.*, p. 663.

Findlay (1954). *J. Amer. Chem. Soc.*, **76**, 2855.

Findlay (1956). *J. Org. Chem.*, **21**, 644.

Findlay and Dougherty (1946). *J. Amer. Chem. Soc.*, **68**, 1666.

Fischer (1899). *Berichte*, **32**, 498.

Fischer and Orth (1934–40) *Die Chemie des Pyrrols* (3 vols.), Leipzig: Akademische Verlagsgesellschaft.

Fodor, Kovács and Weisz (1954). *Nature*, **174**, 131.

Fonseka (1947). *J. Chem. Soc.*, p. 1683.

Ford and Mackay (1956). *J. Chem. Soc.*, p. 4985.

Forster (1947). *Z. Naturforsch.*, **2a**, 149.

Fowden (1956). *Biochem. J.*, **64**, 323.

Frank, Blegen, Dearborn, Myers and Woodward (1946). *J. Amer. Chem. Soc.*, **68**, 1368.

FREUDENBERG (1952). In Elderfield's *Heterocyclic Compounds*, Vol. 3, New York: Wiley.

FREUND and FLEISCHER (1915). *Annalen*, **409**, 188.

FREUNDLICH and KROEPELIN (1926). *Z. physik. Chem.*, **122**, 39.

FRIED (1950). In Elderfield's *Heterocyclic Compounds*, Vol. 1, New York: Wiley.

FRIED and ELDERFIELD (1941). *J. Org. Chem.*, **6**, 569.

FRIEDEL and ORCHIN (1951). *Ultraviolet Spectra of Aromatic Compounds*, New York: Wiley.

FRIEDEL, ORCHIN and REGGEL (1948). *J. Amer. Chem. Soc.*, **70**, 199.

FRIEDMAN and GOTS (1952). *Arch. Biochem. Biophys.*, **39**, 254.

FRIES, FABEL and ECKHARDT (1941). *Annalen*, **550**, 31.

FRIES, HEERING, HEMMECKE and SIEBERT (1937). *Annalen*, **527**, 83.

FRUTON (1950). In Elderfield's *Heterocyclic Compounds*, Vol. 1, New York: Wiley.

FRUTON and SIMMONDS (1953). *General Biochemistry*, New York: Wiley.

FUKUSHIMA (1951). In Elderfield's *Heterocyclic Compounds*, Vol. 2, New York: Wiley.

FUSON (1935). *Chem. Revs.*, **16**, 1.

GANAPATHI and VENKATARAMAN (1945). *Proc. Indian Acad. Sci.*, **22**A, 362.

GARDNER and KATRITZKY (1957). *J. Chem. Soc.*, p. 4375.

GARDNER and NAYLOR (1943). *Org. Synth.*, coll. vol. **2**, 526.

GEISSMAN and MEHLQUIST (1947). *Genetics*, **32**, 410.

GENSLER (1951). *Organic Reactions*, **6**, 191.

GENSLER (1952). In Elderfield's *Heterocyclic Compounds*, Vol. 4, New York: Wiley.

GERBER (1957). In Elderfield's *Heterocyclic Compounds*, Vol. 6, New York: Wiley.

GERNGROSS (1913). *Berichte*, **46**, 1913.

GERRARD, GREEN and NUTKINS (1952). *J. Chem. Soc.*, p. 4076.

GIBBS, JOHNSON and HUGHES (1930). *J. Amer. Chem. Soc.*, **52**, 4895.

GILMAN and BREUER (1934). *J. Amer. Chem. Soc.*, **56**, 1123.

GILMAN and MOORE (1957). *J. Amer. Chem. Soc.*, **79**, 3485.

GILMAN and SWAYAMPATI (1957). *J. Amer. Chem. Soc.*, **79**, 991.

GLEU and NITZSCHE (1939). *J. prakt. Chem.*, **153**, 200.

GLOVER and JONES (1956). *Chem. & Ind.*, p. 1456.

GOERDELER, OHM and TEGTMEYER (1956). *Berichte*, **89**, 1534.

GOGTE (1938). *Proc. Indian Acad. Sci.*, **7**A, 214.

GOLDACRE and PHILLIPS (1949). *J. Chem. Soc.*, p. 1724.

GOLDSCHMIDT and LLEWELLYN (1950). *Acta Cryst.*, **3**, 294.

GOLDSTEIN and VAYMATCHAR (1928). *Helv. Chim. Acta*, **11**, 245.

GOMPPER (1956). *Berichte*, **89**, 1748.

GOMPPER and HERLINGER (1956). *Berichte*, **89**, 2825.

GORDY (1956). In West's *Chemical Applications of Spectroscopy* (Vol. IX of Weissberger's *Technique of Organic Chemistry*), New York: Interscience.

GORE (1955). In Braude and Nachod's *Determination of Organic Structures by Physical Methods*, New York: Academic Press.

GOTTSCHALK (1955). *Biochem. J.*, **61**, 298.

GOULDEN (1952). *J. Chem. Soc.*, p. 2939.

GRAY (1955). *J. Amer. Chem. Soc.*, **77**, 5930.

GREEN and TONG (1956). *J. Amer. Chem. Soc.*, **78**, 4896.

GRESHAM, JANSEN and SHAVER (1948). *J. Amer. Chem. Soc.*, **70**, 998, 1004.

GRIMISON and RIDD (1956). *Chem. & Ind.*, p. 983.

GROB and ANKLI (1949). *Helv. Chim. Acta*, **32**, 2010, 2023.

GROB and UTZINGER (1954). *Helv. Chim. Acta*, **37**, 1256.

GRUNDMANN and KREUTZBERGER (1954). *J. Amer. Chem. Soc.*, **76**, 5646.

GRUNDMANN and SCHRÖDER (1954). *Berichte*, **87**, 747.

GRUNDMANN, SCHRÖDER and RUSKE (1954). *Berichte*, **87**, 1865.

GRUNDMANN and WEISSE (1951). *Berichte*, **84**, 684.

GUADIANO, QUILICO and RICCA (1956). *Atti acad. Lincei*, Classe Sci. fis, **21**, 253 (per *Chem. Abs.*, 1957, **51**, 10500).

GULLAND and HOLIDAY (1936). *J. Chem. Soc.*, p. 765.

HALCROW and KERMACK (1945). *J. Chem. Soc.*, p. 415.

HALCROW and KERMACK (1946). *J. Chem. Soc.*, p. 155.

HALE and VIBRANS (1918). *J. Amer. Chem. Soc.*, **40**, 1059.

HALL (1930). *J. Amer. Chem. Soc.*, **52**, 5123.

HALL and SPRINKLE (1932). *J. Amer. Chem. Soc.*, **54**, 3469.

HALVORSEN and HIRT (1951). *J. Chem. Phys.*, **19**, 711.

HAMER (1950). *Quart. Revs.*, **4**, 327.

HAMPTON (1957). *J. Amer. Chem. Soc.*, **79**, 503.

HANBY, HARTLEY, POWELL and RYDON (1947). *J. Chem. Soc.*, p. 519.

HANSCH (1947). *J. Amer. Chem. Soc.*, **69**, 2908.

HANSCH, SCOTT and KELLER (1950). *Indust. Eng. Chem.*, **42**, 2114.

HARLEY-MASON (1953). *J. Chem. Soc.*, p. 200.

HARLEY-MASON and JACKSON (1954). *J. Chem. Soc.*, p. 1158.

HART (1954). *J. Chem. Soc.*, p. 1879.

HARTOUGH (1952). *Thiophene and its Derivatives*, New York: Interscience.

HARTOUGH and CONLEY (1947). *J. Amer. Chem. Soc.*, **69**, 3096.

HARTOUGH and MEISEL (1954). *Compounds with Condensed Thiophene Rings*, New York: Interscience.

HARTSHORN and BAIRD (1946). *J. Amer. Chem. Soc.*, **68**, 1562.

HAUSCH and GODFREY (1951). *J. Amer. Chem. Soc.*, **73**, 3518.

HAUSER and REYNOLDS (1950). *J. Org. Chem.*, **15**, 1224.

HAWORTH and SYKES (1944). *J. Chem. Soc.*, p. 311.

HAYNES (1927). *Stain Technology*, **2**, 8.

HAZELWOOD, HUGHES and LIONS (1938). *J. Proc. Roy. Soc., N.S.W.*, **71**, 462.

HEARN, MORTON and SIMPSON (1951). (a) *J. Chem. Soc.*, p. 3329; (b) *ibid.*, p. 3318.

DE HEER (1954). *J. Amer. Chem. Soc.*, **76**, 4802.

HEILBRON (1949). *J. Chem. Soc.*, p. 2099.

HENBEST, JONES and WALLS (1950). *J. Chem. Soc.*, p. 3646.

HENRY and FINNEGAN (1954). *J. Amer. Chem. Soc.*, **76**, 290.

HERINGTON (1950). *Trans. Farad. Soc. (Discussions)*, p. 26.

DEN HERTOG and COMBE (1951). *Rec. Trav. Chim. Pays-Bas*, **70**, 581.

DEN HERTOG and OVERHOFF (1930). *Rec. Trav. Chim. Pays-Bas*, **49**, 552.

DEN HERTOG and OVERHOFF (1950). *Rec. Trav. Chim. Pays-Bas*, **69**, 468.

DEN HERTOG, SCHOGT, DE BRUYN and DE KLERK (1950). *Rec. Trav. Chim. Pays-Bas*, **69**, 673.

HEWITT (1950). *Oxidation-Reduction Potentials in Bacteriology and Biochemistry* (6th edn.), Edinburgh: Livingstone.

HEY, STIRLING and WILLIAMS (1955). *J. Chem. Soc.*, p. 3963.

HEY and WILLIAMS (1953). *Discuss. Farad. Soc.*, **14**, 216.

HIDY and ten others (1955). *J. Amer. Chem. Soc.*, **77**, 2345.

HIETALA and WAHLROOS (1956). *Acta Chem. Scand.*, **10**, 1197.

HILL (1936). *Chem. Revs.*, **19**, 27.

HODGKIN, JOHNSON and TODD (1955). In *Naturally occurring nitrogen heterocyclic compounds*, Special Publication No. 3 of the Chemical Society (London), p. 109.

HODGKIN, KAMPER, MACKAY, PICKWORTH, TRUEBLOOD and WHITE (1956). *Nature*, **178**, 64.

HODGSON and DAVIES (1939). *J. Chem. Soc.*, pp. 806, 1013.

HOEHN (1936). *Iowa State College J. Sci.*, **11**, 66.

HOFMANN (1953). *Imidazole and its Derivatives*, New York: Interscience.

HOGGARTH (1949). *J. Chem. Soc.*, p. 3311.

HOLDREN and HIXON (1946). *J. Amer. Chem. Soc.*, **68**, 1198.

HOLLEMAN (1941). *Org. Syntheses*, **1**, 552.

HOLLEY (1953). *Science*, **117**, 23.

HOLMES (1948). *Organic Reactions*, **4**, 60.

HOOVER and DAY (1956). *J. Amer. Chem. Soc.*, **78**, 5832.

HORNER (1939). *Annalen*, **540**, 73.

HORNING, HORNING and WALKER (1948). *J. Amer. Chem. Soc.*, **70**, 3935.

HOSHINO (1932). *Annalen*, **500**, 35.

HÜCKEL, DATOW and SIMMERSBACH (1940). *Z. physik. Chem.*, A. **186**, 129.

HÜCKEL and JAHNENTZ (1942). *Berichte*, **75**, 1438.

HÜCKEL and NABIH (1956). *Berichte*, **89**, 2115.

HUISGEN (1948). *Annalen*, **559**, 103.

HUISGEN (1957). *Angew. Chem.*, **69**, 341.

HUISGEN and UGI (1957). *Berichte*, **90**, 2914.

HULL (1951). *J. Chem. Soc.*, p. 2214.

HULL (1956). *J. Chem. Soc.*, p. 2033.

HUNTER (1945). *J. Chem. Soc.*, p. 213.

HUNTER and PARKEN (1935). *J. Chem. Soc.*, p. 1755.

HUNTER and PARTINGTON (1933). *J. Chem. Soc.*, p. 87.

HURD and KREUZ (1950). *J. Amer. Chem. Soc.*, **72**, 5543.

HURD and LUI (1935). *J. Amer. Chem. Soc.*, **57**, 2656.

HURD and PRIESTLEY (1947). *J. Amer. Chem. Soc.*, **69**, 859.

HURD and RUDNER (1951). *J. Amer. Chem. Soc.*, **73**, 5157.

HURD and SAUNDERS (1952). *J. Amer. Chem. Soc.*, **74**, 5324.

HURST (1956). *Pharmacol. Revs.*, **8**, 199.

HÜTTEL, BÜCHELE and JOCHUM (1955). *Berichte*, **88**, 1577.

Hüttel and Gebhardt (1947). *Annalen*, **558**, 34.
Hüttel, Wagner and Jochum (1955). *Annalen*, **593**, 179.

I. G. Farben (1934). Brit. Pat. 418,291 (per *Chem. Abs.*, 1935, **29**, 819).
Ikekawa, Sato and Maeda (1954). *Pharmaceutical Bulletin* (Japan), **2**, 205 (in English).
Ing (1952). In Elderfield's *Heterocyclic Compounds*, Vol. 3, New York: Wiley.
Ingold (1933). *J. Chem. Soc.*, p. 1127.
Ingold (1953). *Structure and Mechanism in Organic Chemistry*, London: Bell (p. 174).

Jacini (1940). *Gazz. Chim. Ital.*, **70**, 621.
Jackman and Packham (1955). *Chem. & Ind.*, p. 360.
Jacobs (1957). In Elderfield's *Heterocyclic Compounds*, Vols. 5 and 6, New York: Wiley.
Jacobs, Winstein, Henderson and Spaeth (1946). *J. Amer. Chem. Soc.*, **68**, 1310.
Jacobson (1952). *J. Path. Bact.*, **64**, 245.
Jaffé (1954). *J. Amer. Chem. Soc.*, **76**, 3527.
Jaffé (1955). *J. Chem. Phys.*, **23**, 1.
Jaffé and Doak (1955). *J. Amer. Chem. Soc.*, **77**, 4441.
Jansen and Wibaut (1937). *Rec. Trav. Chim.*, **56**, 699.
Jensen and Friediger (1943). *Kgl. Dansk. Vidensk. Selskab*, **20**, No. 20.
Jerchel, Fischer and Thomas (1956). *Berichte*, **89**, 2921.
Jerchel and Möhle (1944), *Berichte*, **77**, 591.
Johnson (1908). *Amer. Chem. J.*, **40**, 24.
Johnson (1946). *J. Chem. Soc.*, p. 895.
Johnson and Joyce (1915). *J. Amer. Chem. Soc.*, **37**, 2163.
Jones (1945). *J. Amer. Chem. Soc.*, **67**, 2127.
Jones (1948). *Nature*, **162**, 524.
Jones (1949). *J. Amer. Chem. Soc.*, **71**, 78.
Jones (1956). *Chem. & Ind.*, p. 1454.
Jones and Sandorfy (1956). In West's *Chemical Applications of Spectroscopy* (Vol. IX of Weissberger's *Technique of Organic Chemistry*), New York: Interscience.
Jones and Taylor (1950). *Quart. Revs.*, **4**, 195.
Julian, Meyer and Printy (1952). In Elderfield's *Heterocyclic Compounds*, Vol. 3, New York: Wiley.

Kahovec and Kohlrausch (1942). *Berichte*, **75**, 627.
Karmas and Spoerri (1957). *J. Amer. Chem. Soc.*, **79**, 680.
Karrer, Fritzsche, Ringier and Salomon (1938). *Helv. Chim. Acta*, **21**, 520.
Karrer and Seyhan (1950). *Helv. Chim. Acta*, **33**, 2209.
Katritzky (1955). *Chem. & Ind.*, p. 521.
Katritzky (1956). *Quart. Revs.*, **10**, 395.
Katritzky, Randall and Sutton (1957). *J. Chem. Soc.*, p. 1769.

KAYE and STONEHILL (1951). *J. Chem. Soc.*, pp. 27, 2638.

KEBRLE and HOFFMANN (1956). *Helv. Chim. Acta*, **39**, 116.

KEHRMANN and MERMOD (1927). *Helv. Chim. Acta*, **10**, 62.

KELLIE, O'SULLIVAN and SADLER (1956). *J. Chem. Soc.*, p. 3809.

KENDALL (1935). Brit. Pat. 424,559 (per *Chem. Abs.*, **29**, 4596).

KENDALL (1951). *Phot. J.*, **91B**, 124.

KENEFORD, MORLEY, SIMPSON and WRIGHT (1950). *J. Chem. Soc.*, p. 1104.

KENEFORD, SCHOFIELD and SIMPSON (1948). *J. Chem. Soc.*, p. 358.

KENNER, LYTHGOE, TODD and TOPHAM (1943). *J. Chem. Soc.*, p. 574.

KENNER, RODDA and TODD (1949). *J. Chem. Soc.*, p. 1613.

KENNER and TODD (1957). In Elderfield's *Heterocyclic Compounds*, Vol. 6, New York: Wiley.

KERMACK and MUIR (1931). *J. Chem. Soc.*, p. 3092.

KERMACK and TEBRICH (1945). *J. Chem. Soc.*, p. 375.

KERMACK and WEATHERHEAD (1940). *J. Chem. Soc.*, p. 1164.

KERMACK and WEBSTER (1942). *J. Chem. Soc.*, p. 213.

KHROMOV-BORISOV (1955). *Zhur. Obshchei Khim.*, **25**, 2520.

KING, HENSHALL and WHITEHEAD (1948). *J. Chem. Soc.*, p. 1373.

KING and NORD (1949). *J. Org. Chem.*, **14**, 405.

KIPRIYANOV and TOLMATSCHEV (1957). *J. Gen. Chem.* (U.S.S.R.), **27**, pp. 142, 486.

KIRK, JOHNSON and BLOMQUIST (1943). *J. Org. Chem.*, **8**, 557.

KLEIN and PRIJS (1954). *Helv. Chim. Acta*, **37**, 2057.

KLEINSPEHN (1955). *J. Amer. Chem. Soc.*, **77**, 1546.

KLEVENS and PLATT (1953). *Survey of Vacuum Ultraviolet Spectra*. Technical Report: U.S.A. Office of Naval Research.

KLINGSBERG and PAPA (1951). *J. Amer. Chem. Soc.*, **73**, 4988.

KLOETZEL (1948). *Org. Reactions*, **4**, 1.

KNAGGS and LONSDALE (1940). *Proc. Roy. Soc.*, A, **177**, 140.

KNIGHT, WALLICH and BALCH (1955). *J. Amer. Chem. Soc.*, **77**, 2577.

KNOWLES and WATT (1943). *J. Amer. Chem. Soc.*, **65**, 410.

KÖGL, VAN DER WANT and SALEMINK (1948). *Rec. Trav. Chim. Pays-Bas*, **67**, 29.

KOLLER (1927). *Berichte*, **60**, 1918.

KOLTHOFF (1925). *Biochem. Zeits.*, **162**, 289.

KÖNIGS, BUEREN and JUNG (1936). *Berichte*, **69**, 2690.

KÖNIGS, GERDES and SIROT (1928). *Berichte*, **61**, 1022.

KÖNIGS and GREINER (1931). *Berichte*, **64**, 1045.

KORTE (1952). *Berichte*, **85**, 1012.

KORTE and LÖHMER (1958). *Berichte*, **91**, 1397.

KREMER and ROCHEN (1957). In Elderfield's *Heterocyclic Compounds*, Vol. 6, New York: Wiley.

KREMS and SPOERRI (1947). *Chem. Revs.*, **40**, 279.

KUHN and JERCHEL (1941). *Berichte*, p. 941.

KUHN and JERCHEL (1943). *Berichte*, **76**, 413.

KÜHN and STEIN (1937). *Berichte*, **70**, 567.

KUMLER and HALVERSTADT (1941). *J. Amer. Chem. Soc.*, **63**, 2182.

Küng (1941). U.S. Pat. 2,356,459.

Landor and Rydon (1955). *J. Chem. Soc.*, p. 1113.
Langmuir (1919). *J. Amer. Chem. Soc.*, **41**, 1543.
Lankelma and Sharnoff (1931). *J. Amer. Chem. Soc.*, **53**, 2654.
Leach, Baxendale and Evans (1953). *Austral. J. Chem.*, **6**, 395.
Leese and Rydon (1955). *J. Chem. Soc.*, p. 303.
Le Fèvre (1934). *J. Chem. Soc.*, p. 450.
Le Fèvre (1948). *Dipole Moments*, London: Methuen.
Le Fèvre and Le Fèvre (1936). *J. Chem. Soc.*, p. 398.
Le Fèvre and Le Fèvre (1937). *J. Chem. Soc.*, p. 1088.
Leffler (1942). *Organic Reactions*, **1**, New York: Wiley, p. 91.
Lehmstedt (1931). *Berichte*, **64**, 2381.
Lehmstedt and Schrader (1937). *Berichte*, **70**, 838.
Lehmstedt and Wirth (1928). *Berichte*, **61**, 2044.
Leis and Curran (1945). *J. Amer. Chem. Soc.*, **67**, 79.
Lemberg (1955). *J. Proc. Roy. Soc., N.S.W.*, **88**, 114.
Lemberg and Falk (1951). *Biochem. J.*, **49**, 674.
Lemberg and Legge (1949). *Hematin Compounds and Bile Pigments*, New York: Interscience.
Lennard-Jones and Coulson (1939). *Trans. Farad. Soc.*, **35**, 811.
Leonard and Gash (1954). *J. Amer. Chem. Soc.*, **76**, 2781.
Leonard and Hauck (1957). *J. Amer. Chem. Soc.*, **79**, 5279.
Leonard and Locke (1955). *J. Amer. Chem. Soc.*, **77**, 437.
Letsinger and Lasco (1956). *J. Org. Chem.*, **21**, 812.
Levenberg and Buchanan (1956). *J. Amer. Chem. Soc.*, **78**, 504.
Levisalles (1957). *Bull. Soc. Chim. France*, p. 997.
Lewis (1945). *J. Amer. Chem. Soc.*, **67**, 770.
Lewis (1957). *J. Chem. Soc.*, p. 531.
Ley and Specker (1939). *Berichte*, **72**, 192 (cf. Ault, Hirst and Martin, *J. Chem. Soc.*, 1935, p. 653).
Lieber, Patinkin and Tao (1951). *J. Amer. Chem. Soc.*, **73**, 1792.
Link (1943). In Gilman's *Organic Chemistry*, Vol. 2, New York: Wiley, p. 1314.
Linsker and Evans (1946). *J. Amer. Chem. Soc.*, **68**, 403.
Linstead (1937). *Ann. Repts. Chem. Soc.*, **34**, 369.
Linstead and Lowe (1934). *J. Chem. Soc.*, p. 1022.
Linton (1940). *J. Amer. Chem. Soc.*, **62**, 1945.
Lisk and Stacy (1946). *J. Amer. Chem. Soc.*, **68**, 2686.
Lister and Ramage (1953). *J. Chem. Soc.*, p. 2234.
Lister, Ramage and Coates (1954). *J. Chem. Soc.*, p. 4109.
Löfgren and Lüning (1953). *Acta Chem. Scand.*, **7**, 15.
Longster and Walker (1953). *Trans. Farad. Soc.*, **49**, 228.
Longuet-Higgins (1949). *Trans. Farad. Soc.*, **45**, 173.
Longuet-Higgins and Coulson (1947). *Trans. Farad. Soc.*, **43**, 87.
Longuet-Higgins and Coulson (1949). *J. Chem. Soc.*, p. 971.
Lord and Miller (1942). *J. Chem. Phys.*, **10**, 328.

LUKEŠ and PRELOG (1926). *Bull. Internat. Acad. Sci. Bohême*, **35**, 1 (per *Chem. Zent.*, 1929, **1**, 523).

LUZ and FALLAB (1956). *Helv. Chim. Acta*, **39**, 1163.

LYTHGOE (1949). *Quart. Revs.*, **3**, 181.

LYTHGOE and RAYNER (1951). *J. Chem. Soc.*, p. 2323.

LYTHGOE, TODD and TOPHAM (1944). *J. Chem. Soc.*, p. 315.

McDANIEL and BROWN (1955). *J. Amer. Chem. Soc.*, **77**, 3756.

McELVAIN and BOLLIGER (1941). *Org. Synth.*, coll. vol. **1**, 473 (2nd edn.).

McELVAIN and GOESE (1943). *J. Amer. Chem. Soc.*, **65**, pp. 2227, 2233.

McEWEN (1946). *J. Amer. Chem. Soc.*, **68**, 711.

McFARLANE (1936). *Biochem. J.*, **30**, 1199.

McILWAIN (1937). *J. Chem. Soc.*, p. 1704.

MACKAY and HITCHINGS (1956). *J. Amer. Chem. Soc.*, **78**, 3511.

McOMIE and CHESTERFIELD (1956). *Chem. & Ind.*, p. 1453.

MAFFEI, PIETRA and CATTANEO (1953). *Gazz. Chim. Ital.*, **83**, 327 (per *Chem. Abs.*, 1954, **48**, 12123).

MAGGIOLO and PHILLIPS (1951). *J. Org. Chem.*, **16**, 336.

MAIER-BODE and ALTPETER (1934). *Das Pyridin*, Halle: W. Knapp.

MANN (1950). *The Heterocyclic Derivatives of Phosphorus, Arsenic, Antimony, Bismuth and Silicon*, New York: Interscience.

MANN (1958). In Cook's *Progress in Organic Chemistry*, **4**, London: Butterworth.

MANNICH (1942). *Berichte*, **75**, 1480.

MANSKE and HOLMES (1952). *The Alkaloids*, New York: Academic Press.

MANSKE and KULKA (1953). *Organic Reactions*, **7**, 59.

MARION (1952). In Manske and Holmes' *The Alkaloids*, New York: Academic Press.

MARSCHALK (1913). *J. Prakt. Chem.*, **88**, 227.

MARSHALL and WALKER (1951). *J. Chem. Soc.*, p. 1004.

MARTELL and CALVIN (1952). *Chemistry of the Chelate Compounds*, New York: Prentice-Hall.

MARTINET and COISSET (1921). *Comptes rendus*, **172**, 1234.

MARVEL and HIERS (1941). *Org. Syntheses*, Coll. Vol. **1**, 327.

MASON (1954). *J. Chem. Soc.*, p. 2071.

MASON (1955). In *Naturally occurring nitrogen heterocyclic compounds*, Special Publication No. 3 of the Chemical Society (London), p. 139.

MASON (1957). *J. Chem. Soc.*, pp. 4874, 5010.

MASON (1958). *J. Chem. Soc.*, p. 674.

MASSIE (1954). *Chem. Revs.*, **54**, 797.

MASUDA (1956). *Pharm. Bull.* (Japan), **4**, 375 (in English).

MATSEN (1956). In West's *Chemical Applications of Spectroscopy* (Vol. IX of Weissberger's *Technique of Organic Chemistry*) New York: Interscience.

MATTOO (1956). *Trans. Farad. Soc.*, **52**, 1184.

MAY and six others (1951). *J. Amer. Chem. Soc.*, **73**, 3067.

DE MAYO and RIGBY (1950). *Nature*, **166**, 1075.

MEDAWAR, ROBINSON and ROBINSON (1943). *Nature*, **151**, 195.

MENCZEL (1927). *Z. physik. Chem.*, **125**, 161.

METZGER and KOETHER (1953). *Bull. Soc. Chim. France*, **20**, 708.

METZLER and SNELL (1955). *J. Amer. Chem. Soc.*, **77**, 2431.

MEUNIER, MENTZER and VINET (1946). *Helv. Chim. Acta*, **29**, 1291.

MEYER-BODE (1936). *Berichte*, **69**, 1534.

MICHAELIS (1940). *Ann. N.Y. Acad. Science*, **40**, Art. 2, p. 39.

MICHELS and AMSTUTZ (1950). *J. Amer. Chem. Soc.*, **72**, 888.

MIĆOVIĆ and MIHAILOVIĆ (1952). *Rec. Trav. Chim.*, **71**, 970.

MILLER, SKOOG, OKUMURA, VON SALTZA and STRONG (1955). *J. Amer. Chem. Soc.*, **77**, 2662.

MIRZA and ROBINSON (1950). *Nature*, **166**, 997.

MISANI and BOGERT (1945). *J. Org. Chem.*, **10**, 347.

MISSONI and SPOERRI (1951). *J. Amer. Chem. Soc.*, **73**, 1873.

MOEWUS (1950). *Angew. Chem.*, **62**, 496.

MONTGOMERY (1956). *J. Amer. Chem. Soc.*, **78**, 1928.

MOOKERJEE and GUPTA (1939). *Indian J. Physics*, **13**, 439.

MOORE and THOMSON (1955). *Science*, **122**, 594.

MORGAN and MITCHELL (1931). *J. Chem. Soc.*, 3283.

MORGAN and WALLS (1931). *J. Chem. Soc.*, p. 2447.

MORLEY (1951). *J. Chem. Soc.*, p. 1972.

MORLEY and SIMPSON (1948). *J. Chem. Soc.*, p. 360.

MORLEY and SIMPSON (1949). *J. Chem. Soc.*, p. 1354.

MORTON and ROGERS (1925). *J. Chem. Soc.*, **127**, 2699.

MORTON and STUBBS (1939). *J. Chem. Soc.*, p. 1321.

MORTON and STUBBS (1940). *J. Chem. Soc.*, p. 1347.

MOSHER (1950). In Elderfield's *Heterocyclic Compounds*, Vol. 1, New York: Wiley.

MOZINGO (1941). *Org. Syntheses*, **21**, 42.

MOZINGO and five others (1945). *J. Amer. Chem. Soc.*, **67**, 2092.

MUEHLMAN and DAY (1956). *J. Amer. Chem. Soc.*, **78**, 242.

MUMM and PETZOLD (1938). *Annalen*, **536**, 1.

MURPHY and PICARD (1954). *J. Org. Chem.*, **19**, 1807.

MURRAY and HAUSER (1954). *J. Org. Chem.*, **19**, 2008.

NEUBERGER and SCOTT (1952). *Proc. Roy. Soc.*, A, **213**, 307.

NEUBERGER and SCOTT (1953). *Nature*, **172**, 1093.

NEWBOLD, SPRING and SWEENY (1950). *J. Chem. Soc.*, p. 909.

NEWMAN and BADGER (1952). *J. Amer. Chem. Soc.*, **74**, 3545.

NEWTON and ABRAHAM (1953). *Biochem. J.*, **53**, 604.

NINEHAM (1955). *Chem. Revs.*, **55**, 355.

NORMANT (1949). *Comptes rendus*, **228**, 102.

NOYCE, RYDER and WALKER (1955). *J. Org. Chem.*, **20**, 1681.

OAKES, PASCOE and RYDON (1956). *J. Chem. Soc.*, p. 1045.

OCHIAI (1938). *J. Pharm. Soc. Japan*, **58**, 1040 (per *Chem. Abs.*, 1939, **33**, 3791).

OCHIAI (1939). *J. Pharm. Soc. Japan*, **59**, 20 (in German).

OCHIAI (1953). *J. Org. Chem.*, **18**, 534.

OCHIAI and HAYASHI (1947). *J. Pharm. Soc. Japan*, **67**, 34 (per *Chem. Abs.*, 1951, **45**, 9533).

OCHIAI, IKEHARA, KATO and IKEKAWA (1951). *J. Pharm. Soc. Japan*, **71**, 1385.

OCHIAI, ISHIDA, NOMURA, HAMANA and ISHII (1945). *J. Pharm. Soc. Japan*, **65**, 69 (per *Chem. Abs.*, 1951, **45**, 8018).

OCHIAI and NAGASAWA (1939). *Berichte*, **72**, 1470.

OCHIAI and NAGASAWA (1940). *J. Pharm. Soc. Japan*, **60**, pp. 43, 132 (per *Chem. Abs.*, 1940, **34**, 5082).

OCHIAI and YAMANAKA (1955). *Pharm. Bull.* (Japan), **3**, 173 (in German).

OCKENDEN and SCHOFIELD (1957). *J. Chem. Soc.*, p. 1375.

ODDO and ALBERTI (1933). *Gazz. Chim. Ital.*, **63**, 236.

ORGEL, COTTRELL, DICK and SUTTON (1951). *Trans. Farad. Soc.*, **47**, 113.

O'ROURKE, CLAPP and EDWARDS (1956). *J. Amer. Chem. Soc.*, **78**, 2159.

OSBORN, SCHOFIELD and SHORT (1956). *J. Chem. Soc.*, p. 4196.

OSDENE and TIMMIS (1955). (a) *J. Chem. Soc.*, p. 2027; (b) *ibid.*, p. 2032; (c) *ibid.*, p. 2036.

O'SULLIVAN and SADLER (1956). *J. Chem. Soc.*, p. 2202.

O'SULLIVAN and SADLER (1957). *J. Chem. Soc.*, p. 2916.

OTOMASU (1954). *Pharm. Bull.* (Japan), **2**, 283 (in English).

OTOMASU (1958). *Pharm. Bull.* (Japan), **6**, 77.

PANOUSE (1951). *Comptes rendus*, **233**, 260.

PANOUSE (1953). *Bull. Soc. Chim. France*, **20**, pp. 53, 60.

PARHAM (1951). In Elderfield's *Heterocyclic Compounds*, Vol. 2, New York: Wiley.

PARHAM and five others (1954). *J. Amer. Chem. Soc.*, **76**, 4957.

PARHAM, RODER and HASEK (1953). *J. Amer. Chem. Soc.*, **75**, 1647.

PARHAM, WYNBERG and RAMP (1953). *J. Amer. Chem. Soc.*, **75**, 2065.

PARKER and SHIVE (1947). *J. Amer. Chem. Soc.*, **69**, 63.

PARRY (1954). *Acta Cryst.*, **7**, 313.

PASSERINI (1954). *J. Chem. Soc.*, p. 2256.

PAUL (1933). *Bull. Soc. Chim. France*, **53**, 1489.

PAUL (1944). *Comptes rendus*, **218**, 122.

PAUL and TCHELITCHEFF (1947). *Comptes rendus*, **224**, 1722.

PAULING (1939). *Fortschr. Chem. Org. Naturstoffe*, **3**, 219.

PAULING (1940). *The Nature of the Chemical Bond*, Cornell University Press, Ithaca.

PAULING and SHERMAN (1933). *J. Chem. Phys.*, **1**, 606.

PAUSACKER and SCHUBERT (1950). *J. Chem. Soc.*, p. 1814.

PEARSON (1957). In Elderfield's *Heterocyclic Compounds*, Vol. 6, New York: Wiley.

PECHMANN (1895). *Berichte*, **28**, 1625.

PENFOLD (1953). *Acta Cryst.*, **6**, 591.

PERRINE and SARGENT (1949). *J. Org. Chem.*, **14**, 583.

PETFIELD and AMSTUTZ (1954). *J. Org. Chem.*, **19**, 1944.

PETROW and SAPER (1948). *J. Chem. Soc.*, p. 1389.

PHILLIPS (1958). *Current Trends in Heterocyclic Chemistry*, London: Butterworth.

PICTET and PATRY (1902). *Berichte*, **35**, 2534.

PLANT, ROGERS and WILLIAMS (1935). *J. Chem. Soc.*, p. 741.

PLANT and TOMLINSON (1931). *J. Chem. Soc.*, p. 3324.

PLANT and TOMLINSON (1933). *J. Chem. Soc.*, p. 955.

PLANT and WILLIAMS (1934). *J. Chem. Soc.*, p. 1142.

PLATT (1951). *J. Chem. Phys.*, **19**, 263.

PLAZEK (1936). *Roczniki Chem.*, **16**, 403 (per *Chem. Abs.*, 1937, **31**, 1808).

PLAZEK (1939). *Berichte*, **72**, 577.

PLAZEK and RODEWALD (1936). *Roczniki Chem.*, **16**, 502.

PLIENINGER (1955). *Berichte*, **88**, 370.

PLIENINGER and WERST (1958). *Angew. Chem.*, **70**, 272.

POHLAND, FLYNN, JONES and SHINE (1951). *J. Amer. Chem. Soc.*, **73**, 3247.

POLONOVSKI and PESSON (1948). *Bull. Soc. Chim. France*, **15**, 688.

POLONOVSKI and SCHMITT (1950). *Bull. Soc. Chim. France*, **17**, 616.

POTTS and SMITH (1957). *J. Chem. Soc.*, p. 4018.

PRATESI (1935). *Gazz. Chim. Ital.*, **65**, 43.

PRATT (1957). In Elderfield's *Heterocyclic Compounds*, Vol. 6, New York: Wiley.

PRELOG and BOZICEVIC (1939). *Berichte*, **72**, 1103.

PRELOG and GEYER (1945). *Helv. Chim. Acta*, **28**, 1677.

PRICE (1952). In Manske and Holmes' *The Alkaloids*, New York: Academic Press.

PRICE and ROBERTS (1946). *J. Amer. Chem. Soc.*, **68**, 1204.

PRICE and WALSH (1947). *Proc. Roy. Soc.*, A, **191**, 22.

PRIJS (1952). *Kartothek der Thiazolverbindungen*, Basel and New York: Karger.

PRIJS, OSTERTAG and ERLENMEYER (1947). *Helv. Chim. Acta*, **30**, 2110.

PRUCKNER (1941). *Z. physik. Chem.*, A, **190**, 101.

PRUCKNER and WITKOP (1943). *Annalen*, **554**, 127.

PULLMAN, A. (1947). *Ann. Chim.*, **2**, 5.

PULLMAN, A. and METZGER (1948). *Bull. Soc. Chim. France*, **15**, 1021.

PULLMAN, B. (1946). *Comptes rendus* **222**, 1396.

PULLMAN, B. (1948). *Bull. Soc. Chim. France*, **15**, 533.

PULLMAN, B. and PULLMAN, A. (1952). *Théories Electroniques de la Chimie Organique*, Paris: Masson & Cie.

PULLMAN, M., SAN PIETRO and COLOWICK (1954). *J. Biol. Chem.*, **206**, 129.

PURRMANN (1940). *Annalen*, **546**, 98.

QUILICO (1932). *Gazz. Chim. Ital.*, **62**, 822.

QUILICO, FUSCO and ROSNATI (1946). *Gazz. Chim. Ital.*, **76**, 87.

QUILICO and MUSANTE (1941). *Gazz. Chim. Ital.*, **71**, 327.

RADULESCU and OSTROGOVICH (1931), *Berichte*, **64**, 2233.

RAMPINO and NORD (1941). *J. Amer. Chem. Soc.*, **63**, 2745.

RANDALL, FOWLER, FUSON and DANGL (1949). *Infrared Determination of Organic Structures*, New York: Van Nostrand.

RASMUSSEN, HANSFORD and SACHANEN (1946). *Indust. Eng. Chem.*, **38**, 376.

RATNER and CLARKE (1937). *J. Amer. Chem. Soc.*, **59**, 200.

REED and NIU (1955). *J. Amer. Chem. Soc.*, **77**, 416.

REICHSTEIN and STAUDINGER (1950). *Angew. Chem.*, **62**, 292.

REID (1930). *Berichte*, **63**, 1920.

RENSHAW and CONN (1938). *J. Amer. Chem. Soc.*, **60**, 745.

REPPE (1941). D.R. Pat. 701,825 (per *Chem. Abs.*, 1941, **35**, 7976).

REYNOLDS (1957). *J. Amer. Chem. Soc.*, **79**, 4951.

RICE and LONDERGAN (1955). *J. Amer. Chem. Soc.*, **77**, 4678.

RICHTER and SMITH (1944). *J. Amer. Chem. Soc.*, **66**, 396.

RICHTER and TAYLOR (1955). *Angew. Chem.*, **67**, 303.

RIEDEL (1905). D.R. Pat. 174,941 (1905) (per *Friedländers Fortschritte*, **8**, 1238).

RIMINGTON (1955). *Endeavour*, **14**, 126.

RIMINGTON (1956). *Brit. Med. J.*, **ii**, 189.

RINKES (1932). *Rec. Trav. Chim.*, **51**, 1134.

RINKES (1934). *Rec. Trav. Chim. Pays-Bas*, **53**, 1167.

RINKES (1938). *Rec. Trav. Chim.*, **57**, 390.

RINKES (1943). *Org. Synth.*, coll. vol. **2**, 393.

RITCHIE (1945). *J. Proc. Roy. Soc., N.S.W.*, **78**, 134.

ROBERTSON (1932). *J. Chem. Soc.*, p. 1380.

ROBINS (1956). *J. Amer. Chem. Soc.*, **78**, 784.

ROBINS, DILLE, WILLITS and CHRISTENSEN (1953). *J. Amer. Chem. Soc.*, **75**, 263.

ROBINS, FURCHT, GRAUER and JONES (1956). *J. Amer. Chem. Soc.*, **78**, 2418.

ROBINS, JONES and LIN (1956). *J. Org. Chem.*, **21**, 695.

ROBINSON (1916). *J. Chem. Soc.*, **109**, 1038.

ROBINSON (1935). *Nature*, **135**, 732.

ROBINSON and ROBINSON (1924). *J. Chem. Soc.*, **125**, 827.

ROBINSON and ROBINSON (1938). *Biochem. J.*, **32**, 1661.

ROBISON and ROBISON (1955). *J. Amer. Chem. Soc.*, **77**, 457.

ROBLIN and CLAPP (1950). *J. Amer. Chem. Soc.*, **72**, 4890.

ROBLIN, LAMPEN, ENGLISH, COLE and VAUGHAN (1945). *J. Amer. Chem. Soc.*, **67**, 290.

RODDA (1956). *J. Chem. Soc.*, p. 3509.

ROSE (1954). *J. Chem. Soc.*, p. 4116.

ROSENBERG (1942). *The Vitamins*, New York: Interscience.

ROSENMUND, ZYMALKOWSKI and SCHWARTE (1954). *Berichte*, **87**, 1229.

ROSSITER and SAXTON (1953). *J. Chem. Soc.*, p. 3654.

ROYER (1949). *J. Chem. Soc.*, p. 1803.

RUBTSOV and ARENDARUK (1946). *J. Gen. Chem.*, U.S.S.R., **16**, 215 (per *Chem. Abs.*, 1947, **41**, 128).

RUGGLI and PREISWERK (1939). *Helv. Chim. Acta*, **22**, 484.

RUGGLI and SCHETTY (1940). *Helv. Chim. Acta*, **23**, 718.

RUGGLI and STAUB (1937). *Helv. Chim. Acta*, **20**, 919.

RUSSELL, ELION, FALCO and HITCHINGS (1949). *J. Amer. Chem. Soc.*, **71**, 2279.

RUSSELL and HITCHINGS (1951). *J. Amer. Chem. Soc.*, **73**, 3763.

RUSSELL, PURRMANN, SCHMITT and HITCHINGS (1949). *J. Amer. Chem. Soc.*, **71**, 3412.

SALEMINK and VAN DER WANT (1949). *Rec. Trav. Chim. Pays-Bas*, **68**, 1013.

SANDMEYER (1919). *Helv. Chim. Acta*, **2**, 234.

SANDORFY, VROELANT, YVAN, CHALVET and DAUDEL (1950). *Bull. Soc. Chim.* (5), **17**, 304.

SANÉ and JOSKI (1924). *J. Chem. Soc.*, **125**, 2481.

SCHENCK (1947). *Berichte*, **80**, 289.

SCHIPPER and DAY (1957). In Elderfield's *Heterocyclic Compounds*, Vol. 5, New York: Wiley.

SCHMID and KARRER (1946). *Helv. Chim. Acta*, **29**, 573.

SCHMID and KARRER (1949). *Helv. Chim. Acta*, **32**, 960.

SCHMIDT and DRUEY (1956). *Helv. Chim. Acta*, **39**, 986.

SCHNEIDER (1941). *Berichte*, **74**, 1252.

SCHNIEPP and GELLER (1946). *J. Amer. Chem. Soc.*, **68**, 1646.

SCHOFIELD (1950). *Quart. Revs.*, **4**, 382.

SCHOFIELD (1955). In discussion to Albert (1955, a).

SCHOFIELD and SIMPSON (1945). *J. Chem. Soc.*, p. 512.

SCHOFIELD and SWAIN (1949). *J. Chem. Soc.*, p. 1367.

SCHOFIELD, SWAIN and THEOBALD (1952). *J. Chem. Soc.*, p. 1924.

SCHOFIELD and THEOBALD (1949). *J. Chem. Soc.*, p. 2404.

SCHOMAKER and PAULING (1939). *J. Amer. Chem. Soc.*, **61**, 1769.

SCHÖNBERG and MOSTAFA (1943). *J. Chem. Soc.*, p. 654.

SCHÖPF, KOMZAK, BRAUN and JACOBI (1948). *Annalen*, **559**, 1.

SCHWARTZ (1945). *Org. Syntheses*, **25**, 35.

SCHWARZENBACH and LUTZ (1940). *Helv. Chim. Acta*, **23**, 1147.

SEARLES, TAMRES, BLOCK and QUARTERMAN (1956). *J. Amer. Chem. Soc.*, **78**, 4917.

SEELEY, YATES and NOLLER (1951). *J. Amer. Chem. Soc.*, **73**, 772.

SETHNA and SHAH (1945). *Chem. Revs.*, **36**, 1.

SHABICA, HOWE, ZEIGLER and TISHLER (1946). *J. Amer. Chem. Soc.*, **68**, 1156.

SHAW (1950). *J. Biol. Chem.*, **185**, 439.

SHEEHAN and COREY (1957). *Organic Reactions*, **9**, 388.

SHEMIN and RUSSELL (1953). *J. Amer. Chem. Soc.*, **75**, 4873.

SHEPARD, WINSLOW and JOHNSON (1930). *J. Amer. Chem. Soc.*, **52**, 2083.

SHORT (1952). *J. Chem. Soc.*, p. 4584.

SILVERSTEIN, RYSKIEWICZ, WILLARD and KOEHLER (1955). *J. Org. Chem.*, **20**, 668.

SIMPSON (1953). *Condensed Pyridazine and Pyrazine Rings, Cinnolines, Phthalazines and Quinoxalines*, New York: Interscience.

SIMPSON and WRIGHT (1948). *J. Chem. Soc.*, pp. 1707, 2003.

SKLAR (1942). *J. Chem. Phys.*, **10**, 135.

SKRAUP (1919). *Annalen*, **419**, 1.

SMITH (1930). *J. Amer. Chem. Soc.*, **52**, 397.

SMITH (1954). *Chem. & Ind.*, p. 1451.

SMITH (1955). *Electric Dipole Moments*, London: Butterworths.

SMITH and CHRISTENSEN (1955). *J. Org. Chem.*, **20**, 829.

SMITH and RUOFF (1940). *J. Amer. Chem. Soc.*, **62**, 145.

SNYDER and FREER (1946). *J. Amer. Chem. Soc.*, **68**, 1320.

SNYDER, HANDRICH, BROOKS, ALLEN, KIBLER and VAN ALLAN (1942). *Org. Syntheses*, **22**, 65.

SNYDER and PILGRIM (1948). *J. Amer. Chem. Soc.*, **70**, 3770.

SORKIN, ROTH and ERLENMEYER (1952). *Helv. Chim. Acta*, **35**, 1736.

SORM (1948). *Coll. Czech. Chem. Commun.*, **12**, 71.

SORM and ARNOLD (1947). *Coll. Czech. Chem. Commun.*, **12**, 467.

SPÄTH and GALINOWSKI (1936). *Berichte*, **69**, 2059.

SPEAKMAN (1954). *Annual Reports Chem. Soc.*, **51**, 377.

SPECKER and GAWROSCH (1942). *Berichte*, **75**, 1338.

SPENSER (1956). *J. Chem. Soc.*, p. 3659.

SPRAGUE and LAND (1957). In Elderfield's *Heterocyclic Compounds*, Vol. 5, New York: Wiley.

SPRING (1945). *Ann. Reports Chem. Soc.*, **42**, 188.

STAAB (1956). *Berichte*, **89**, 1927.

STAAB (1957). *Berichte*, **90**, 1320.

STECK and EWING (1948). *J. Amer. Chem. Soc.*, **70**, 3397.

STECK, NACHOD, EWING and GORMAN (1948). *J. Amer. Chem. Soc.*, **70**, 3406.

STEDMAN and MACDONALD (1955). *Canad. J. Chem.*, **33**, 468.

STEIN and STIASNY (1955). *Nature*, **176**, 734.

STEINKOPF (1941). *Die Chemie des Thiophens*, Dresden: Verlag Steinkopff.

STEINKOPF and HANSKE (1939). *Annalen*, **541**, 238.

STEINKOPF and HÖPNER (1933). *Annalen*, **501**, 174.

STEINKOPF and KILLINGSTAD (1937). *Annalen*, **532**, 288.

STEINKOPF and OHSE (1933). *Annalen*, **437**, 14.

STERN and MOLVIG (1936). *Z. physik. Chem.*, A, **177**, 365.

STEPHENSON (1957). *Chem. & Ind.*, p. 174.

STEVENSON and JOHNSON (1937). *J. Amer. Chem. Soc.*, **59**, 2525.

STOCK (1949). *J. Chem. Soc.*, pp. 586, 763.

STOLLÉ, BERGDOLL, LUTHER, AUERHAN and WACKER (1930). *J. Prakt. Chem.*, **128**, 1.

STOLLÉ, HECHT and BECKER (1932). *J. Prakt. Chem.*, **135**, 345.

STRAUSS and LEMMEL (1921). *Berichte*, **54**, 25.

SUGASAWA, SATODA and YANAGISAWA (1938). *J. Pharm. Soc. Japan*, **58**, 139.

SUMMERBELL and UMHOEFER (1939). *J. Amer. Chem. Soc.*, **61**, 3020.

SUMPTER and MILLER (1954). *Heterocyclic Compounds with Indole and Carbazole Systems*, New York: Interscience.

SUMPTER, MILLER and HENDRICK (1945). *J. Amer. Chem. Soc.*, **67**, 1656.

SUMPTER, MILLER and MAGAN (1945). *J. Amer. Chem. Soc.*, **67**, 499.

SUNNER (1955). *Acta Chem. Scand.*, **9**, 847.

SUREAU (1956). *Bull. Soc. Chim. France*, p. 622.

SURREY and HAMMER (1946). *J. Amer. Chem. Soc.*, **68**, 113.

SUTER and MAXWELL (1938). *Org. Syntheses*, **18**, 64.

SUTTER-KOSTIC and KARRER (1956). *Helv. Chim. Acta*, **39**, 677.

SUTTON (1955). In Braude and Nachod's *Determination of Organic Structures by Physical Methods*, New York: Academic Press.

SWAN and FELTON (1957). *The Phenazines*, New York: Interscience.

TALLEY, FITZPATRICK and PORTER (1956). *J. Amer. Chem. Soc.*, **78**, 5836.

TANAKA, SUGAWA, NAKAMORI, SANNO and ANDO (1955). *J. Pharm. Soc. Japan*, **75**, 770 (per *Chem. Abs.*, 1955, **49**, 14001).

TANNER (1956). *Spectrochim. Acta*, **8**, 9.

TARBELL (1951). In Elderfield's *Heterocyclic Compounds*, Vol. 2, New York: Wiley.

TAVORMINA, GIBBS and HUFF (1956). *J. Amer. Chem. Soc.*, **78**, 4498.

TAYLOR (1948). *J. Chem. Soc.*, p. 765.

TAYLOR (1950). *Helv. Chim. Acta*, **33**, 164.

TAYLOR (1954). In *Chemistry and Biology of Pteridines*, a Ciba Foundation Symposium, London: Churchill.

TAYLOR and BAKER (1937). In Sidgwick's *Organic Chemistry of Nitrogen*, Oxford: 1937.

TAYLOR and KALENDA (1954). *J. Amer. Chem. Soc.*, **76**, 1699.

TEAGUE and ROE (1951). *J. Amer. Chem. Soc.*, **73**, 688.

TERENTEV, BELENKII and YANOVSKAYA (1954). *J. Gen. Chem.* U.S.S.R., **24**, 1265 (per *Chem. Abs.*, 1955, **49**, 12327).

TERENTEV and GOLUBEVA (1946). *Compt. rend. Acad. Sci.*, U.S.S.R. (Doklady), **51**, 689 (per *Chem. Abs.*, 1947, **41**, 2033).

TERENTEV and KAZITSYNA (1946). *Compt. rend. Acad. Sci.* U.S.S.R., **51**, 603 (in English), (per *Chem. Abs.*, 1947, **41**, 2033).

TERENTEV and SHADKINA (1947). *Compt. rend. Acad. Sci.*, U.S.S.R., **55**, 227 (per *Chem. Abs.*, 1947, **41**, 5873).

THIELIG (1953). *Berichte*, **86**, 96.

THIRTLE (1946). *J. Amer. Chem. Soc.*, **68**, 342.

TODD, BERGEL and KARIMULLAH (1936). *J. Chem. Soc.*, p. 1557.

TOMLINSON (1939). *J. Chem. Soc.*, p. 158.

TREIBE and KOLM (1957). *Annalen*, **606**, 166.

TSCHICHIBABIN (1932). *Berichte*, **56**, 1879.

TSCHICHIBABIN (1936). *Bull. Soc. Chim. France*, **3**, 1607.

TSCHICHIBABIN (1938). *Bull. Soc. Chim. France*, **5**, pp. 429, 436.

TSCHICHIBABIN and KURSANOVA (1930). *J. Russ. Phys. Chem. Soc.*, **62**, 1211 (per *Chem. Abs.*, 1931, **25**, 2727).

TSCHICHIBABIN and RJAZANCEV (1915). *J. Russ. Phys. Chem. Soc.*, **47**, 1571 (per *Chem. Abs.*, 1916, **10**, 2898).

TUCKER and IRVIN (1951). *J. Amer. Chem. Soc.*, **73**, 1923 (cf. Edsall and Blanchard, *ibid.*, 1933, **55**, 2337).

TURNER (1949). *J. Amer. Chem. Soc.*, **71**, 3472.

TURNER and OSOL (1949). *J. Amer. Pharm. Assoc.*, **38**, 158.

TYSON (1950). *J. Amer. Chem. Soc.*, **72**, 2801 (cf. *Org. Synth.*, 1943, **23**, 42).

TYSON and SHAW (1952). *J. Amer. Chem. Soc.*, **74**, 2273.

UTERMOHLEN (1943). *J. Org. Chem.*, **8**, 544.

VAN ALLAN and DEACON (1950). *Org. Synth.*, **30**, 56.

VARYUKHINA and PUSHKAREVA (1956). *J. Gen. Chem. Russ.*, **26**, 1740 (per *Chem. Abs.*, 1957, **51**, 1960).

VEIBEL and LINHOLT (1955). *Acta Chem. Scand.*, **9**, 970.
VIRTANEN and HIETALA (1955). *Acta Chem. Scand.*, **9**, 1543.
VIVIAN (1956). *J. Org. Chem.*, **21**, 565.
VOTOČEK and MALACHTA (1932). *Coll. Czechoslov. Chem. Communs.*, **4**, 87.

WAGNER and FEGLEY (1947). *Org. Synth.*, **27**, 45.
WAGNER and SIMONS (1936). *J. Chem. Educ.*, **13**, 265.
WALBA and ISENSEE (1956). *J. Org. Chem.*, **21**, 702.
WALKER (1947). *J. Chem. Soc.*, p. 1552.
WALLER, FRYTH, HUTCHINGS and WILLIAMS (1953). *J. Amer. Chem. Soc.*, **75**, 2025.
WALLER, WOLF, STEIN and HUTCHINGS (1957). *J. Amer. Chem. Soc.*, **79**, 1265.
WALLS (1935). *J. Chem. Soc.*, p. 1405.
WALLS (1945). *J. Chem. Soc.*, p. 294.
WALLS (1952). In Elderfield's *Heterocyclic Compounds*, Vol. 4, New York: Wiley.
WALSH (1948). *Quart. Revs.*, **2**, 73.
WANG, APICELLA and STONE (1956). *J. Amer. Chem. Soc.*, **78**, 4180.
VAN DER WANT (1948). *Rec. Trav. Chim. Pays-Bas*, **67**, 45.
WARE (1950). *Chem. Revs.*, **46**, 403.
WATERMAN and HARBERTS (1936). *Bull. Soc. Chim. France*, **3**, 643.
WATERMAN and VIVIAN (1949). *J. Org. Chem.*, **14**, 289.
WATSON and CRICK (1953). *Nature*, **171**, 964.
WAWZONEK (1951). In Elderfield's *Heterocyclic Compounds*, Vol. 2, New York: Wiley.
WEIDENHAGEN and WEEDEN (1938). *Berichte*, **71**, 2349.
WEIJLARD, TISHLER and ERICKSON (1945). *J. Amer. Chem. Soc.*, **67**, 802.
WEINSTEIN and WYMAN (1956). *J. Amer. Chem. Soc.*, **78**, 4007.
WEISSMANN, BROMBERG and GUTMAN (1955). *Nature*, **176**, 1217.
WEIZMANN (1940). *Trans. Farad. Soc.*, **36**, 978.
WENIG and KOPECKÝ (1943). *Časopis Českoslov, Leckárnictva*, **56**, 49 (per *Chem. Abs.*, 1945, **39**, 3120).
WENKER (1935). *J. Amer. Chem. Soc.*, **57**, 1079.
WENKER (1938). *J. Amer. Chem. Soc.*, **60**, 2152.
WENNER and PLATI (1946). *J. Org. Chem.*, **11**, 751.
WESSON (1948). *Tables of Electric Dipole Moments*, Massachusetts Institute of Technology.
WEST (1956). In West's *Chemical Applications of Spectroscopy* (Vol. IX of Weissberger's *Technique of Organic Chemistry*) New York: Interscience.
WEYGAND and RICHTER (1955). *Berichte*, **88**, 499.
WHALEY and GOVINDACHARI (1951). *Organic Reactions*, **6**, 74.
WHALLEY (1955). Special Publication No. 3: *Naturally occurring nitrogen heterocyclic compounds*, London: The Chemical Society, p. 98.
WHELAND (1942). *J. Amer. Chem. Soc.*, **64**, 900.
WHELAND (1944). *The Theory of Resonance*, New York: Wiley.
WHELAND (1949). *Advanced Organic Chemistry*, New York: Wiley.
WHELAND and PAULING (1935). *J. Amer. Chem. Soc.*, **57**, 2091.

WHITE and CLEWS (1956). *Acta Cryst.*, **9**, 586.

WHITEHEAD (1952). *J. Amer. Chem. Soc.*, **74**, 4267.

WHITEHEAD (1953). *J. Amer. Chem. Soc.*, **75**, 671.

WHITELEY (1937). In Thorpe's *Dictionary of Applied Chemistry*, under 'Alloxan', London: Longmans.

WHITELEY and THORPE (1937). In Thorpe's *Dictionary of Applied Chemistry*, under 'Barbituric Acid', London: Longmans.

WHITTAKER (1951). *J. Chem. Soc.*, p. 1565.

WHITTAKER (1953). *J. Chem. Soc.*, p. 1646.

WIBAUT (1939). *Berichte*, **72**, 1708.

WIBAUT and NICOLAI (1939). *Rec. Trav. Chim.*, **58**, 709.

WILCOX and GOLDSTEIN (1952). *J. Chem. Phys.*, **20**, 1656.

WILEY (1947). *J. Org. Chem.*, **12**, 43.

WILEY and BENNETT (1949). *Chem. Revs.*, **44**, 447.

WILEY, ENGLAND and BEHR (1951). *Org. Reactions*, **6**, 367.

WILEY, HUSSUNG and MOFFAT (1956). *J. Org. Chem.*, **21**, 190.

WILLIAMS and RUEHLE (1935). *J. Amer. Chem. Soc.*, **57**, 1856.

WILLIAMS, RUEHLE and FINKELSTEIN (1937). *J. Amer. Chem. Soc.*, **59**, 526.

WILLIAMSON (1957). In Elderfield's *Heterocyclic Compounds*, Vol. 6, New York: Wiley.

WILSON (1945). *J. Chem. Soc.*, pp. 52, 61.

WILSON (1948). *J. Chem. Soc.*, p. 1157.

WINSTEIN and HENDERSON (1950). In Elderfield's *Heterocyclic Compounds*, Vol. 1, New York: Wiley.

WITKOP (1956). *J. Amer. Chem. Soc.*, **78**, 2873.

WITTIG, CLOSS and MINDERMANN (1955). *Annalen*, **594**, 89.

WITTIG, TENHAEFF, SCHOCH and KOENIG (1951). *Annalen*, **572**, 1.

WOHL (1901). *Berichte*, **34**, 2444.

WOLF and FOLKERS (1951). *Org. Reactions*, **6**, 410.

WOOLLEY, SHAW, SMITH and SINGER (1951). *J. Biol. Chem.*, **189**, 401.

WORK (1942). *J. Chem. Soc.*, p. 426.

WRIGHT (1951). *Chem. Revs.*, **48**, 397.

WRIGHT (1955). *J. Amer. Chem. Soc.*, **77**, 3930.

WYMAN (1956). *J. Amer. Chem. Soc.*, **78**, 4599.

YALE and BERNSTEIN (1948). *J. Amer. Chem. Soc.*, **70**, 254.

YOUNG and AMSTUTZ (1951). *J. Amer. Chem. Soc.*, **73**, 4773.

ZAUGG (1954). *Organic Reactions*, **8**, 305.

ZECHMEISTER and SEASE (1947). *J. Amer. Chem. Soc.*, **69**, 273.

ZIEGLER and ZEISER (1930). *Berichte*, **63**, 1874.

ZUMWALT and BADGER (1939). *J. Chem. Phys.*, **7**, 629.

Index

All entries should be read *also* as if in the plural. Thus 'pyridine' includes all derivations of pyridine not separately indexed. Likewise 'pyridine, hydroxy-' includes mono- and poly-hydroxypyridines.

Hydrogenated nuclei. Tetrahydropyridine is indexed under T (not P), dihydrothiazole under D (not T), and so on.

2D

2E